PHOTOPERIODISM AND SEASONAL DEVELOPMENT OF INSECTS

PHOTOPERIODISM AND SEASONAL DEVELOPMENT OF INSECTS

A. S. DANILEVSKII

PROFESSOR: DEPARTMENT OF ZOOLOGY
UNIVERSITY OF LENINGRAD

Translated by
J. JOHNSTON, M.A.
with editorial assistance from
N. WALOFF, PH.D

OLIVER & BOYD
EDINBURGH AND LONDON

OLIVER AND BOYD LTD

Tweeddale Court
Edinburgh 1

39 Welbeck Street
London W.1

This is a translation of Фотопериодизм и сезонное развитие насекомых, by А. С. Данилевский, published in 1961 by Издательство Ленинградского Университета, Leningrad, U.S.S.R.

First English Edition 1965

Printed in Great Britain by
Robert Cunningham & Sons Ltd, Alva

PREFACE

The ability to determine day-length with precision and to react to changes in it is a unique adaptation that has arisen independently in various groups of organism. The comparative study of photoperiodic adaptations is a very interesting problem of evolutionary physiology and ecology. Up to the present, however, this problem has been studied mainly in plants, and in the animal kingdom mainly in birds and mammals. The important results obtained in the latter field are well known. For other groups of animals, and particularly for invertebrates, there was until recently only scattered information.

In entomology the subject of photoperiodism has attracted close attention only during the last few years. It has been conclusively shown by much experimental work that for insects also day-length is a vitally important factor regulating development and reproduction in accordance with the succession of ecological conditions during the year. It has become clear that, unless the reactions to seasonal and geographical variations in day-length are taken into account it is impossible fully to understand the phenology, distribution, and population dynamics of insects, i.e. the phenomena with which the fundamental practical tasks of entomology are concerned. The significance of photoperiodic adaptations in the formation of physiologically different local races has also been demonstrated, enabling us to approach from a new angle the problems of understanding the first stages of intraspecific differentiation and of evaluating the possibilities of acclimatization and extending the distribution range of insects.

Extensive and varied data on the photoperiodic adaptations of insects have already been accumulated, and it has become necessary to analyse and systematize them.

The present work is based primarily on the results of experimental investigations in the entomological laboratories of the University of Leningrad, which to a considerable extent devised and planned these investigations. In the bibliographical appendix are listed, as completely as possible, publications on the influence of day-length on arthropods.

In this work only the ecological side of the problem is examined. Questions concerning the physiological mechanism of the photoperiodic reaction of insects are here almost untouched, as data in this field are still extremely limited. Special attention is paid to the dependence of the photoperiodic reaction on other ecological factors, and also to the problems of intraspecific adaptations to geographical variations in light and temperature conditions. An attempt has been made to estimate the possibility of using the experimental data in the analysis and prognosis of the development of insects in nature.

Most of the original data in this book relate to Lepidoptera, since I am most familiar with the systematics and ecology of that group. For purposes of comparison other groups, including several phytophagous ticks, have also been considered.

As the significance of day-length for insects is primarily in its influence on diapause, the main data are preceded by a special chapter in which the role of diapause in the life cycle and ecology of insects is briefly described.

Many questions discussed in the book are, of course, still far from being solved, and in many cases the discussion is necessarily sketchy; but if the book directs attention to this new and important branch of insect ecology, its object will have been attained.

In conclusion I wish to express my sincere gratitude to all who have helped me—to colleagues, students and aspirants in the Department of Entomology in the University of Leningrad, without whose aid the long and difficult experiments on which this book is based could not have been completed. I am particularly indebted to K. F. Geispits, E. I. Glinyanaya, N. I. Goryshin, and G. G. Shel'deshova, in collaboration with whom I began and for more than ten years carried on these investigations.

CONTENTS

Chapter I

DIAPAUSE AND ITS SIGNIFICANCE IN INSECT ECOLOGY

The seasonal effects of external conditions are among the most important ecological factors in the life of insects. They give rise to a system of special adaptations, which are expressed in the life cycle characteristic of each species. The role of these seasonal adaptations is particularly great in temperate and northern latitudes, where climatic variations during the course of the year are most marked.

The life cycles of insects are extremely varied. Depending on the species and the peculiar features of its biology, differences may appear in the number of generations per year, in the seasonal sequence of the different stages of development, in periodic changes in diet and behaviour, and frequently in seasonal dimorphism or even in alternation of bisexual and parthenogenetic methods of reproduction.

In spite of the extraordinary variation in the life cycles of species, they are always based on an alternation of periods of active development with periods of retardation or complete cessation of growth and formative processes. Such a condition of physiological rest is called 'diapause'.

Ecologically the states of activity and of diapause are widely different and have the definite appearance of adaptations to the two principal periods of the year, i.e. summer and winter in temperate latitudes, and wet and dry seasons in the tropics. Since during diapause the organism is subjected to widely differing and harsh conditions, adaptations of the diapause stages to climatic factors show greater specificity, and are in general more varied and complex than adaptations in the active stages.

Generally diapause is regarded as a passive stage in the life cycle. This state, however, does not merely assure survival through unfavourable seasons. No less important is the fact that diapause determines the constancy of life cycles and the synchronization of developmental stages with periods of the year to which they are adapted. Thus the eco-physiological features of diapause form the basis of the entire life cycle of insects.

1. Ecological prerequisites for the appearance of diapause and the forms of its manifestation

The growth and morphogenetic processes of insects are possible only within a limited range of temperature. The lower limit, depending on the species and the stage of growth, generally fluctuates between 5° and 10°, and the upper limit between 30° and 35°. Thus the range of biologically-effective temperature is only 25° to 30°. In fact development normally takes place within still narrower limits, as conditions near the limits always cause disturbances in growth and heavy mortality. Thermal adaptations linked with the seasonal cycles of insects are not great. They consist in a raising or lowering of the optimum and biologically-effective range of temperature by only a few degrees, and these extensions rarely pass beyond the limits mentioned above. As extreme examples we may mention the highly thermophilic locusts *Locusta migratoria migratorioides* and *Schistocerca gregaria*, whose development is possible in temperatures from 20° to 40-45° (HAMILTON, 1936), and the Winter Moth, active in late autumn, for which the effective temperature zone is from 0° to 20° (KOZHANCHIKOV, 1950b).

Biologically-ineffective temperatures inhibit development, and if their action on the insect is prolonged they inevitably cause death. The active stages of insect life cycles are especially vulnerable to unfavourable temperatures, which are lethal to them even if their action is of short duration.

From these facts it is clear that it is only in tropical and subtropical conditions, where the annual range of temperature does not extend beyond the limits effective for insect development, that no special thermal adaptations in the life cycle are required. In temperate climates and high latitudes, with their prolonged cold periods and frosts, insects can exist only if their life cycle includes a special dormant state such as diapause.

Other ecological factors may also cause periodic pauses in development.

Most insects in the active state are hygrophilic. Therefore in regions with sharply-defined dry and hot seasons many insects develop a special form of diapause, known as aestivation. In the life cycles of several species in temperate latitudes one sometimes observes both aestivation and winter diapause. For example, in the Winter Moth *Operophtera brumata* and the leafroller *Exapate congelatella* there is a summer diapause in the pupal stage and a winter diapause in the egg stage.

Finally, diapause may evolve as an adaptation to periodical scarcity of food, especially in cases where close dependence on plants in a particular phenophase occurs. As a typical example of the significance of food specialization in the formation of a life cycle we may mention the Apple-blossom Weevil *Anthonomus pomorum.* The entire development of this species from egg to imago takes place within the buds of apple-blossom. After emergence the beetle remains in an inactive state for ten or eleven months until the following spring. Similar cycles are characteristic of many carpophagous insects.

In nearly all insects and other terrestrial arthropods diapause is a strictly seasonal adaptation, with which its cyclic character is linked. But sometimes adaptations similar in their physiological mechanisms and ecological function arise in response to environmental factors that do not show periodicity. Thus among blood-sucking arthropods that lie in wait for passing hosts (the bug *Rhodnius*, and many ticks) a pause in development of the diapause type occurs as a result of temporary shortages of food. Diapause without obvious seasonal links is also seen in several dwellers in small lakes, which may dry up, for example in mosquitoes of the genus *Aëdes.* In this way analogous physiological adaptations arise in all cases where the environment is notably changeable and shows frequent deviations from the norm for active development.

Diapause was originally regarded as the result of unfavourable external conditions which exert a direct retarding effect on the organism. This view still persists in the literature. But the regulation of the seasonal cycle of insects has proved to be more complex. In its nature diapause differs widely from non-adaptive torpor, which may arise at any moment as a response to sublethal conditions. In nature, torpor caused by cold is very frequently observed; but such a state cannot be greatly prolonged, as gradual pathological changes, ultimately leading to death, take place in the organism.

Unlike torpor, diapause is a special adaptation in the life cycle, and its ecological norm comprises conditions unfavourable to active stages. Special physiological preparation, to enable the organism to survive a very long period of conditions lethal to the development stages, is the chief characteristic of diapause. Another important characteristic of diapause is its partial independence of external factors. Diapause begins and ends without direct dependence on the ecological conditions which the organism is adapted to surviving, and in a natural environment it always precedes their onset.

These characteristics result from the fact that an important part in the regulation of diapause is played by internal cyclic processes that modify the influence of the external environment. Such a dual regulation by factors that are largely independent of each other—physiological and ecological—is characteristic of all seasonal-cyclical adaptations and, as will be shown later, is of great importance in the mechanism of synchronization of life cycles with the dynamics of external conditions.

The correlation of external and internal factors in the regulation of diapause may be of various kinds. In monocyclic species diapause is usually an essential stage in individual development. It begins at a definite stage in each generation and is thus due to internal mechanisms fixed by heredity. In polycyclic species it is facultative, appearing only in certain generations under the influence of specific external conditions. Finally, species with homodynamic development generally have no diapause.

The intensity and duration of diapause vary within wide limits. In some species development is halted for several months or even years, whereas in others one observes only a brief cessation of activity, which comes to an end spontaneously within a few days. Sometimes that depends on the external conditions in which the onset of diapause occurs. For example, in the caterpillar of the Pine Moth *Dendrolimus pini*, diapause, when it begins under the influence of short day-length at a temperature of 12°, continues for about 1½ months, whereas it lasts only one or two days when it begins at a temperature of 30°. Even in the latter case, however, all the characteristics of diapause are shown, including resistance to low temperatures.

We must now briefly consider the question of the so-called hibernation of insects, as a special type of adaptation to surviving the unfavourable periods of the year. In the literature the view is widely expressed that hibernation is sharply distinguished from diapause in that it is determined exclusively by external conditions without the participation of internal preparatory processes. It begins as a direct response to unfavourable conditions and ends immediately after these have returned to normal. From that point of view, the state of hibernation essentially is almost the same as torpor.

The phenomenon of hibernation is still not thoroughly investigated, but all existing data indicate that it is very difficult to distinguish it from diapause. Hibernation is not merely the direct result of unfavourable conditions, but, like diapause, is possible only at a definite stage of the life cycle of a species, which indicates its dependence on internal physiological processes. USHATINSKAYA (1957) comes to the conclusion that the onset of hibernation is preceded by a special physiological preparation, and that its termination is accompanied by a special recuperative period. These two processes in no way differ from those observed in diapause. It is characteristic that the resting period in species such as *Agrotis segetum*, *Dendrolimus pini*, *Arctia caia*, and *Locusta migratoria*, formerly regarded as examples of hibernation (KOZHANCHIKOV, 1939a; LOZINA-LOZINSKII and SOKOLOV, 1938), appear after much more detailed investigation to be indubitably diapause, regulated by indirect factors.

From the ecological point of view the varying depth of diapause undoubtedly has an adaptive significance. The great mobility of the resting period known as hibernation has its own ecological advantages over deep diapause and apparently is a particular form of specialization of the life cycle.

Like other seasonal adaptations diapause may occur at any stage of the life cycle, but it is always strictly specific for each species. Table 1 contains a few typical examples of diapause in different morphological stages in Lepidoptera.

Even within the limits of a single ontogenetic stage, there are apparently no periods when temporary cessation of development is potentially impossible. Thus, for instance, in spite of very intensive morphogenesis, diapause has been observed in embryonic and pupal development at the most diverse stages. In the imaginal stage the resting period occurs most frequently just before sexual maturation, but sometimes diapause may interrupt the early part of the sexual cycle, leading to resorption of eggs already formed, as in blood-sucking mosquitoes (Beklemishev, 1944) and in the Colorado Beetle *Leptinotarsa decemlineata* (de Wilde, Duintjer and Mook, 1959).

In some systematic groups predominance of one form of diapause is observed; e.g. embryonic in most locusts, imaginal in leaf-eating beetles and many bugs, pupal in most moths, and so on. But still the linking of diapause with morphological stages primarily depends not on the systematic relationships of a species but on the particular features of its ecology. Even in closely-

Table 1

The occurrence of diapause in different developmental stages of some Lepidoptera

Species*	Family*	Diapause stage
Bombyx mori	Bombycidae	Early embryonic stages
Orgyia antiqua	Lymantriidae	do.
Tortrix viridana	Tortricidae	do.
Lymantria dispar	Lymantriidae	Formation of larva in egg
Antheraea yamamai	Attacidae	do.
Yponomeuta (*Hyponomeuta*) *malinellus*	Yponomeutidae	Emerged larva before feeding
Aporia crataegi	Pieridae	Larvae in early instars
Orgyia gonostigma	Lymantriidae	do.
Dasychira fascelina	Lymantriidae	do.
Dendrolimus pini	Lasiocampidae	Larvae of any age
Loxostege sticticalis	Pyralididae	Prepupa
Enarmonia (*Carpocapsa*) *pomonella*	Eucosmidae	do.
Eriocrania sparmanella	Eriocraniidae	do.
Antheraea pernyi	Saturniidae	Pupa
Pieris brassicae	Pieridae	do.
Dasychira pudibunda	Lymantriidae	do.
Gonopteryx rhamni	Pieridae	Imago, sexually immature
Scoliopteryx libatrix	Noctuidae	do.
Vanessa io	Nymphalidae	do.

* Classification as in Danilevskii's Russian text.

related species of a single genus diapause occurs in entirely different stages, whereas in species belonging to unrelated families it often occurs at the same stage (see Table 1). Many such examples may be cited for different orders of insects. This shows that diapause is an easily attained adaptation (from the evolutionary point of view), since it appears independently at parallel stages in different groups.

The state of diapause, regardless of its type and the stage at which it appears, is characterized by a number of general physiological features, of which the most essential is an abrupt lowering of metabolism. The following features also are typical: profound changes in the system of oxidizing enzymes; decrease in the total amount of water in the body and its transfer from a free to a colloidal state; presence in the tissues of abundant deposits of reserve food material, by means of which the vital processes are maintained during the resting period; and absence or extremely low level of feeding and movement.

Some of these features are so characteristic that they have often been looked upon as the direct physiological causes of the onset of diapause; but none of them is absolutely indispensable. In each feature one may find all degrees of transition from the level characteristic of active life to that typical of diapause. Only their whole complex clearly distinguishes an organism in diapause from one that is actively developing.

2. Characteristics of the response of the diapause stages to external conditions

The resistance to unfavourable environmental factors

In contrast to active stages, whose ecological adaptations are usually much specialized, the diapause stages always have a broad and complex resistance to external conditions. That feature is observed even when diapause is an adaptation to one of the unfavourable factors, e.g. to negative temperatures during hibernation or to drought during aestivation. The necessity for many-faceted resistance is dictated by the fact that with the onset of unfavourable seasons the whole complex of climatic and food conditions changes. But we must bear in mind that the physiological features of diapause, particularly the low level of metabolism, also strengthen the resistance of the organism to unfavourable effects of external conditions. As a result non-adaptive resistance, e.g. to poisons, may also appear during the resting period.

In all ecological types of diapause the ability to dispense with food for a long period is developed. Only in comparatively rare instances, mainly in imaginal diapause, is active feeding continued, as in the mosquitoes *Anopheles maculipennis atroparvus*, *A. m. sacharovi*, *A. superpictus*, butterflies of the genus *Vanessa*, and a number of moths. The life-processes during diapause continue mostly at the expense of endogenous nutriment, the source of which is special reserves stored in fatty tissues during the preparatory period. Therefore histological examination of fatty tissues provides one of the clearest indicators of diapause (POSPELOV, 1910; LARCHENKO, 1937, 1956; KUZNETSOVA, 1955).

In the composition of the food reserves a high fat content is most notable. Special deposits of proteins have been described, often entering into close combination with fat, forming within cells in the fatty tissue fat-protein granules characteristic of diapause stages (POSPELOV, 1910; LARCHENKO, 1937, 1956). Abundant deposits of carbohydrates in the form of glycogen have also been observed (USHATINSKAYA, 1957). These deposits closely resemble the reserves that enable active development to take place in a non-feeding stage, such as egg yolk or deposits in fatty tissues during pupal metamorphosis.

The low metabolic level permits very economical expenditure of the stored nutriment, as a consequence of which diapause may sometimes last for many months or even years. The lower the metabolic rate, the greater the duration of diapause (HELLER, 1926; DANILEVSKII, 1951).

Another general peculiarity of the diapause stage is high resistance to desiccation, which inevitably results from limitation of water absorption through the intestines as a result of cessation of feeding. Resistance to desiccation becomes most important in diapause of the summer type (aestivation), particularly in the conditions of arid tropical and subtropical regions. This feature, however, is always found also in diapause of the winter type, and frequently determines emergence from hibernation (USHATINSKAYA, 1957).

The main source of water during diapause, apparently, is the reserve nutriment, through oxidation of which the so-called metabolic water is formed. Maintenance of the necessary water balance is achieved by simple fixation of water in hydrophilic plasma colloids and by reduction of evaporation through the cuticle and the respiratory system. The latter is due primarily to a low respiratory rate, but also to a special condition of the spiracles, which during diapause are usually closed, or are open only periodically (PUNT, 1950; SCHNEIDERMAN and WILLIAMS, 1953). During egg diapause the formation of waxy protective layers is observed in several locusts and in the Spider Mite *Petrobius* (*Machilis*) *latens* (LEES, 1955).

Temperature strongly affects the water balance during diapause. According to USHATINSKAYA (1949, 1957), while the caterpillar of the Codling Moth *Enarmonia* (*Carpocapsa*) *pomonella* is in diapause in winter at a raised temperature (11°) the amount of metabolic water formed does not compensate for evaporation, and the water content of the body decreases. The same takes place at temperatures below freezing-point (−5°, −10°), when oxidation in the organism proceeds at a lower rate than evaporation, which may lead to death from desiccation. A temperature of about 0° is most favourable. In such conditions the water content of the organism remains constant or even increases in many cases. This optimal condition differs in different species. According to KARLASH (1954), the optimum temperature for the diapausing pupa of the Chinese Oak Silk-worm *Antheraea pernyi* is approximately +10°. It is possible that the effect of temperature on breaking diapause is also linked with fluctuations in water balance.

Cold-resistance is an adaptation that is very important in the climatic conditions of temperate and northern latitudes and has thus attracted the close attention of investigators. An extensive literature, summarized in the reviews by USHATINSKAYA (1957) and LOZINA-LOZINSKII (1952), is devoted to the subject. We shall therefore touch on only a few aspects of it. We have to distinguish two modes of resistance to low temperatures by insects, based on their physiological mechanism and their ecological significance, namely: capacity for prolonged resistance to low positive temperatures unfavourable to development (from 0° to 10°), which are lethal to the active stages; and resistance to frost, i.e. ability to survive temperatures below freezing-point.

Tolerance of the prolonged action of low positive temperatures is very high in all types of diapause. Its physiological basis has not been adequately investigated, but it is certain that it is linked with metabolic characteristics—the ability to feed on internal reserves and to maintain the necessary level of respiration (KOZHANCHIKOV, 1938c, 1939a).

Frost-resistance is a more specialized adaptation, which is strongly manifested only in the winter type of diapause in species living in northern latitudes. In typical cases, frost-resistance in insects takes the form of ability to undergo prolonged deep supercooling, whereby many species do not freeze to death even at $-30°$ or $-40°$. The low temperature limit at which water begins to crystallize in the tissues, causing irreversible damage, depends on the species and the conditions of hibernation. The ability to undergo deep freezing is not confined to the diapause stage. In a number of cases active pupae of several species, e.g. *Pieris brassicae* and *Chloridea obsoleta*, can be supercooled to the same degree as when in diapause. In active stages, however, the supercooled state is unstable and soon ends spontaneously or as a result of external conditions, whereas in diapause it may last for months.

The cause of the stability in supercooling, as explained long ago (ROBINSON, 1928; SAKHAROV, 1928, 1930; PAYNE, 1926, 1929), lies in a relative desiccation of the organism and a conversion of free water in the tissues into a colloid-bound state. In this respect the frost-resistant mechanism has much in common with resistance to desiccation. It is therefore not surprising that in southern species (*Philosamia cynthia, Platyedra gossypiella*) diapause takes the form of an adaptation to periods of drought, and increased resistance to negative temperatures is found.

Several insects possess, besides the ability to undergo supercooling, another form of frost-resistance, whereby they are able to survive formation of ice in the tissues. This is observed in the prepupa of the Corn Borer, the caterpillar of *Macrothylacia rubi, Arctia caia* (LOZINA-LOZINSKII, 1937, 1942, 1952), the larva of the sawfly *Croesus septentrionalis*, and the caterpillar of *Lasiocampa quercus* (KOZHANCHIKOV, 1939a). The prepupa of the Corn Borer may remain for an indefinite period in the frozen state, surviving a fall in temperature to $-60°$. Meanwhile, as in the supercooled state, tissue-respiration in the insects does not cease (KOZHANCHIKOV, 1938c, 1939a; LOZINA-LOZINSKII, 1942, 1952). Up to the present it is still unexplained why the formation of ice in the tissues and even complete freezing is easily survived in this type of frost-resistance, whereas in most species a comparatively small amount of ice produces severe damage to cell structure and death.

There is almost no information in the literature about the resistance of diapausing insects to excessive heat. Probably that is because few studies have been made on diapause in insects in arid tropical regions, and because there are no ecological reasons for developing such physiological adaptations. In natural conditions, maximum temperatures dangerous to insect life are usually of short duration, and insects can easily avoid them by taking refuge in the soil and other cool shelters. Diapausing insects usually survive moderately high temperatures well over a prolonged period. Unfavourable effects are observed only when such conditions persist too long.

Features of the ecological requirements of stages in diapause

Diapause is often described as a state of physiological rest; it is not, however, a completely inactive state. During diapause physiological changes continue, although very slowly, following a definite direction, which ultimately results in the capacity for active development.

ZOLOTAREV (1947, 1950a, 1950b) stresses the importance and adaptive character of these changes, which he calls the diapause processes. ANDREWARTHA (1952) and other authors following him (LEES, 1955) apply to the same phenomena the name 'diapause development'; but this term cannot be considered to be well-chosen. The internal processes taking place during diapause differ essentially from biological development in the usual sense of the term, which is indissolubly linked with progressive growth and differentiation. The phenomena occurring during diapause are simpler, amounting to 'unblocking' of development, i.e. to building up a condition in which activity can recommence. Therefore it is more precise to describe this process as reactivation. When one speaks of the specificity of the ecological requirements of diapause stages, one is actually thinking of conditions necessary for the resumption of development.

At the basis of reactivation there are physiological processes that take place spontaneously. The reason for the known autonomous nature of diapause, and for the possibility of its spontaneous termination even while external conditions remain constant, lies in that fact. But external factors still, to a large extent, affect reactivation, hastening or delaying its course and consequently affecting the duration of diapause. One of the most characteristic features of diapause is the unique dependence of reactivation on temperature.

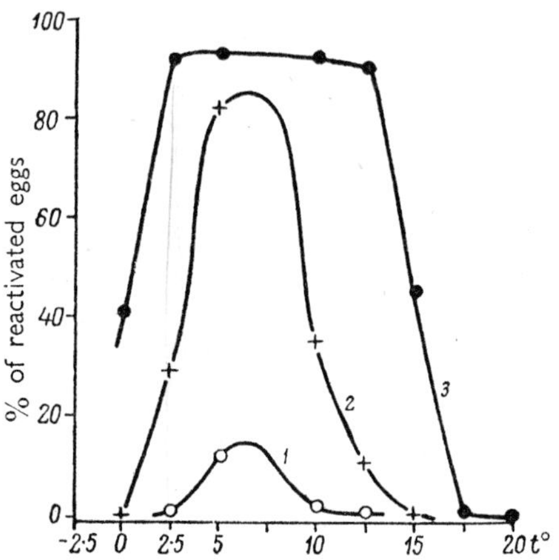

FIG. 1. The effect of temperature on the rate of reactivation of diapausing eggs of *Bombyx mori* (after Muroga, from Lees, 1955).

Curves: the percentage of developing eggs with incubation at a temperature of 22·5° after different periods of cooling: 1, 40 days; 2, 60 days; 3, 120 days.

As is well known, in a developing organism the rates of growth and of other life processes increase with a rise in temperature, and the curve of the relation between these, within the limits of biologically-effective temperatures, is generally a straight line. The process of reactivation in diapause is not subject to that direct relation and is therefore sharply distinguished from other biological phenomena.

The characteristic reactions of diapause stages to temperature were first observed by DUCLAUX (1869, 1871, 1876) in experiments with silkworms. He showed that without sufficient cooling the development of the embryo is not resumed. At a temperature of 20°, diapause can last more than a year, and the eggs ultimately perish. The rate of reactivation is greatly increased by lowering the temperature; but that is observed only on the positive side of the scale. A negative temperature again sharply checks resumption of development. Thus the process of reactivation does not always display a linear relation with temperature, but—as for other biological phenomena—there exist a definite optimum and limits of temperature. This is well illustrated by the data of MUROGA (1951), also obtained from silkworms (Fig. 1).

The important ecological significance of Duclaux's findings was understood only recently, when similar phenomena were observed by several authors in a large number of insects.

The above temperature relation is characteristic of diapause adapted to cold winter conditions. It is important to stress that in this type the zone of reactivating temperatures lies below the threshold necessary for active development. Optimal temperatures are most often about 5°-10°, but—depending on the species—they may fluctuate from 12° to 15°, e.g. in *Austroicetes cruciata* (ANDREWARTHA, 1943, 1952), *Polychrosis botrana* (KOMAROVA, 1954), *Gryllulus commodus* (BROWNING, 1952a, 1952b), down to close to 0° in *Malacosoma disstria* (HODSON and WEINMAN, 1945), *Gilpinia polytoma* (PREBBLE, 1941), *Phalera bucephala*, *Sphinx ligustri*, and others (DANILEVSKII, 1950). It is possible that species exist for which freezing is essential, but there are no sufficiently precise data on this aspect.

There is no doubt that specific differences in optimum temperatures have adaptive significance. Reactivation in unsuitable conditions prevents further development and causes decreased viability, irregular growth, and finally lowered fertility in the imaginal state. Therefore knowledge of the temperature requirements of the diapause states is necessary for understanding the ecology of a species.

Comparative studies of species with different geographical distribution have revealed great variations in their temperature requirements during diapause, and the close connection of these with climatic conditions within their ranges of distribution (DANILEVSKII, 1946, 1949, 1950). Examples of specific differences in the upper temperature limits of reactivation are illustrated in Fig. 2.

In diapause the pupae of *Philosamia cynthia*, a species found mainly in tropical regions of Asia, differ from other, more northern species in not requiring freezing; their reactivation is even accelerated by a rise in temperature. A similar reaction was observed by GORYSHIN (1958b) in diapausing pupae of the Cotton-boll Worm *Chloridea obsoleta*. Another typical example of such thermophilic diapause is found in the moth *Diparopsis castanea*, a pest of cotton in tropical Africa, in which the highest rate of reactivation is observed at 28°, whereas much lower or higher temperatures greatly prolong diapause in the pupae (LEES, 1955). This type of diapause, no doubt, arose as an adaptation to survive hot dry periods.

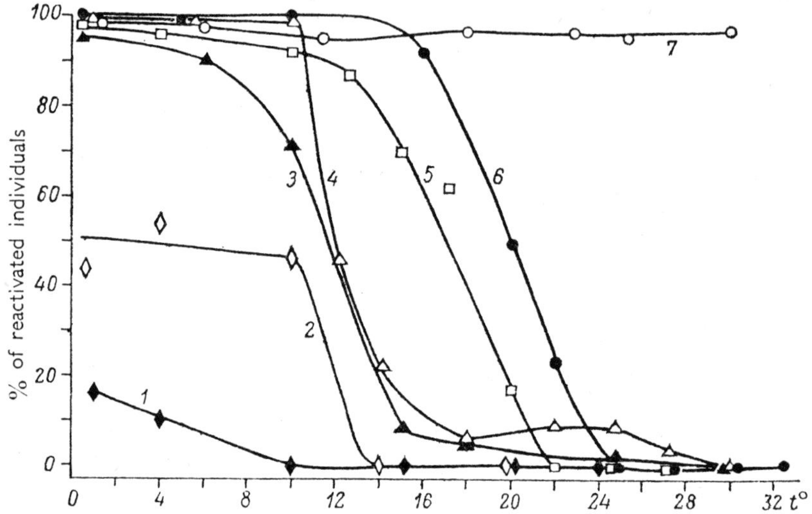

FIG. 2. The specific differences in temperature thresholds of reactivation.

Curves: the percentage of reactivated pupae with incubation at 25° after 5 months at the temperatures shown: 1, *Eriogaster lanestris*; 2, *Saturnia pavonia*; 3, *Smerinthus ocellatus*; 4, *Phalera bucephala*; 5, *Pieris brassicae*; 6, *Antheraea pernyi*; 7, *Philosamia cynthia*.

The specific humidity requirements for diapause are much less clearly known. This question has been studied mainly from the physiological point of view, as dehydration of an organism has been frequently regarded as the principal cause of diapause.

An intensive intake of water during renewal of development has been observed in many insects, but it is difficult to determine whether this is a cause or a consequence of reactivation. The significance of water in the regulation of embryonic development has been most thoroughly studied in locusts, where this development is always accompanied by intensive absorption of moisture from the environment. According to SLIFER (1938, 1946), the development of diapausing eggs of *Melanoplus differentialis* begins only after destruction of a waxy layer that covers a special apparatus —the hydropyle—through which the egg absorbs water. Removal of this layer by dissolving it in xylene, and consequent increase of water-content in the egg, can terminate diapause at any time. The directly reactivating role of water is also shown by the immediate resumption of development in an isolated embryo of *Melanoplus differentialis* by immersing it in Ringer's solution (BUCKLIN, 1953).

On the other hand, comparative data regarding other locusts —*Austroicetes cruciata* (BIRCH and ANDREWARTHA, 1942), *Melanoplus bivittatus* (SALT, 1949, 1952), *Locustana pardalina* (MATTHEE, 1951), and *Locusta migratoria* (SHUMAKOV and YAKHIMOVICH, 1950)—indicate that absorption of water does not regulate the onset and termination of diapause, but on the contrary the change in the activity of the hydropyle apparatus is a result of internal physiological processes taking place in the embryo. Reactivation is sometimes even stimulated by drought. Thus diapausing eggs of the African locust *Locustana pardalina*, when kept at 35° in a humid environment, begin development slowly and very unevenly (over a period of 36 to 95 days), but when held for 1½ months in dry conditions after moistening they hatch simultaneously in 8 days (MATTHEE, 1951).

Similar phenomena are found also in other types of diapause: in all cases that have been studied in sufficient detail, no obligatory requirement of water for the reactivation process itself has been observed. Restoration of the water balance in the organism, apparently, merely accompanies reactivation, as has been shown in the case of *Cephus cinctus* (CHURCH, 1953, 1955b), and a high requirement of contact water usually occurs after the termination of diapause. The often-quoted data of TOWNSEND (1926) on the possibility of artificially terminating diapause in the caterpillar of the Codling Moth *Enarmonia* (*Carpocapsa*) *pomonella* by giving it abundant moisture are not borne out by other authors (THÉRON, 1943; ANDREWARTHA, 1952). In the case of the European Corn Borer *Pyrausta nubilalis* it is particularly clear that the necessity of absorbing water for resuming development arises only in larvae fully reactivated by the effects of low temperatures (Babcock, 1927a; Monchadskii, 1935; Ladyzhenskaya, 1935). According to Roubaud (1928), during diapause the larvae of this species even require complete desiccation, which, like low temperature, accelerates the process of reactivation.

Moisture, therefore—unlike temperature, which directly affects the process of reactivation—apparently has a more indirect effect on it. It does not follow from this, of course, that the water relationships have no significance during the diapause period. Thus in northern species the highest rate of reactivation is observed at temperatures between 0° and 12°, when, according to Ushatinskaya (1949), a positive water balance is established in the organism. A different relation to water conditions may also be produced by the varying resistance of the diapause states to desiccation.

In several cases the rate of reactivation depends on the light relationships. Thus, according to Geispits (1953), diapause in larvae of the Pine Moth *Dendrolimus pini* in conditions of 12-hour daylight and a temperature of 20° lasts about a month, whereas at the same temperature with continuous illumination activity begins after 17 days. The author has observed the strong effect of light on the rate of reactivation in diapausing *Arctia caia* and *Parasemia plantaginis*. Similar facts have also been established for the diapause states of various moths (Baker, 1935). Most species, however, are neutral towards the light factor while in diapause.

3. Diapause as a regulator of the life cycle

The significance of diapause in synchronizing insect phenology with the seasonal rhythm of external conditions

The origin of the peculiar temperature requirements of diapause stages can be explained only by their function in the mechanism for synchronizing the life cycle with the seasonal rhythm of external conditions.

The synchronizing role of the resting period is shown most clearly in species with diapause of the winter type. During the active part of their cycle, because the rate of development depends directly on temperature and the diversity of microclimatic conditions, asynchronism of development inevitably occurs and increases with each successive generation. Consequently by the end of the vegetative period one may find polycyclic species in all stages of their life cycle simultaneously. Without a special adaptation to harmonize their phenology, this would regularly lead to the death of a considerable part of the population with the onset of cold weather, as they would be in stages unsuitable for hibernation. The unusual reaction to positive temperature observed in diapause of the winter type, which is almost diametrically opposite to the reaction of the active stages, serves as protection against such losses.

Diapause always comes on at a temperature that permits development. If in such conditions the reaction process is checked, individuals that have entered diapause remain in that state until autumn. This guards against resumption of development in conditions when there might not remain enough time—or rather effective heat—for the completion of the next generation. It is also important that the higher the temperature, the more strongly should the reactivation process be checked, so that individuals entering diapause at different times should arrive at the beginning of winter in the same physiological condition. In this way there gradually accumulates a uniform wintering stock, resistant to negative temperatures, embracing the entire population.

In autumn, when the temperature falls below the threshold for active development, the next stage in the condition of diapausing insects begins. While the temperature remains between 10° and 0° reactivation continues intensively. Usually it does not stop completely before the period of frost begins, and slowly tapers off through the winter and early spring. Field observations show that, because of individual variation in the degree of diapause, the proportion of reactivated insects increases more or less gradually throughout the winter. But as the temperature then is considerably below the developmental threshold, reactivated individuals remain in an obligatory state of rest, maintaining the peculiar frost-resistance of diapause. Ultimately, by spring, the whole wintering stock appears to be potentially capable of resuming development immediately, and this begins uniformly as soon as the temperature rises to the necessary level.

In this way the wide divergence among temperature optima

for active growth is a fundamental mechanism for regulating the course of the seasonal cycle.

The above pattern, which is typical for species in temperate latitudes, is often complicated by additional adaptations. These include, for example, the requirement of water, without which the development of over-wintering reactivated larvae of several Lepidoptera and also that of locust eggs is not resumed. The resumption of development in spring may be greatly delayed by a raised threshold for the first stages of post-diapause development, as is observed in *Chloridea obsoleta* (GORYSHIN, 1958b). Such partial and as yet insufficiently-studied adaptations, together with adaptations of the active stages based on stable phenology, create great diversity in the phenological patterns of species in nature. We must also point out that diapause, by limiting the period of active development, to a considerable extent also limits the number of generations.

Very little is known of the synchronization of insect development with seasonal variations in climate in tropical and subtropical countries. It has been adequately described only for the geometrid *Abraxas miranda* and the Cabbage Moth *Barathra brassicae* in Japan (MASAKI, 1956a, 1958). Field and laboratory observations on other southern species—*Nomadacris septemfasciata* (NORRIS, 1959), *Platyedra gossypiella* (SQUIRE, 1939, 1940), *Diatrea lineolata* (KEVAN, 1944), *Diparopsis castanea* (PEARSON and MITCHELL, 1945), and *Chloridea obsoleta* (PARSONS and ULLYETT, 1934)—have shown that, in all cases where there is seasonal development and constant harmony between the calendar and the different phases of the cycle, this has been achieved by means of special types of diapause. The mechanism of synchronization in tropical conditions, however, is substantially different from that described for species in a temperate climate with cold reactivation. Judging from the data of Masaki and Norris, the fundamental role in it is played not by temperature conditions during diapause but by ecological factors acting during the period of preparation for diapause, under the influence of which the duration of the resting period proves to be variable.

The significance of diapause in the geographical distribution of insects

Comparison of the temperature adaptations of active stages in the life cycles of insects does not show in tropical and temperate-zone species any differences that adequately explain their attachment to a particular climatic zone (DANILEVSKII, 1946, 1949, 1950). That is because of the relatively slight variation in the geographical aspect of temperatures during the active period. Temperature adaptations of the diapause states are much more diverse, as has been noted above, and this may be naturally explained by the great differences in temperature conditions in winter at different latitudes. A cardinal role in establishing the present ranges is taken by these historically-originating features of the diapause states.

The most obvious relation is that between geographical distribution and the degree of frost-resistance in the diapause states.

It has long been known that the northern limits of insect distribution coincide with the isotherms of winter minima (GREVILLIUS, 1905; SANDERSON, 1908; UVAROV, 1931). According to Grevillius, for instance, the range of *Euproctis chrysorrhoea* is limited by the $-35°$ isotherm, which closely corresponds to a temperature lethal to the larvae in diapause. Kozhanchikov has shown in a number of special studies that several general types of northern range limits of palaearctic species may be fairly accurately determined on the basis of specific frost-resistance and the amounts of effective heat required for a complete cycle.

With high frost-resistance in the diapause stages, e.g. in *Pyrausta nubilalis* (the European Corn Borer), *Phaedon cochleariae*, and *Loxostege sticticalis* (KOZHANCHIKOV, 1938b, 1939c, 1941), minimum winter temperatures do not prevent extension of the range to the north. Such species are widely distributed in Eurasia, and the northern limits of their ranges are determined mainly by the total of effective temperatures necessary for their development, i.e. by summer conditions. In species with low frost-resistance the total of summer temperatures limits extension to the north only in western regions with mild winters, and the north-eastern limit is determined by winter minima. Therefore, for instance, *Pieris brassicae* and *Gastroidea viridula* (KOZHANCHIKOV, 1936, 1939c) do not extend into continental regions of Siberia. In some widely-distributed species the northern limit there, following the course of winter isotherms, becomes sinuous —e.g. in the case of *Agrotis segetum* (KOZHANCHIKOV, 1937b). The less resistant the species is to negative temperatures, the more strongly this feature is shown. Consequently complete segregation of the western and eastern parts of the range may occur, as is seen in the Winter Moth *Operophtera brumata* (KOZHANCHIKOV, 1950c). Finally, the western limits of distribution of southern species may be entirely determined by low frost-resistance in the diapause stages. This is seen in the cases of *Philosamia cynthia* (DANILEVSKII, 1940), *Polychrosis botrana* (KOMAROVA, 1954), and *Chloridea obsoleta* (GORYSHIN, 1958b).

The above data illustrate the importance of hardiness in the diapause stages in determining the extent of the possible range of a species and in its occupation of regions with severe climates.

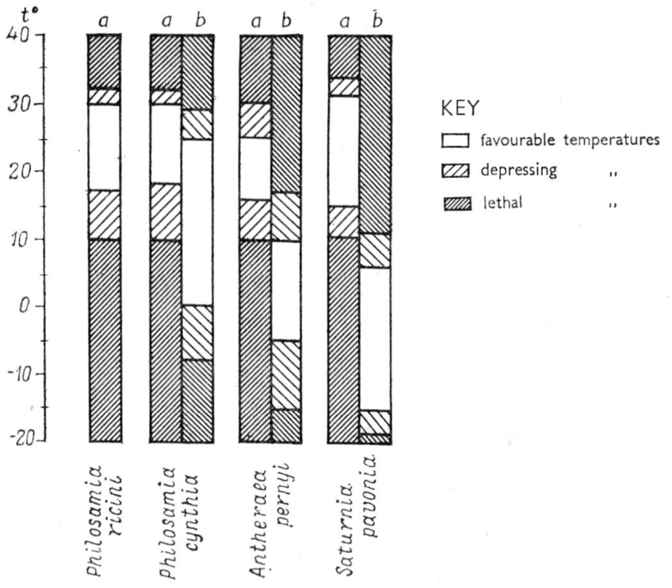

FIG. 3. The relation between the temperature norms of active and diapausing stages in different species of the family *Attacidae*.

a, active stages; *b*, diapausing stages.

On the other hand, specialization of the life cycle and temperature requirements during diapause, which arise primarily as a mechanism for coordinating phenology and the seasonal effects of external conditions, may prove to be a limiting factor in the geographical distribution of a species. For instance, the absence of the Beet Webworm *Loxostege sticticalis* from southern districts of the U.S.A. may be explained by the fact that the winters are too warm, and prevent reactivation of the prepupae in diapause (PEPPER, 1938).

The importance of differentiation of the life cycle and the seasonal effects of temperature as factors determining the geographical distribution in general may be traced in species with sharply-defined ranges (DANILEVSKII, 1946, 1949). Fig. 3 shows the relation between temperature norms for active and resting phases in the life cycles of four representatives of the family *Attacidae* with different geographical distribution. *Philosamia ricini* is found only in tropical Asia; *Philosamia cynthia* inhabits mainly tropical and subtropical countries in Asia; *Antheraea pernyi* occurs in temperate provinces of China; and *Saturnia pavonia* is a typical trans-palaearctic species, extending as far as the Arctic Circle. The first of these has no diapause, and the others have diapause in the pupal stage.

The phases of active growth and morphogenesis of these species, as shown in Fig. 3, are characterized by similar and narrowly-limited requirements. The temperature zone normal for life activity in all lies between 15° and 30°, and the limits for development are about 10° and 33°. Specific differences are insignificant and have no connection with types of range. Requirements in the diapause state, on the contrary, differ greatly. Depending on the relation of these to the requirements of the active stages, a number of sharply-differing types of life cycle are formed, which may be taken as characteristic of definite eco-geographical groupings:

(1) Species of the *Philosamia ricini* type, which have no resting phase, and whose entire development is adapted to a narrow range of temperature, prolonged divergences from this range being lethal to them. Such species are restricted to the tropical zone and to some subtropical countries where seasonal fluctuations in temperature do not exceed a few degrees, making year-round development possible.

(2) Species of the *Philosamia cynthia* type with thermophilic diapause, whose optimum for reactivation coincides partly or wholly with conditions required for the development of their active stages. The existence of such species proves to be possible both in constant high temperatures and in fluctuating temperatures.

This ecological group includes *Chloridea obsoleta* (GORYSHIN, 1958b), *Diparopsis castanea* (PEARSON and MITCHELL, 1945),

Platyedra gossypiella, and other southern forms. Their range embraces regions of tropical and subtropical climate without a definite winter period. Their diapause is primarily an adaptation for survival in drought and heat, but because of the similarity of the mechanisms for resistance to drought and to low temperatures species of this group are capable of prolonged survival in comparatively low temperatures and even slight frosts. Some of them therefore extend into southern regions of the Palaearctic with definite cold seasons.

(3) Finally, a special eco-geographical group is composed of species of the *Saturnia pavonia* and *Antheraea pernyi* type, with diapause at low temperatures, reactivation from which takes place only at a temperature below the threshold for active development. In consequence of the sharp divergence between the requirements for the active and the diapause stages, existence of such forms is not possible in constant temperatures. Fluctuation in temperature during ontogenesis is for them an indispensable condition for life.

This group includes the majority of species that occur in temperate latitudes. As typical, and fairly well studied, examples we may mention: *Pieris brassicae*, *Pieris napi*, *Lymantria dispar*, *Leucoma salicis*, *Acronycta rumicis*, *Pyrausta nubilalis*, etc.

This group includes forms differing greatly in their modes of life, their diets and their ranges. Many of them occupy extensive territories from the subarctic to the Mediterranean, with extremely varied climatic conditions, but the southern limits of their ranges are very similar. The annual temperature fluctuations in the regions occupied by them have a marked seasonal rhythm, with average temperature in the winter months not lower than +12°, and regular frosts. None of these species passes beyond this ecological limit, or penetrates into the tropics, because of the absence there of the temperature fluctuations necessary for their complete cycle.

The following bioclimatogram (Fig. 4), compiled from experimental data on the Chinese Oak Silkworm *Antheraea pernyi*, shows how closely the seasonal adaptations of insects reflect the temperature rhythm within their range. It shows the annual temperature curves at several points in Eastern Asia in relation to the norms required for the active and diapause phases. At all points lying within the range of the species from north-eastern China (Siyangtsi) to the south (Chengtu), the temperature in summer corresponds to the norm for the active stages and that in winter to the norm for the diapause stages. At points lying north

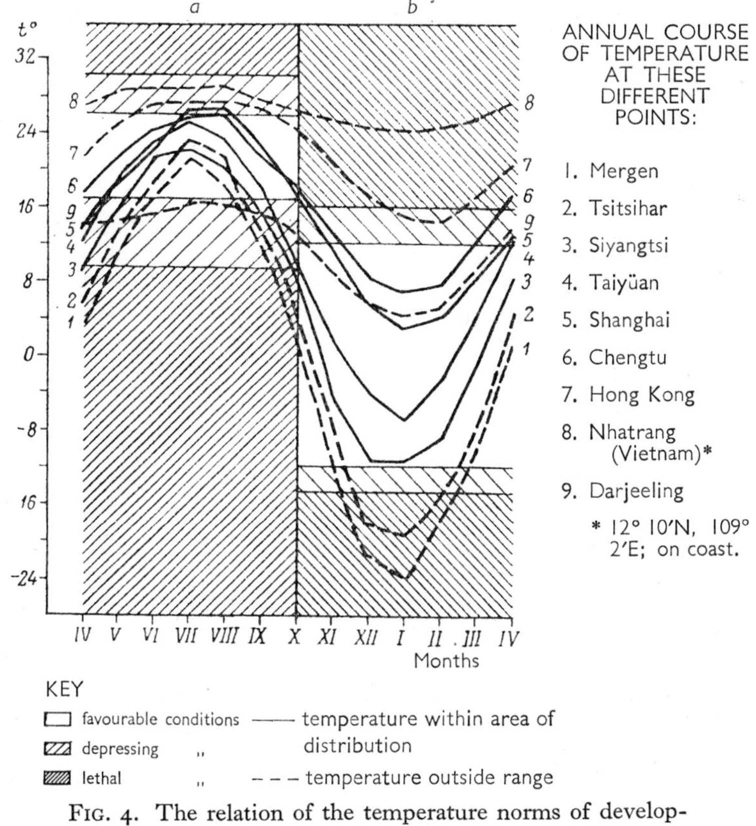

FIG. 4. The relation of the temperature norms of development of different stages of the seasonal cycle of *Antheraea pernyi* to annual course of temperature in Eastern Asia.

a, active stages; *b*, diapausing pupae.

(TRANSLATOR'S NOTE: the names transliterated as Sivan'tszy and Chendu have been tentatively identified as Siyangtsi (33°26′N., 116°21′E.) and Chengtu (30°37′N., 104°06′E.), although the text suggests a greater difference in latitude.)

of the limits of distribution of the species (towards Blagoveshchensk) summer conditions are still favourable, but the winter temperature falls below the limits of frost-resistance for diapausing pupae (– 18°, – 20°). Places lying south of the range limits have winter temperatures too high for diapausing pupae, hence development of the full cycle is impossible there also. The Chinese Oak Silkworm, like other species of this ecological type, does not penetrate into the tropics even along mountain systems, e.g. at Darjeeling, because of the equable temperature there.

Confirmation of the primary importance of seasonal fluctuations in temperature as a factor in the distribution of species of temperate climates is given by the results of acclimatizing them beyond the limits of their natural range. When species of this type were taken from Europe to America, none of them extended southward in the new area beyond the climatic limits characteristic of the original range. When taken to the southern hemisphere they can adapt themselves to the reversed seasonal cycle, which fact DUCLAUX (1871) has explained as being due to reactivation being delayed by high temperature. It is remarkable, however, that even south of the Equator acclimatization is always restricted to regions similar to the original in the annual range of temperature. This was very clearly demonstrated by SHEL'DESHOVA (1956) for the Codling Moth *Enarmonia* (*Carpocapsa*) *pomonella*, which originated in Europe and central Asia. The equatorial boundaries of the present vast range of the Codling Moth in the northern and southern hemispheres follow precisely the mid-winter isotherms of $+12°$ and $+14°$, in January for the northern hemisphere and in July for the southern. In areas lying nearer to the Equator acclimatization has proved to be impossible, because seasonal fluctuations in temperature are too small.

The absence of species of the above ecological type from regions where the winter is too warm should not be looked upon merely as the result of the physical impossibility of reactivating their diapause stages. Rather is it explained by the impossibility (on the principle of cold reactivation) of coordinating the life cycle and the seasonal sequence of external conditions there, since for the normal functioning of the mechanism it is necessary to have a prolonged period of temperatures that inhibit the resumption of development. The inconstancy of the winter conditions in marginal subtropical areas, where the average temperature remains at a level intermediate between the norms for active and diapause stages and is always marked by sharp rises and dangerous frosts, may produce serious disturbance of the life cycle in species adapted to winters of constant cold. This important question remains almost untouched by investigators.

MILYANOVSKII (1956b), discussing the reasons for the absence of many northern species of Lepidoptera from the subtropical littoral zone of Abkhazia (Sukhumi) although they are common in adjoining mountain districts, concluded that this could not be explained by the humidity and temperature conditions in summer and the related food conditions. He considered the main reason to be the warm and very changeable winters on the coast, which produce—particularly during the unstable diapause in the larval stages—reactivation during a period when the availability of food and temperature required for development is doubtful. In the mountain districts, which have colder and more uniform winters, the development of these species proceeds normally. It is of interest that for several southern non-diapausing species the winter, even on the coast, is too cold. For instance, the population of the Oleander Sphinx Moth *Daphnis nerii* dies off there every year, and continues to exist only because adults migrate from more southerly areas. KUZNETSOV (1958) came to a similar conclusion about the effect of winter conditions, by analysing the altitudinal distribution of Lepidoptera in subtropical districts of Kopet-Dagh.

The great zoogeographical importance of the seasonal rhythm of climate and of physiological adaptations to it is shown by the precise correspondence of the boundaries dividing the holarctic and tropical areas with the winter-month 12° isotherm and the limit of possible frosts down to −5° and −10°, i.e. with conditions which make year-round development difficult. This zone serves as an ecological barrier, preventing passage to the north of non-cold-resistant tropical fauna and passage to the south of specialized fauna of the regions with cold winters.

Species able to pass this barrier are of particular interest. They are relatively few. They consist either of species with thermophilic diapause (*Philosamia*, *Chloridea* and *Platyedra* spp.) or species having movable resting periods of the quiescence type, e.g. *Plutella maculipennis*, *Agrotis segetum*, *A. margaritosa*, etc. (DANILEVSKII, 1949). Quiescence, which provides the possibility of surviving unfavourable temperature conditions, does not prevent continuous development in conditions that are steadily favourable. The world-wide distribution of *Plutella* shows the exceptional adaptability of this type of cycle. Unfortunately, it remains entirely uninvestigated.

4. The physiological mechanism of diapause

A number of hypotheses have been put forward to explain the physiological factors that induce diapause, but most of them have not been supported by experimental data and have now been discarded.

After the work of WIGGLESWORTH (1934, 1936, 1954), WILLIAMS (1946, 1956), FUKUDA (1951a, 1951b, 1951c, 1952), HASEGAWA (1952), and many other authors there is no longer any doubt that the state of diapause is caused primarily by changes taking place in the endocrine system, which regulates the growth and development of insects. Abundant experimental data confirming this conclusion are cited in the summaries and reviews by WIGGLESWORTH (1954), LEES (1955, 1956, 1959a), and NOVAK (1959). To understand the seasonal cyclic nature of development and its dependence on external conditions, however, it is necessary to state briefly modern concepts of the hormonal mechanism for regulation of diapause.

Three different types of regulation of diapause are distinguished, depending on the developmental stage at which diapause begins.

The first type is characteristic of diapause beginning in the period of growth and metamorphosis. According to the data of Williams and his colleagues, who studied this type in detail in *Platysamia cecropia*, diapause in the pupa of this species is caused by a temporary inactivity of the gland system, which produces a hormone activating growth and development. The primary link in this system is the neurosecretory cells of the protocerebrum, which secrete a substance that stimulates the endocrine organs, in particular the prothoracic gland. The hormone discharged by the latter into the haemolymph serves as a direct stimulant to metamorphosis and moulting. Possibly the corpora cardiaca take part in this process as intermediate links (NOVAK, 1959).

BUTENANDT and KARLSON (1954) succeeded in isolating from *Bombyx* pupae the prothoracic gland hormone ('ecdysone') in crystalline form. It is not peculiar to sex or species, and shows the same effect even on representatives of other orders. Transplantation of the brain and prothoracic gland from active individuals into diapausing pupae, and also injection of the pure hormone, have the effect of breaking diapause and reinducing development at any time. The process of natural reactivation of the diapause stages is due to gradual restoration of the secretory activity of the brain centres, which takes place spontaneously, but is greatly accelerated by cold.

There are adequate grounds for believing that the above regulatory mechanism applies also to larval diapause (SELLIER, 1949; RAHM, 1952; CHURCH, 1955a) and to late embryonic diapause, when development is halted at the stage of complete formation of the larva in possession of a functioning neuro-humoral system.

The second type of regulation is observed in imaginal diapause, a principal feature of which is arrest of development of the sex organs. The mechanism regulating sexual maturation has not been adequately explained, and there are substantial contradictions in the experimental data, but it certainly cannot be due to the action of the prothoracic gland, since in the imaginal phase it usually degenerates. Apparently the principal role is assumed by the gonadotropic hormone, secreted by the corpora allata, whose activity is controlled by the neurosecretory centres of the brain. The gonadotropic hormone of the corpora allata acts on the sex cells not directly but through the follicular cells that nourish them.

DETINOVA (1945) has pointed out the dependence of imaginal diapause in the mosquito *Anopheles maculipennis* on the activity of the corpora allata. According to JOLY (1945), imaginal diapause in the beetle *Dytiscus* may be terminated by implantation of active corpora allata. It is possible that even there, as in pupal diapause, the primary stimulus is produced in the brain, because in diapausing females of *Leptinotarsa decemlineata* sexual maturation can be produced not only by the secretion of the corpora allata (DE WILDE, 1959b) but also by that of the epipharyngeal ganglia taken from active individuals (GRISON, 1949). Natural reactivation in imaginal diapause is accelerated by lowered temperature.

Lastly, the third type of regulation has been described for diapause beginning in early embryonic stages, when the embryo has not yet formed its neural and endocrinal systems. This type has been most fully studied in the silkworm by Japanese investigators, and to some extent in embryonic diapause in locusts (JONES, 1956a, 1956b). It has been pointed out long ago (UMEYA, 1926) that the factor inducing diapause in eggs of the silkworm is found in the haemolymph of the female and is transmitted through the ovary. But only the recent work of FUKUDA (1951a, 1951b, 1951c, 1952, 1953a, 1953b, 1953c) and HASEGAWA (1952) has established that the source of this 'diapause hormone' is the neurosecretory cells of the suboesophageal ganglion, whose activity is controlled to a definite extent by the brain through the neural commissures (FUKUDA, 1953c; MOROHOSHI, 1959; LYUI KHUN-SHEN, 1960). The hormone is not peculiar to the species. Diapause can be induced in silkworm eggs by transplanting into the pupae suboesophageal ganglia from other species of Lepidoptera, both those diapausing in the egg stage (*Antheraea yamamai*, *Lymantria dispar*) and those without embryonic diapause (*Antheraea pernyi*). HASEGAWA (1957) obtained from silkworms an active hormone extract that induced diapause. As in other cases, termination of embryonic diapause takes place under the influence of low temperatures, which apparently destroy an inhibiting hormone in the egg.

Therefore we may consider it proved that diapause can be induced by different causes. These are either the absence of hormones which stimulate growth, in the cases of pupal and imaginal diapause; or the presence of a special 'diapause hormone' that checks growth in the early embryonic stages. Although most of the experimental data on which these views are founded are quite convincing in themselves, all the general deductions can hardly be regarded as conclusive and as completely expressing the nature of the observed phenomena. In the work of various authors, carried out on different subjects, there are many contradictory or ambiguous data, and new investigations frequently lead to unexpected results.

A serious shortcoming in most studies is the absence of a comparative approach to the problem and a certain narrowness of view. Thus all studies of pupal and larval diapause are based only on experiments on its termination, and in embryonic diapause of the silkworm only the process of its initiation has been studied. It has been suggested that both initiation and termination of diapause are due to a single hormonal factor. This, however, has not been demonstrated and is even doubtful. Preparation for diapause, which begins during a period of active growth and leads to profound physiological changes in the organism, has not been studied from the point of view of its hormonal mechanism. It is nevertheless very important, and probably several components of the endocrine system participate. If the organism is not prepared physiologically, simple removal of the brain or of the prothoracic gland cannot produce the typical diapause picture in species or stages that do not usually possess it. Thus in the experiments of NOVAK (1599), when the brain is removed from silkworm pupae, although a halt in development and also a decrease in respiration and increased resistance to cyanide are observed, the latter are much less marked than in pupae in normal diapause. In my experiments, when the first section of the body was removed from non-diapausing larvae of *Galleria melonella*, *Dendrolimus pini*, and *Enarmonia pomonella*, respiration and transpiration continued at a considerably higher level than in diapause. As a result the individuals operated upon soon died from emaciation and desiccation.

It may be suggested that with more complete knowledge of the functions of separate hormones in regulating normal growth and development we may succeed in unifying the general pattern of these varied physiological mechanisms, which have been discovered up to the present for different stages of ontogenesis. A number of interesting ideas on this subject have been propounded by HINTON (1953, 1957), who attempted to formulate a general theory of diapause based on the simultaneous action of inhibiting hormones and of activators. Within that framework new data by MOROHOSHI (1959), obtained from *Bombyx mori*, acquire great significance. He showed that in addition to the hormone from the suboesophageal ganglion which induces diapause, there is in this species also an antagonistic hormone, secreted by the corpora allata, which inhibits it. The secretory activity of both organs is controlled by the brain through nerve paths. Peculiarities of voltinism in different races are determined by the balance of these two factors. Both hormones not only take part in regulating diapause but also affect the duration of larval development, the number of moults, and the amount of silk secreted. Morohoshi looks upon the hormone of the suboesophageal gland as a general inhibitor of growth, and the hormone of the corpora allata as a stimulator of growth.

A similar pattern is very probable in other types of diapause also. That is indicated by the existence of a 'hormone of embryonic diapause', secreted by the suboesophageal gland, in species with pupal diapause (such as *Antheraea pernyi*), for which its significance is not clear. Apparently diapause is not determined by a special physiological mechanism but is merely a result of quantitative changes in the balance of the hormonal system which regulates normal growth and metamorphosis in insects. From this point of view one can understand better the possibility of similar types of diapause evolving independently in widely-differing systematic groups, and different types in closely-related species. Comparative study of species and races with different life cycles will doubtless lead to the discovery of the physiological mechanism that determines diapause and of the paths by which it was produced in the course of evolution.

5. The conditions regulating the initiation of diapause in the seasonal cycle

In discussing the biological significance of diapause we have not touched on the question of causes regulating the time at which it appears during the season. This problem, however, is exceedingly important from the ecological standpoint, as it is only by the timely initiation of diapause, as of other seasonal adaptations, that its adaptational role can become apparent. Agreement between the time of onset of diapause and the effects of external conditions is always very clearly manifest; consequently a special mechanism must exist to maintain this synchronization. Many different views about this have been put forward in the literature, but they are often contradictory or inadequately based.

The great constancy in the calendar dates of onset of diapause for every locality and species certainly cannot be explained by the existence of an endogenous annual rhythm of development independent of external conditions. The periods of development and the date of commencement of the resting stage can easily be altered experimentally by changing external conditions, even in monocyclic species, which develop throughout the year in a single generation. At the same time, regulation of diapause cannot be explained as being due only to external causes.

A neurohumoral mechanism as the basis of diapause enables the internal and external factors that regulate the course in time of seasonal development to be combined into a single system. The neurosecretory activity of the brain may depend both on the internal conditions of the organism and on external stimuli received by special receptors, or which directly activate the nervous system. On this basis we perceive the possibility of two different methods of regulating diapause: (1) endogenous, causing internal physiological processes, and (2) exogenous, controlled by external environmental factors.

An example of endogenous regulation is provided by monocyclic species with obligatory diapause, which occurs in each generation at a stage determined for that species by internal, genetic, fixed correlations. Such strict monocyclism is found in all orders of insects. Although the initiation of diapause in these cases does not depend on external conditions, the annual cycle as a whole remains under the influence of the environment, especially of temperature, which determines the rate of reactivation and also the dates and duration of development of the active stages. It is on this basis that synchronization of the development of monocyclic species with the seasonal effects of external conditions is achieved.

Monocyclism fixed by heredity is the simplest and surest method of synchronizing the life cycle of insects with the seasonal sequence of external conditions in cases where, because of temperature or other factors, development of only one generation a year is possible. Therefore such cycles predominate among insects in northern latitudes, and also in desert ephemerals or species that are biologically linked with strictly limited phenophases of plants.

On the other hand, where conditions during the vegetative period permit development of more than one generation, monocyclism becomes biologically unprofitable, as it restricts the possibilities of multiplication of a species. In such conditions a polycyclic type of development evolves, with facultative diapause, the beginning and end of which are controlled mainly by external factors. Such species have an unbroken series of successive generations during the vegetative period, and diapause comes only with the approach of unfavourable conditions. This type of seasonal development is ecologically more fluid than the monocyclic, and permits fuller use of the potentialities of multiplication. It is, therefore, the most prevalent among insects.

The cause of initiation of diapause has been sought among the external conditions in which survival is due to this adaptation.

There is a widespread opinion that diapause is a response to unfavourable conditions that accompany development (COUSIN, 1932; MAERCKS, 1934; KOZHANCHIKOV, 1937a; and others). Experimental data exist that point to its initiation under the influence of external factors: low or very high temperature, low atmospheric humidity, decrease of the water content in the diet, and changes in the biochemical composition of food plants.

The problem of regulating the seasonal cycle of insects has taken on a new aspect in recent years on account of the discovery of the great dependence of diapause on photoperiodic conditions.

The duration of daylight occupies a unique place among ecological factors. Unlike hygrothermic and food conditions, light is not essential to the fundamental processes of life activity. Growth and development even of insects living in exposed conditions may take place normally with any day-length, or even in total darkness. It is therefore quite evident that diapause and other phenomena that occur under the influence of changes in day-length are not direct adaptations to the light factor. Day-length is only an indirect factor, which regulates in time the adaptations of insects to changes in other vitally important conditions.

This 'signal' role of photoperiod compels us to re-examine the established concepts of the mechanism of action of other ecological factors in the initiation of diapause.

The results of experimental investigations of the photoperiodic reaction of insects and their physiological condition during the period of diapause indicate that diapause should not be regarded as a reaction to unfavourable growth conditions. Moreover, the process of formation of diapause, associated with intensive assimilation and accumulation of the food reserves necessary to support life during the resting period, requires conditions favourable for active life processes. The special role of diapause in the equalization of phenology is based on the onset of the resting period long before autumnal chilling. Consequently the regulation of diapause in nature can be performed only by factors of a 'signal' type, i.e. those regularly preceding the onset of seasons unfavourable to development. These may be any external factors having a sufficiently regular seasonal course. Changes in temperature, humidity, and food composition by autumn are also in essence signals of the approach of winter.

Thus the timeliness of onset of diapause in nature is ensured by a very safe regulating system, founded upon the parallel action of various factors. The hormonal mechanism of diapause, which enables it to be regulated by diverse influences which directly or indirectly affect the neuro-endocrinal system, explains why factors entirely different in their nature may produce similar effects.

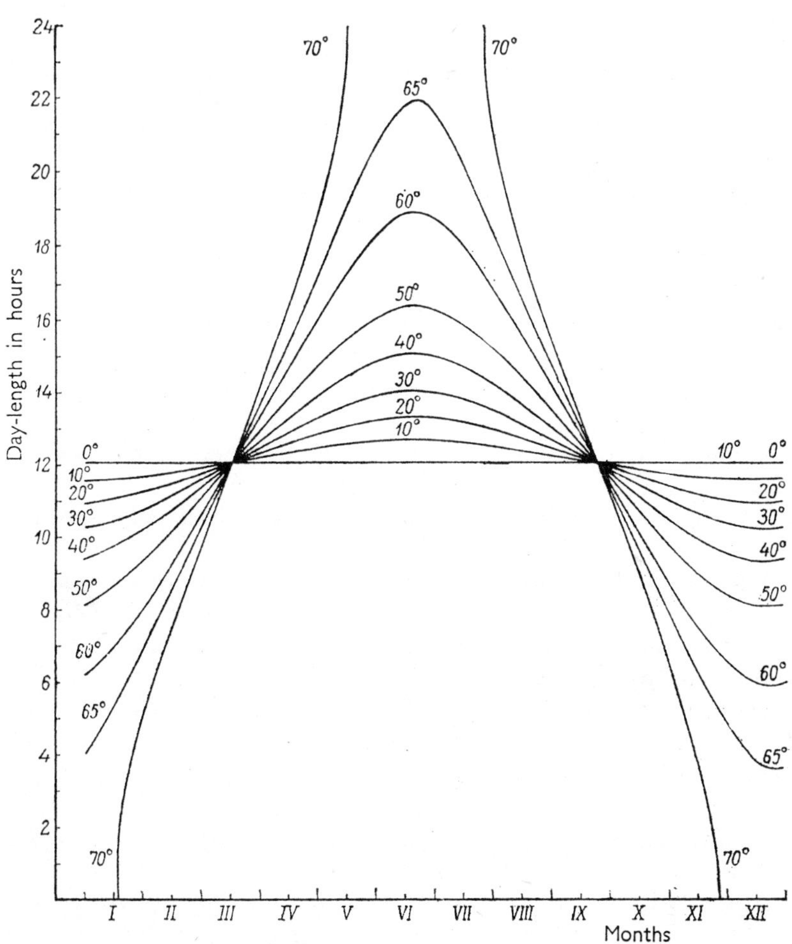

FIG. 5. The seasonal changes in day-length at different latitudes in the northern hemisphere.

The yearly course of day-length differs in its constancy and astronomical precision from other ecological conditions that determine the onset of diapause and other seasonal adaptations. For that very reason it serves as the principal regulator of the seasonal cycle. It is noteworthy that, in the process of adaptation by insects to living in a reversed-seasonal environment, the chief role in regulating seasonal-cyclic adaptations has been taken by changes in day-length—not a factor of direct physiological significance, but a prime cause of seasonal fluctuations in climate.

It is important to evaluate the biological role of photoperiodism in insects from a geographical point of view. The seasonal amplitude of fluctuations in day-length varies with the latitude (Fig. 5). At the Equator day-length is always constant at 12 hours. This provides for an even flow of energy throughout the year, and great stability of temperature. With distance from the Equator seasonal fluctuations in day-length and in the amount of radiation received increase progressively, producing greater variations in the seasonal rhythm of climate, especially of temperature. The biological role of photoperiodism in different geographical zones cannot be uniform. The great significance of this factor in the temperate zone, with its marked seasonal changes in temperature and day-length, is easily understood. In subarctic latitudes the regulatory role of day-length is necessarily diminished because of the shortness of the vegetative period and the low summer temperature, which practically exclude polycyclism.

On the other hand, the view is often expressed that in low latitudes, because of the very small seasonal fluctuations in day-length and the constant high temperature, which allow continuous development, an acyclic or homodynamic type of development predominates; hence photoperiod cannot play a substantial role there. But since in tropical regions continuous development often proves to be impossible because of sharp seasonal fluctuations in humidity, which lead to diapause as an adaptation to ensure survival through drought periods, there is a need for a precise indicator of the approach of such periods. The data of NORRIS (1959) are of special interest in this respect, showing that in the locust *Nomadacris septemfasciata*, which lives in Africa at about latitude 10° (where variations in day-length through the year do not exceed one hour), there is a clear photoperiodic reaction which regulates the onset of imaginal diapause. It is therefore very probable that in tropical countries with definite seasonal changes in humidity, day-length is a more important ecological factor than is generally believed.

Chapter II

THE PRINCIPAL FEATURES OF THE PHOTOPERIODIC REACTION IN INSECTS

The first experimental proofs of the influence of seasonal fluctuations in day-length on insect development were obtained soon after discovery of the phenomenon of photoperiodism in plants. Marcovitch (1923, 1924) discovered that the sequence of seasonal forms in the complex life cycle of aphids was determined by the duration of daylight. Later Shull (1928, 1929, 1930) studied in detail the influence of photoperiodic conditions on the emergence of winged forms of the aphid *Macrosiphum solanifolii*. But these important works, as well as the detailed investigation of Kogure (1933), which showed the importance of day-length in regulating embryonic diapause in bivoltine and multivoltine races of silkworms, were not appreciated at the time, and the full investigation of photoperiodism in entomology was delayed for a long time. During the next two decades only isolated studies produced data dealing with the effect of light conditions on the development of various species of insects (Sabrosky, Larsen and Nabours, 1933; Baker, 1935; Tate and Vincent, 1936). Thus the role of photoperiodic conditions in insect ecology had not been studied at all until recently. Moreover, in several special investigations the influence of the light factor on insect development was doubted or even denied (Janisch and Maercks, 1933).

The little attention paid to so important a factor can be explained only by the ecological role of seasonal adaptations of insects—i.e. the very phenomena regulated by day-length—still not being adequately appreciated at that time. Only when the paramount importance of these adaptations in the life of insects was demonstrated was definite appreciation given to the problem of photoperiodic regulation of development and its practical value in the field of entomology understood.

Fairly recently several authors, simultaneously and independently, again demonstrated the outstanding role of seasonal day-length fluctuations in the regulation of diapause and the seasonal rhythm of insect development (ANDRIANOVA, 1948; DANILEVSKII and GEISPITS, 1948; DANILEVSKII, 1948; DICKSON, 1949; WAY and HOPKINS, 1950). Unlike earlier studies, which had dealt with insects having very specialized seasonal cycles, these studies were made on species with relatively simple cycles, typical of a wide variety of insects. Thus the significance of day-length as a general and important ecological factor became clearer. From then on studies of photoperiodism in insects have developed intensively and continuously. Experimental data of wide scope have now accumulated, which give a general outline of the photoperiodic reactions of insects.

1. The distribution of photoperiodic reactions among insects

In the comparative investigation of photoperiodic reactions in our laboratory, we studied in greater or less detail about 90 species of insects and phytophagous mites. Including data from other authors, the total number of species studied in this connection is now about 130. A list of them, with a brief indication of their reactions, is given in the Appendix. In spite of the unequal extent to which different orders have been studied, the data available enable us to make a fairly definite estimate of the distribution of photoperiodic adaptations in the various systematic and biological groups.

Lepidoptera have received the most systematic and detailed study. Dependence of development on the daily rhythm of light has been discovered in more than 60 species belonging to families in widely-separated groups—from the primitive (Tortricidae, Gelechiidae) to the highly-specialized (Lymantriidae, Arctiidae, Noctuidae). There are fairly extensive data for Diptera. Day-length strongly affects the development of various mosquitoes (Culicidae, Tendipedidae, Heleidae) and also the higher flies (Muscidae, Larvivoridae). The remaining orders with complete metamorphosis have been little studied, but clear reactions to day-length have been discovered in sawflies (*Athalia*, *Lygaeonematus*) and parasitic Hymenoptera (*Apanteles*, *Pteromalus*), leaf-eating beetles (*Leptinotarsa*, *Chrysomela*, *Haltica*) and Neuroptera

(*Chrysopa*). In orders with incomplete metamorphosis photoperiodic reactions are widespread among Homoptera—in aphids, cicadas, and leaf-hoppers; they are also found in several locusts (*Acrydium*, *Nomadacris*, *Schistocerca*) and dragonflies (*Anax*).

Thus the ability to react to changes in day-length has been found in representatives of all the principal orders of insects, namely: Lepidoptera, Diptera, Hymenoptera, Neuroptera, Coleoptera, Rhynchota, Orthoptera, and Odonata. If one adds data on the influence of day-length on the seasonal cycles of spider mites and ixodids, it becomes clear that photoperiodic reaction is one of the most general ecological adaptations of the most diverse groups of arthropods.

Photoperiodic adaptations have been observed in species with extremely varied modes of life. These include both terrestrial and aquatic forms; both phytophagous and carnivorous —blood-sucking, predatory, and endoparasitic—species. Many of the forms studied lead exposed lives, but day-length adaptations are also found among forms that live in concealment with marked negative phototropism. Thus the caterpillars of *Barathra brassicae*, *Pyrausta nubilalis*, *Plodia interpunctella*, *Laspeyresia molesta* and *Enarmonia* (*Carpocapsa*) *pomonella* are very sensitive to photoperiod. Even larvae of the fly *Hylemyia brassicae*, which live in the soil on the roots of plants, react to day-length. Thus photoperiodic reactions may occur even in species living in places with very slight illumination. The reaction, however, is not obligatory. Among all the groups studied there are species with little reaction, or even entirely unresponsive to changes in day-length.

The connection between photoperiodic adaptations and the type of seasonal cycle is very clearly marked. Close dependence of development on the light conditions is particularly typical of polycyclic species with facultative diapause. Day-length does not affect homodynamic species or species with only slightly differentiated seasonal cycles. Examples studied in our laboratory are the flies *Musca domestica* and *Calliphora erythrocephala*, the Diamond-back Moth *Plutella maculipennis*, and the mite *Metatetranychus citri*.

It has been shown in the literature that strictly monocyclic forms also do not react to day-length (KOGURE, 1933; DANILEVSKII and GEISPITS, 1948). Among such species neutral to the light conditions are *Lymantria dispar*, *Sphinx ligustri*, *Aporia crataegi*, *Cacoecia rosana*, and *Tortrix viridana*. It has been found, however, that in many Lepidoptera, especially those that hibernate in the caterpillar stage, the seasonal cycle—believed to be fixed by heredity and not dependent on external conditions—proves to be to some extent affected by day-length. This has been found in *Arctia caia*, *Agrotis triangulum*, *Agrotis occulta*, and *Cosmotriche potatoria*, as well as in the closely-studied Tussock Moth (GEISPITS, 1953) and *Spilosoma menthastri* (DANILEVSKII, 1957a, 1957b). In nature these species are monocyclic everywhere, but in experiments with artificially-determined light conditions a considerable decrease in the diapause period, or its complete disappearance, has been observed.

The connection between photoperiodic reactions and seasonal-cyclic adaptations is particularly well shown in the mosquitoes *Anopheles maculipennis* and *Culex pipiens*, of which only fertilized females in diapause survive the winter. Day-length strongly affects the nature of the development of females of these species, determining the course of the gonadotropic cycle and the initiation of diapause; at the same time the light conditions have no effect on the development and physiological condition of males (DANILEVSKII and GLINYANAYA, 1958). A similar phenomenon is also observed in several spider mites, e.g. *Tetranychus urticae* and *Schizotetranychus tiliarium*, of which also only females survive the winter.

Up to the present the attention of investigators has been given only to typical cases of photoperiodic reaction, taking place in a wide variety of external conditions. There are, however, many species in which it is only slightly apparent or occurs only in certain conditions. This group includes, for example, *Agrotis segetum*, *Peridroma margaritosa*, *Athetis ambigua*, *Notodonta ziczac*, *Protophormia terrae-novae*, etc. Such mild forms of the reaction occur even among species living in the open with typical facultative diapause. Study of them may help to explain the conditions for the evolution of photoperiodic adaptations.

The nature of the distribution of photoperiodic reactions among insects enables us to conclude that this adaptation to seasonal changes in external conditions arose independently and by parallel means among different systematic groups. In this respect the reaction to day-length resembles the phenomenon of diapause, whose independent development in different groups is beyond doubt.

2. The phenomena regulated by seasonal fluctuations in day-length

The field of biological phenomena regulated by photoperiodic conditions holds great variety. The effect of day-length on the initiation of diapause has been most fully investigated. Light conditions may also determine the type of diapause, including embryonic diapause (*Bombyx mori*), larval diapause (*Pandemis ribeana*, *Dendrolimus pini*, *D. sibiricus*, *Euproctis chrysorrhoea*, *E. similis*, *Agrotis triangulum*, etc.), prepupal diapause (*Loxostege sticticalis*, *Plodia interpunctella*, *Enarmonia* (*Carpocapsa*) *pomonella*, *Apanteles glomeratus*, *Chrysopa* sp.), pupal diapause (*Acronycta rumicis*, *Pieris brassicae* and many other Lepidoptera), and imaginal diapause (*Anopheles maculipennis*, *Culex pipiens*, *Leptinotarsa decemlineata*, etc.).

In some insect species changes in day-length may also affect ontogenesis (in addition to diapause and the rhythm of seasonal development), determining, in particular, seasonal metamorphoses. Such regulation may take place either directly, or indirectly through diapause. The latter type is clearly shown in the nymphalid *Araschnia levana-prorsa*, known as the classic example of seasonal dimorphism. Adults of the spring generation, emerging from wintering pupae, have a russet-red colour with black spots (the *levana* form); their progeny, developing in summer, are black with white spots (the *prorsa* form). This phenomenon has long been attributed to the effect of temperature on the pupae, and that view is still widely held. The data of SÜFFERT (1924), however, have shown that temperature plays a limited role there and that the chief factor determining the colour-form of the butterflies is diapause. Diapausing pupae, regardless of the temperature, produce the spring red form (*levana*), and active pupae the summer black form (*prorsa*). Diapause in *Araschnia* has in turn proved to be entirely dependent on day-length during the period of larval development (DANILEVSKII, 1948; MÜLLER, 1955c, 1956, 1957b, 1959), and therefore the seasonal colour changes are also regulated by the photoperiodic conditions (Table 2).

We have observed a similar phenomenon in the butterfly

TABLE 2

The effect of photoperiodic conditions on the appearance of seasonal forms of *Araschnia levana-prorsa*. Temperature 26°

Day-length in hours	% of diapausing pupae	% of active pupae	Form
24	0	100	only *f. prorsa*
9	100	0	only *f. levana*
Darkness	77·6	22·4	77·6% *f. levana* 22·4% *f. prorsa*

Hylophila prasinana L. When caterpillars of the southern race of this species (from Sukhumi) were raised in short-day (10-hour) conditions diapausing pupae were produced, from which butterflies of the typical form *prasinana* emerged after hibernation. But in long-day (24-hour) conditions development proceeded without diapause, and in that case butterflies differing sharply in form and colour were obtained. The latter form had previously been placed by systematists in the independent species *Hylophila hongarica* Warr.

A similar mechanism regulates the seasonal alternation of coloured forms of the leafroller *Peronea fimbriana* Thnbg-*lubricana* Mn., formerly considered to be independent species and only recently recognized as synonymous (KUZNETSOV, 1955). Adults of the summer non-diapausing generation, developing in long-day conditions, have an orange-ochre colour (*lubricana*), but the autumn forms are dark-grey (*fimbriana*). When larvae of the autumn form were raised in artificial long-day conditions, Kuznetsov succeeded in obtaining adults with summer-type colouring.

Seasonal changes in colour and structural features in many cicadas have also proved to be connected with changes in day-length. As in Lepidoptera, in most cases the effect of photoperiod on these metamorphoses is expressed through diapause. Thus larvae of the Rice Leaf-hopper *Nephotettix cincticeps*, which enter diapause under the influence of short days, produce a small and relatively short-winged imago, but when developing in continuous long-day conditions they produce a larger long-winged summer form (KISIMOTO, 1959a, 1959b). In the delphacid *Delphacodes striatella*, as the result of diapause induced by short days, the number of short-winged individuals increases in the spring generation as compared with the summer one (KISIMOTO, 1956). Morphological changes connected with diapause are also clearly shown in *Stenocranus minutus*, but with this species (unlike the preceding species) diapausing individuals are larger than those that develop without interruption (MÜLLER, 1957a).

The direct effect of photoperiod, apparently without the participation of diapause, on seasonal metamorphoses of Jassids of the genus *Euscelis* has been established by the detailed investigations of MÜLLER (1954, 1955a, 1955b, 1957b, 1958b, 1959). It is of particular interest that in that case day-length determines not only colour and body-size but also the structure of the genital apparatus—a feature on which species-identification of members of that group had been based.

Fig. 6 shows how much the structure and dimensions of the genitals of male jassids vary in accordance with day-length during the period of larval development. In short-day (4 to 15 hours) conditions only the form known as *incisus* is obtained; in nature it occurs in spring and emerges from hibernating pupae. Characteristic of it are small body-size, dark colour, and the absence of uncinate processes on the surface of the aedeagus. With a long day (16 hours or more) the summer form *plebejus* is obtained. It is considerably larger, lighter in colour, and characterized by the presence of strong uncinate processes on the aedeagus. Transitional forms are observed only in a narrow zone of marginal photoperiods. Temperature has an insignificant effect on the differentiation of these forms. In a constant photoperiodic regime (short-day or long-day) the forms *incisus* and *plebejus* develop continuously, even up to the fourteenth observed generation, retaining all their characteristic features unchanged. In spite of the great morphological differences in the genital apparatus, the two forms easily mate with each other and in such cases are perfectly fertile.

On the basis of experimental analysis, MÜLLER (1958b) has shown that a number of the species of *Euscelis* described by systematists should be combined into two groups of seasonal forms of the species *Euscelis plebejus-incisus* and *Euscelis lineolatus-bilobatus*. It is of interest that the males of seasonal forms of one species can be distinguished from each other by the structure of their genital apparatus better than can those of several fully-independent species. The direct biological significance of these different forms of jassids, like the above-described change of colour in Lepidoptera, is still unknown, but their connection with seasonal climatic changes and with their wintering condition is beyond doubt.

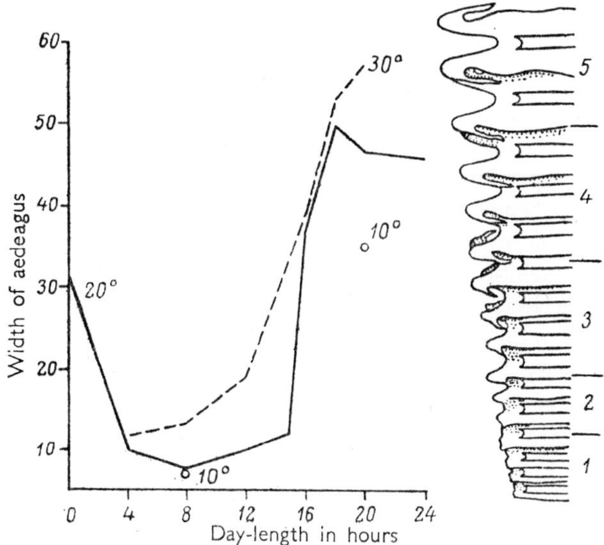

FIG. 6. The changes in the structure of the male genitalia in the jassid *Euscelis plebejus* in accordance with the photoperiodic conditons during post-embryonic development (from Müller, 1959). The ordinates give the breadth of the aedeagus in divisions of the ocular micrometer and the forms corresponding thereto:

1, *incisus*; 2, *abbingensis*; 3, *subplebejus*; 4, *plebejus*; 5, *superplebejus*. ——, at a temperature of 20°; - - -, at 30°; o o o, at 10°.

Changes in day-length have a great effect on the complex seasonal cycles of aphids. Much of the literature is devoted to this important problem. The first data, as already stated, were obtained by MARCOVITCH (1923, 1924), who demonstrated by experiments on *Aphis forbesi* and various migratory species that the change from bisexual to parthenogenetic reproduction, which in them occurs in autumn, and also the development of migratory forms, are due to seasonal changes in day-length. These conclusions were confirmed and developed by work of the following authors on various aphid species: *Macrosiphum solanifolii*=*M. euphorbiae* (SHULL, 1928, 1929), *Aphis fabae* (DAVIDSON, 1929), *Aphis chloris* (WILSON, 1938), *Brevicoryne brassicae* and *Myzus persicae* (BONNEMAISON, 1951), *Acyrthosiphon pisum* (KENTEN, 1955). Among these works the extensive studies of BONNEMAISON (1951) are outstanding.

The mechanism of the photoperiodic regulation of development in aphids has been most fully investigated for *Megoura viciae* (LEES, 1959b). The seasonal cycle of this aphid is comparatively simple. During spring and summer a series of generations of viviparous parthenogenetic females develops (*virginipara*), with or without wings. In spite of their obligatory parthenogenesis, each generation usually contains some males. In autumn the cycle changes to production of a bisexual generation with winged egg-laying females (*ovipara*), which after fertilization produce wintering, diapausing eggs. In this way parthenogenetic females may produce different kinds of offspring, including (as well as males) three types of females: wingless parthenogenetic, winged parthenogenetic, and winged egg-laying females in a bisexual generation.

Lees has demonstrated that viviparous parthenogenetic females of *Megoura viciae* have a special regulatory mechanism, apparently of a humoral nature, which—depending on external conditions—directs the development of the embryo along one of the possible paths. By applying short-day or long-day conditions to different stages of development of maternal individuals, Lees established a chronological succession in the determination of the forms of offspring and a sensitivity to such conditions in the embryonic stages.

Sex is first determined. This takes place in the first larval stage of the mother, apparently in the process of oogenesis, and is controlled by the temperature conditions. Limiting high (25°) and low (11°) temperatures suppress production of males. Photoperiod does not affect sex determination in *Megoura viciae*, but in other species its action is very pronounced. For instance, in *Brevicoryne brassicae* and *Myzus persicae* the number of males in the progeny is greatly reduced in long-day conditions (BONNEMAISON, 1951); and in *Acyrthosiphon pisum* males are completely absent in such conditions, and appear only with short days (KENTEN, 1955).

Later, but still in early embryonic stages, differentiation of the embryos of future females of *Megoura viciae* into parthenogenetic and sexual begins. This process takes place as the embryo appears, beginning with the second larval stage of the mother. It is regulated entirely by the photoperiodic and temperature conditions. High temperatures and long days lead to the formation of parthenogenetic females, and lower temperatures and short days to the formation of oviparous females in a bisexual generation.

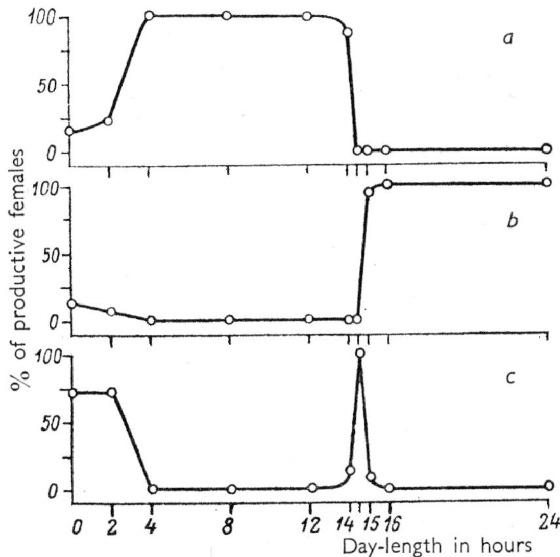

FIG. 7. The dependence of the form of offspring of types of the aphid *Megoura viciae* on the photoperiodic conditions affecting the mothers (from Lees, 1959).

a, % of females producing only *ovipara*; *b*, producing only *virginipara*; *c*, producing both forms. Temperature 15°.

Fig. 7 shows how the appearance of different filial forms of aphids depends on day-length during the development of the mothers. The clearness of the reaction, and the complete change in form of the offspring on either side of the critical photoperiod of $14\frac{1}{2}$ hours, are characteristic. Only in the vicinity of that threshold, and also in darkness, do the females produce mixed offspring.

In later stages of embryonic development the formation of wings on parthenogenetic females is determined. In contradiction to the data of SHULL (1928, 1929) for *Macrosiphum solanifolii*

(*M. euphorbiae*), day-length produces no noticeable effect on this process. The stimulus for formation of winged parthenogenetic females is mainly disturbance of normal diet, and also over-population (Bonnemaison, 1951). (In the opinion of Bonnemaison, after he had checked the reaction of *Macrosiphum euphorbiae*, Shull's conclusions were due to the fact that he mistook migrant *gynoparae* for winged parthenogenetic females.)

The regulation of the seasonal cycle observed in *Megoura viciae* is in general typical for non-migratory, sedentary species of aphids. In multi-host species, for which there are necessarily variations in the plant species used for food during the parthenogenetic part of the cycle, the picture is somewhat more complex. The appearance of special migratory forms, which travel to secondary food plants, is mainly due to deterioration of feeding conditions on the primary plant host (Shaposhnikov, 1959). But the formation of sexually-reproductive individuals (*gynoparae*), that return in autumn to the principal plants (re-migrants) on which they produce a bisexual generation, takes place—as Marcovitch (1924) has shown in *Aphis rumicis*, *A. sorbi*, and *Capitophorus hippophaes*—as a result of shortening the day.

The above data enable us to conclude that the life cycles of aphids are based to a great degree on independent adaptations to two groups of seasonally-fluctuating factors—dietetic and climatic.

The appearance of migratory parthenogenetic females is linked with deterioration of food conditions; in its simplest form it occurs in single-host species, but in two-host species it is accompanied by profound changes in the food-specialization of the migrants. Migrations, which permit transfer to plants more favourable for feeding and reproduction, are the principal means whereby high numbers of aphids are maintained. These phenomena occur during the spring and summer and are not restricted in time by weather conditions critical for life. Therefore the appearance of migratory forms does not require great precision of calendar dates. This apparently is the reason why a photoperiodic signal is not involved in the mechanism regulating the formation of migrants.

The bisexual generation of aphids has a different ecological significance. Because of a general reduction in numbers and fertility, it does not play a substantial role in increasing the population. But it is directly connected with the appearance of the hibernating stages—usually in the form of fertilized diapausing eggs. In the quickly-changing conditions, with critical temperatures, of autumn, the timeliness of the appearance of a bisexual generation becomes very important. Therefore the photoperiodic conditions, together with temperature, acquire primary significance in determining the bisexual generation and its predecessor forms—the sexually-reproductive re-migrants. From the ecological point of view, the dependence of the bisexual generation of aphids on external conditions may be looked upon as a complex case of regulation of winter diapause.

Among all the varied phenomena mentioned above—diapause, colour and structural polymorphism, appearance of re-migrants, and even sex determination in aphids—there is one common feature: that all the phenomena are cyclic, expressing adaptation of a species to seasonal changes in external conditions, and closely connected with the wintering stages. The great similarity in the dependence of the above phenomena on photoperiod (see Figs. 6-9) gives grounds for supposing that the internal directing mechanism for all of them has a common basis. One cannot doubt that all these phenomena are regulated by the activity of the neurohumoral system.

All available experimental data, however, definitely indicate that the photoperiodic conditions exert no substantial influence on the principal life processes in the active stages: intensity of growth, duration of development, resistance to unfavourable conditions, fertility, etc. Therefore, unlike other ecological factors, changes in day-length act selectively on seasonal-cyclical adaptations only. This important fact also accounts for the peculiar forms in which photoperiodic reactions appear.

3. The principal types of reaction to day-length

In the insects that react to changes in day-length two main types of photoperiodic reaction are observed, analogous in an ecological sense to those found in plants.

The long-day type of development, several examples of which are illustrated in Fig. 8, is the most widespread among species of our fauna. A characteristic feature of reactions of this type is that non-diapause development and consequent succession of generations take place in conditions of continuous daylight and 'long days' that exceed the threshold of length critical for the species concerned. Development in short-day conditions, with duration of daylight below the critical point, brings on diapause. In experimental conditions another very characteristic feature has been discovered, namely, a tendency to non-diapause development in extreme short-day conditions and particularly in total darkness. That is shown very typically in *Pieris brassicae* (DANILEVSKII and GEISPITS, 1948), *Acronycta rumicis* (DANILEVSKII, 1948), and a

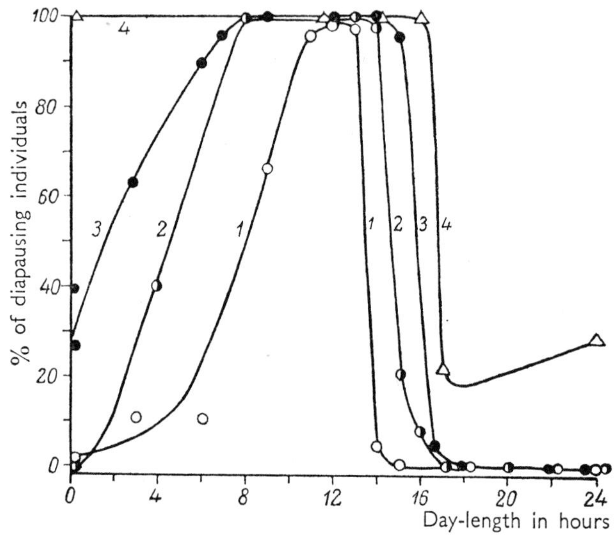

FIG. 8. The photoperiodic reaction of long-day-type species.

1, *Laspeyresia molesta* at 24°; 2, *Pieris brassicae* at 24°; 3, *Acronycta rumicis* at 26°; 4, *Leptinotarsa decemlineata* at 24°.

large number of other Lepidoptera studied in our laboratory. Similar data have been obtained by other authors working on other species: *Laspeyresia molesta* (DICKSON, 1949), *Polia oleracea* (WAY and HOPKINS, 1950), *Antheraea pernyi* (BELOV, 1951; TANAKA, 1950b, 1950c), and the spider mites *Tetranychus urticae* (BONDARENKO, 1950) and *Metatetranychus ulmi* (LEES, 1953a). The similarity in the actions of continuous light and total darkness represents one of the most common features of photoperiodic reaction in terrestrial arthropods. But, as is seen from Fig. 8, the tendency to continuous development in conditions of total darkness may be exhibited to a widely-differing extent in different species, revealing a definite dependence on the critical threshold for the species concerned. As the threshold rises the tendency weakens, or even disappears altogether.

In spite of the similarity of reactions in extreme conditions and the evident symmetry of the photoperiodic curve, different parts of it have quite different biological meanings. The left-hand half, which expresses reaction to day-length below 10 hours, has no ecological significance, as such photoperiods are observed only in winter in high latitudes and consequently special adaptations to them cannot be developed in insects. All that part of the curve is a non-adaptational result of the physiological mechanism on which the principal reaction to natural light-rhythms is based. This aspect is of great interest, but only from the physiological point of view.

The right-hand part of the curve has an entirely different meaning. It expresses adaptation to the daily light conditions in summer and autumn, and so covers the whole ecology of photoperiodic reactions. In regulating the seasonal cycle in nature the critical threshold, which determines the transition from non-diapause to diapause development, has a decisive significance. In most species this transition occurs suddenly when the critical day-length is reached, which is shown in the graph by abrupt bends in the curves. In the region of the critical threshold even small changes in day-length (less than one hour) usually lead to complete inversion of the type of development. Individual variations in this response are very few, in contradistinction to what is seen on the left-hand side of the curve, where variability is always clearly evident. The precision of the response to changes in day-length is the result of rigorous selection, which in natural conditions is necessary in the process of photoperiodic regulation of the seasonal cycle and preparation for hibernation.

The long-day type of photoperiodic reaction is especially characteristic of polycyclic forms in temperate climates with facultative winter diapause. It is rarely found in species with a one-year or two-year development cycle. Among Lepidoptera this happens, apparently, only with unstable diapause and hibernation in the caterpillar stages. As examples we may mention the Pine Moth and the Siberian Silkworm Moth, which have been studied in detail (GEISPITS, 1949, 1953). But among monocyclic species one often finds different degenerate forms of reaction, down to mere traces of it. These forms have not been studied at all, and the biological significance of such reactions to the light conditions remains unexplained. We present a few examples of weak reactions of the long-day type. All relate to species that hibernate in younger or medium instars.

Photoperiod exerts a strong and definite influence on *Arctia caia* larvae of the Leningrad population; but individual variations in the reaction, even among specimens from the same brood, are very great. With a temperature of 23° and a 12-hour day larvae that have reached the third instar cease to feed and to develop. Diapause, however, does not last long, and soon some individuals again begin to eat and to grow slowly. In these conditions the full cycle lasts at least three months. With a long day (20 to 21 hours of light) development in most of the larvae proceeds without interruption; but side by side with individuals pupating by the fortieth day, some larvae remain even to the seventieth day at the same level as those in diapause, although they do not cease to feed. The most uniform development of *Arctia caia* larvae is observed with changing light conditions: short days up to the beginning of diapause in the third instar, and long days throughout the rest of the development period.

TABLE 3

The effect of day-length on the development of *Agrotis occulta* larvae. Temperature 23°

Day-length (hours)	Weight of larvae on 20th day (mg)	Duration of larval development (days)
24	58 (23-155)	39 (33-53)
20	46·5 (27-136)	54 (41-62)
16	44·3 (26-105)	61 (50-70)
12	41·0 (32- 51)	65 (51-78)

Larvae of *Agrotis occulta* react less strongly to the light conditions. Changes in day-length affect mainly their rate of development. At 23°, in all light conditions, the larvae feed without ceasing, but their growth proceeds very unevenly and is clearly greatest in long-day conditions (Table 3). Finally, in the lasiocampid *Cosmotriche potatoria*, whose larvae have no diapause, there is still some acceleration of growth in long-day as compared with short-day conditions.

The opposite type of photoperiodic reaction is found in species that may be called 'short-day' species. Continuous

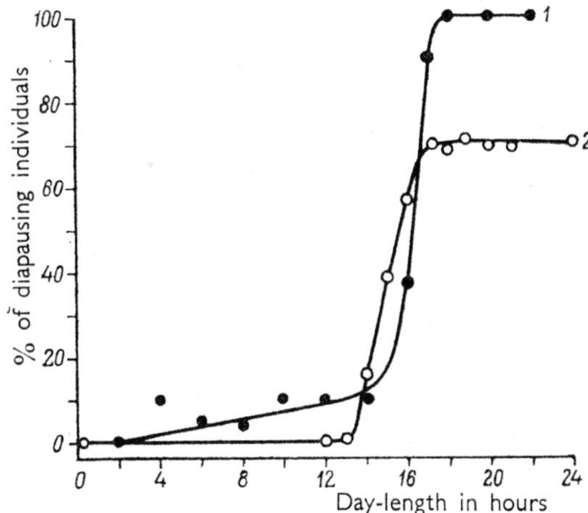

FIG. 9. The photoperiodic reaction of short-day-type species.
1, *Stenocranus minutus*, at 20° (from Müller, 1958);
2, *Bombyx mori*, at 15° (from Kogure, 1933).

development is observed in them only in short-day conditions, whereas long days check growth or induce diapause (Fig. 9). From Table 4 it is seen that total darkness has an effect on them similar to that of long days.

TABLE 4

The effect of day-length on development and diapause in the gor'kovskii univoltine race of *Antheraea pernyi*. Temperature 18°-20°

Day-length (hours)	Duration of larval development (days)	% of diapausing pupae
22-19 (natural day)	52·0	63·7
12	48·4	5·4
8	42·4	6·2
4	50·9	40·0
Darkness	51·3	62·0

In the literature only a few cases of reaction of this type are described. It has been studied in greatest detail in races of silkworms with facultative embryonic diapause. As was first pointed out by KOGURE (1933), regulation of the latter is of a very peculiar type in these insects. As a result of development of the eggs and young larvae in short-day and low-temperature conditions, adults were obtained which laid eggs that developed without interruption, but if incubation took place in long days or higher temperatures the adults laid wintering, diapausing eggs.

The short-day reaction has been observed (DANILEVSKII and GEISPITS, 1948) in the so-called 'gor'kovskii' univoltine race of the Chinese Oak Silkworm *Antheraea pernyi*, bred by Professor S. S. Chetverikov (Table 4). It is of interest that in other races of this species winter diapause of the pupae is regulated by the usual long-day reaction (ANDRIANOVA, 1948; BELOV, 1951; TANAKA, 1944, 1950a, 1950b, 1950c, 1951). The unique seasonal cycle of the geometrid *Abraxas miranda*, with summer diapause in the pupal stage, is also regulated by the short-day type (MASAKI, 1957a, 1958).

Among members of our Lepidoptera the short-day type occurs very rarely and therefore is still not closely investigated. This type of reaction is found in the monocyclic Tussock Moth *Dasychira pudibunda*, in which a long pause in larval development is observed in summer in natural conditions. Experiments by GEISPITS (1953) have shown that development is almost twice as rapid in short days as in long. A definite short-day tendency is found also in the noctuid *Agrotis triangulum* (Table 5). It takes the form of considerable acceleration of the growth of the larvae in short-day conditions. In high temperatures (23°-24°) and short-day condi-

TABLE 5

The effect of day-length on the growth of *Agrotis triangulum* larvae. Temperature 24°

Day-length (hours)	Weight of larvae (mg)			
	20th day	30th day	40th day	50th day
12	66·3 (41-75)	144·7 (141-183)	178·3 (140-279)	180 (147-237)
24	39·3 (25-37)	64·2 (45- 96)	78·4 (63-104)	90·1 (74-120)

tions larvae of the arctiid *Parasemia plantaginis* develop continuously and extremely uniformly. With 24-hour illumination development proceeds slowly and unevenly, and in a certain proportion of the larvae typical diapause is observed.

A very typical case of short-day development was discovered by MÜLLER (1957a, 1958a) in the monocyclic jassid *Stenocranus minutus* (see Fig. 9). In natural conditions it develops in summer during the long-day period, as a result of which it undergoes prolonged imaginal diapause, in which it hibernates. But in short-day experiments that jassid can develop without interruption, with consequent production of a special form, clearly distinguished from the diapausing form by its much smaller size.

All these data show that the short-day type of photoperiodic reaction may be observed in both summer and winter diapause. In our fauna it often occurs in monocyclic species. We may expect this type to be found widely distributed among steppe and desert species that have a summer resting period.

A peculiar type of reaction, which may be called 'intermediate', was discovered by GEISPITS (1953) in several monocyclic Lepidoptera, e.g. in *Leucoma salicis* L., *Euproctis chrysorrhoea* L., and *E. similis* (Fig. 10). Non-diapause development of this type is found only in a very restricted region of optimal day-length (18-20 hours of light per day). With both longer and shorter days diapause always occurs.

The intermediate type of photoperiodic reaction combines the other forms in a single system. In essence it is close to the short-day type seen, for example, in the univoltine race of *Antheraea pernyi* (see Table 4), distinguished only by its zone of development being narrower and displaced towards the long-day type. On the other hand, as GEISPITS (1953) has remarked, there are also features linking it with the long-day type. In many typical long-day species, when developing in continuous light, one constantly observed a small percentage of diapausing individuals, whereas in daylight lasting about 20 hours all of them develop without diapause. Among the species studied one may pick out a series showing gradual transition from the long-day type of development to the intermediate: *Laspeyresia molesta*, *Polia oleracea*, *Leptinotarsa decemlineata*, the northern form of *Pyrausta nubilalis*. Finally, in the intermediate-type species *Euproctis similis*, *E. chrysorrhoea*, and *Leucoma salicis* one sees a gradual weakening of the reaction and contracting of the zone of photoperiod in which continuous development is possible. In *Leucoma salicis*, even with optimum day-length, a considerable proportion of the larvae

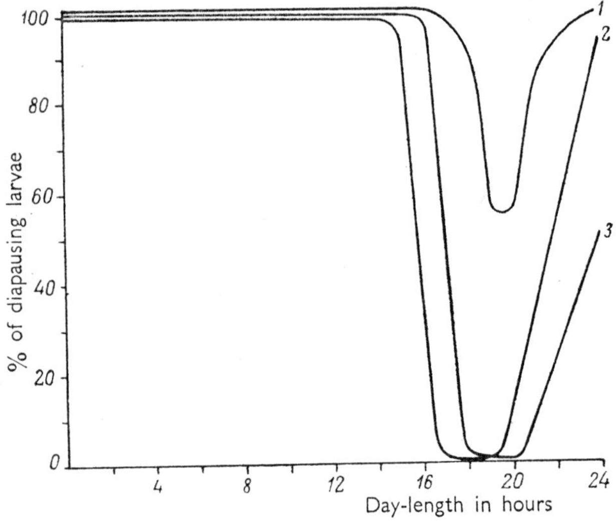

FIG. 10. The photoperiodic reaction of intermediate-type species.

1, *Leucoma salicis*; 2, *Euproctis similis* (from Geispits, 1953); 3, *Pyrausta nubilalis*, northern form (from the data of Du Chzhen'-ven').

enter diapause. From here, there is only one step to monocyclism that is fully independent of light conditions, as, for example, in *Aporia crataegi* or *Lymantria dispar*.

4. The effectiveness of different light rhythms

The photoperiodic effect is based not on simple fluctuation in the amount of light-energy received, but on the specific effect of a rhythmic sequence of light and dark periods of definite length. This is seen in the above-mentioned similarity in the action of continuous light and total darkness. The effectiveness of different light rhythms has been studied in a number of special investigations.

In the experiments with *Acronycta rumicis* we may see how strongly the reaction varies in accordance with the light rhythm

(Table 6). In all the experiments, larvae received equal total numbers of hours of light and darkness during their development period; but the frequency of the photoperiodic rhythm was varied. The data obtained show that the effect of alternate light and darkness is manifested only with rhythms of a definite optimum frequency. Diapause takes place only with an alternation of 12-hour and 24-hour periods of light and darkness. Short periods of 6 hours or less, as well as very long ones exceeding 24 hours, proved to have no photoperiodic effect at all, and in such cases development proceeded continuously.

TABLE 6

The effect of the light rhythm during larval development on the onset of diapause in *Acronycta rumicis*. Temperature 25°-26°

Light rhythm (hours)		Duration of larval development (days)	% of diapausing pupae
Light	Darkness		
3	3	19·2	0
6	6	19·5	0
12	12	21·2	100
24	24	21·0	100
48	48	23·2	0
72	72	19·5	0
120	120	19·5	0
216	216	18·0	0
Continuous light		18·2	0
Continuous darkness		21·3	22

The complete absence of diapause and a somewhat accelerated growth rate of larvae in conditions of too frequent or extremely slow light rhythms show that such rhythms act like continuous illumination. From this fact it follows that in long-day species, such as *Acronycta rumicis*, the reacting system is 'tuned' to continuous development, but diapause is induced by rhythmic illumination, the main role in which is played by the duration of the dark periods.

The following experiments show the minimal length of the effective period of darkness (Table 7). A short-day daily rhythm of 9 hours of light and 15 hours of darkness was taken as the basic pattern (experiment 1). In such conditions diapause was obligatory in all pupae. In the experiments the dark period was interrupted at different times by additional 3-hour periods of light. The total number of light and dark hours in the majority of experiments was the same (12 hours).

TABLE 7

The effect of the duration of darkness on the photoperiodic reaction. Temperature 25°

No. of experiment	Total hours per day		Hours of the day								% of diapausin pupae in repeat experiments	
	light	dark-ness	3	6	9	12	15	18	21	24	I	II
1	9	15	······	······	······	——	——	——	——	——	100	100
2	15	9	······	······	······	······	······	——	——	——	72·8	—
3	12	12	······	······	······	······	——	——	——	——	100	100
4	12	12	······	······	······	——	······	——	——	——	53·1	56·
5	12	12	······	······	······	——	——	······	——	——	4·7	8·
6	12	12	······	······	······	——	——	——	······	——	100	90·
7	12	12	······	······	——	——	······	······	——	——	0	0
8	12	12	······	——	······	——	······	——	······	——	0	0
9	24	0	······	······	······	······	······	······	······	······	0	0
10	0	24	——	——	——	——	——	——	——	——	37·5	18·

Note. Solid lines denote the dark period of the day, and dotted lines the light period.

From the data obtained we may draw the following conclusions. The proportion between the totals of light and dark hours during the day has no significance in the photoperiodic reaction. When the totals are equal (12 hours), by varying the periodicity one may obtain any reaction, from that corresponding to continuous illumination (absence of diapause) to the full effect of a short day (diapause of all pupae). To induce diapause, continuous periods of darkness lasting not less than 9 hours are required: shorter periods are ineffective. A 9-hour period of darkness (experiment 6) exerts a certain depressing effect on a following 3-hour light period, but the effect is weaker than that of light on subsequent darkness (experiment 4).

From the whole study of the effects of rhythms of different frequencies (Tables 6 and 7) we may conclude that in *Acronycta rumicis* diapause is induced only by light rhythms close to those found in nature, with duration of darkness from 9 to 24 hours. This confirms the fact that the photoperiodic reaction has been evolved as an adaptation to natural light conditions.

Similar results were obtained by DICKSON (1949) for the Oriental Fruit Moth *Laspeyresia molesta.* The photoperiodic reaction in it proved to be restricted to even narrower limits than those applying to *Acronycta rumicis.* With a 12-hour-12-hour alternation of light and darkness all pupating larvae entered diapause, whereas with 9-9 or 15-15 alternations no diapause took place. The short-day effect is produced in the Oriental Fruit Moth only by rhythms in which darkness lasts from 11 to 16 hours and light from 7 to 15 hours. In conditions beyond these limits development continues without interruption. The photoperiodic reaction regulating the appearance of re-migrants in the aphid *Macrosiphum solanifolii* also almost disappears if the periods of darkness last less than 10 hours (SHULL, 1929).

Antheraea pernyi reacts somewhat differently to the light rhythm. According to TANAKA (1950c, 1951), diapause occurs in pupae of this species only in light rhythms in which the period of darkness lasts not less than 11 hours, but (in contrast to the situation with the preceding species) the effect of such dark periods persists when they alternate with varying light periods of up to 60 hours. The reaction to light rhythm is displayed even when the dark periods are extended to 39 hours. Consequently, in *Antheraea pernyi* light rhythms differing greatly from those found in nature have a photoperiodic effect.

The photoperiodic reaction of the mite *Metatetranychus ulmi* occurs within very wide light-rhythm limits, far exceeding those found in nature. Females which lay diapausing eggs appear even with a 4-hour alternation of light and darkness. The effect depends more on the proportion between light and dark periods than on their absolute duration. Thus the diapause-inducing effect of darkness is sharply increased when its duration is extended to 12-24 hours. Such periods of darkness induce diapause even when combined with 60 hours of light (Fig. 11). *Meta-*

tetranychus is slightly sensitive to interruptions of the dark periods by light.

It is difficult to give a fully adequate physiological explanation of all of these features of reaction to light rhythms. In this field more searching comparative investigations, covering species with short-day and intermediate types of development as well as those

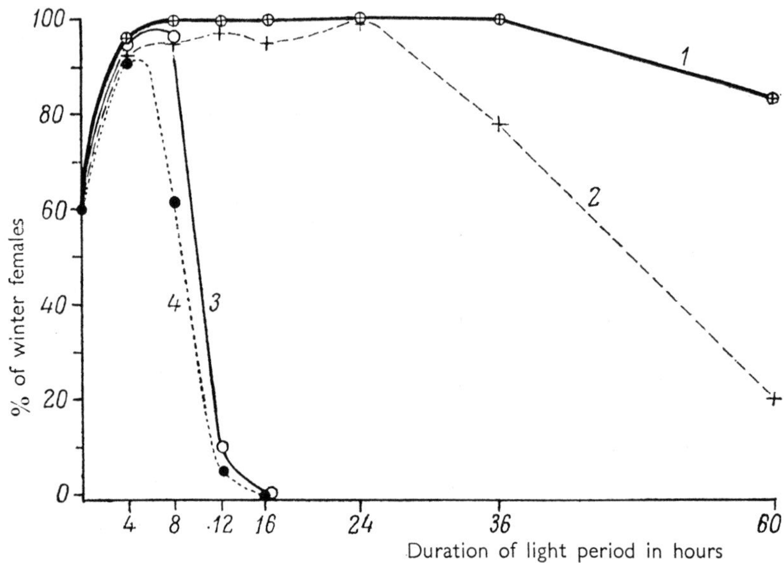

FIG. 11. The effect of different combinations of light and darkness on the induction of diapause in *Metatetranychus ulmi* at a temperature of 15° (from Lees, 1953).

Curves: percentage of winter females; 1, duration of darkness 24 hours; 2, 12 hours; 3, 8 hours; 4, 4 hours.

with the long-day type, are necessary. The majority of authors, however, come to the conclusion that the photoperiodic-reaction mechanism is based on the action of two mutually-antagonistic processes, one of which takes place in light and the other in darkness, with the latter taking the leading role in induction of diapause (DICKSON, 1949; DANILEVSKII and GLINYANAYA, 1949; LEES, 1953b, 1955). There are many factors in favour of this explanation. Results obtained by combining light and temperature rhythms, however (GORYSHIN, 1955; DANILEVSKII and GORYSHIN, 1960), compel us to re-examine the hypothesis. We shall return to it in connection with the survey of data on the effect of temperature on photoperiodic reaction.

5. The significance of gradual changes in day-length

Up to the present the photoperiodic effect has been looked upon merely as the result of the influence of different light-rhythms with constant length of light and dark periods. But such conditions do not exist in nature, and day-length is constantly and gradually changing. This phenomenon is reflected in the photoperiodic reactions of vertebrates. It is known that birds and mammals are greatly affected not only by the absolute duration of daylight but also by the direction of its seasonal changes—by its gradual lengthening or shortening. The possibility of similar effects on insect development was first noted by CORBET (1954, 1955, 1956). While studying the seasonal cycle of the dragonfly *Anax imperator* in England that author found that larvae entering their final instar in spring (before the end of May) continued their metamorphosis and were soon transformed into the imago; with later entrance into the final instar (after the end of May) their development was checked, and metamorphosis did not take place until the following spring, although movement and feeding by the larvae did not cease. Corbet rightly regarded this phenomenon as a special case of diapause regulated by the light conditions; but he suggested that it was impossible to explain the development of *Anax imperator* from the point of view of the determining role of a critical photoperiod, as in that case one would have to expect a second wave of metamorphoses in August and September, when the absolute duration of daylight is the same as in spring and temperature conditions are still entirely favourable. Since that is not observed, Corbet concluded that the regulating factor is not the absolute duration of daylight but the process of its lengthening within the limits of definite photoperiods. Experiments designed to verify this conclusion, however (CORBET, 1956), cannot be considered to be fully decisive.

SHIPITSYNA (1957b, 1959) also, by analysing data on the phenology of *Anopheles maculipennis*, deduced the importance of the changes of day-length in photoperiodic reaction. The different dates of commencement of diapause in *Anopheles* in different climatic zones may, in her opinion, be explained by the specific effect of the shortening of the day, irrespective of its absolute duration.

The regulating role of the absolute duration of daylight, fully proved for insects, does not exclude an additional effect due to the changes of the photoperiodic conditions. Therefore it was necessary to check by experiment the way in which the gradual lengthening and shortening of the day affect the initiation of diapause.

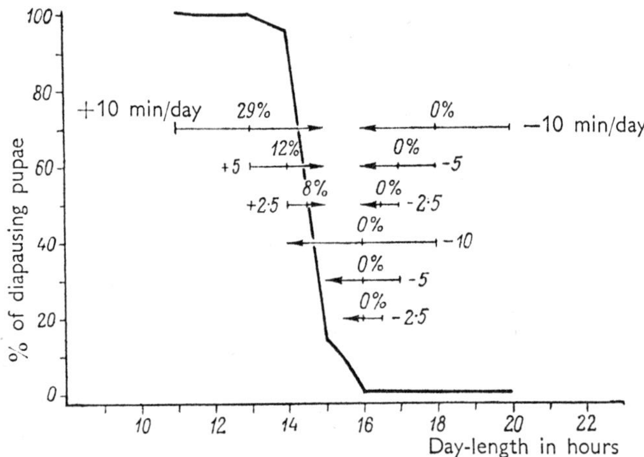

FIG. 12. The significance of constant and varying day-lengths in inducing diapause in *Acronycta rumicis*. Temperature 21° (from the data of G. F. Tsvetaeva).

Curve: the percentage of diapausing pupae with different constant day-lengths acting on their larvae (control). The arrows show the direction and amount of change in the day-length during larval development in experiments with different rates of decrease (−) or increase (+) in the light period of the day. The figures above the arrows denote the percentage of diapausing pupae in the experiment.

Fig. 12 illustrates the results of experiments carried out for this purpose by G. F. Tsvetaeva on the Sukhumi form of *Acronycta rumicis*. In control experiments with constant photoperiod the threshold of reaction was clearly defined at 14 hours 30 minutes. With daylight exceeding 15 hours 30 minutes development proceeded without diapause, and at 13 hours 30 minutes all pupae entered diapause. In experiments with changing conditions, uniform shortening or lengthening of daylight by 2·5, 5, and 10 minutes daily was used throughout the period of development of the larvae, which lasted 24 days.

As is evident from the data obtained, shortening the day in the zone above the critical photoperiod (more than 16 hours) does not strengthen the tendency to diapause, and in such conditions development continues without interruption. Diapause is absent also in a series of experiments in which the average duration of daylight was 16 hours, although in these experiments the second half of the developmental period of the larvae took place in the zone of the critical photoperiod. Consequently shortening of the day is not in itself a factor regulating the initiation of diapause in *Acronycta rumicis*. The effect is entirely determined by the average duration of the photoperiod.

More interesting are the results obtained by lengthening the day in the zone of short photoperiods. As the diagram shows, with average day-length one should expect a high percentage of diapause, in any case over 50%. But in all experiments only a small number of diapausing pupae were obtained. Even when the larvae developed in an average day-length of 13 hours (with increase from 11 to 15 hours), when one might expect diapause in all pupae, the actual proportion of diapausing pupae was only 29%. Thus one gets the impression that gradual lengthening of the day increases the tendency towards continuous development. Unfortunately the diagram has not taken into account an experiment in lengthening of the day with photoperiods shorter than 13 hours 30 minutes, which would have been particularly significant. Very similar results were obtained in parallel experiments with *Barathra brassicae*, but the stimulating action of increasing day-length proved weaker in this case.

If the fact that development is stimulated by lengthening the day is confirmed by further investigations, it will make it easier to understand the reasons for the absence of diapause in the spring generations of several polycyclic species, whose development at that time takes place in near-critical daylight conditions. The experiments that have been made, however, enable us to conclude with assurance that the photoperiodic reaction in insects is based on the action of absolute day-length and definite critical values of it. If the direction of the changes in daylight plays any role it is only secondary, in the nature of an additional adaptation.

Even the seasonal cycle of *Anax imperator* can be fully explained by the action of constant critical photoperiods. This species probably possesses the intermediate type of photoperiodic reaction, in which, as in *Euproctis similis* (see Fig. 10), development is possible only within a narrow photoperiodic range, and a longer or shorter day induces diapause. This is the cause of springtime development and the beginning of diapause with the lengthening days by the end of May. The ineffectiveness of the same day-length in autumn may be due to the fact that the larvae, being in diapause, do not react to the light conditions until their full reactivation has taken place, which according to Corbet (1956) occurs only in February. With regard to the malaria mosquito, the experiments of VINOGRADOVA (1960) have shown that the commencing dates of diapause in different climatic zones are determined by variations in the critical photoperiod.

6. The significance of light intensity

One of the most characteristic features of photoperiodic reaction in insects is that it is fully displayed only in very subdued illumination. SHULL (1929) found that for the photoperiodic reaction of the aphid *Macrosiphum solanifolii* the lower light limit was about 1 lux (candle-metre), but it depends on the amount of contrast in the alternation of light and dark. Thus if in the daily rhythm a 16-hour period of very weak light (1·6 lux) alternates with 8 hours of low-intensity light (up to 323 lux), such conditions have the same effect as continuous illumination and the aphids produce only apterous offspring. But alternation with 8 hours of strong light (9,000 lux) induces a partial photoperiodic effect, and 50% of the offspring are winged. Consequently in this case weak light (1·6 lux) has an effect similar to that of darkness.

A similar limit for effective illumination has been found in the photoperiodic reaction of the Belgorod form of *Acronycta rumicis* (DANILEVSKII, 1948). In these experiments larvae were reared at a temperature of 26° in short-day conditions (9 hours of light and 15 hours of darkness). The intensity of light in different experiments was 65, 35, 16, and 5 lux. With a light intensity lower than that to which the larvae were sensitive, there resulted a decrease in the percentage of the pupae obtained that entered diapause, down to the level observed among larvae reared in constant darkness.

Control larvae developing in constant darkness produced 72%

of non-diapausing pupae, but in all variations in light intensity of 16 lux and over the short-day effect was fully displayed and all pupae entered diapause. Only when the light level was lowered to 5 lux did a few (8%) non-diapausing pupae appear, which points to the nearness of the limit of sensitivity. As the fluctuations took place on the outer surface of the vessels containing the larvae, and a considerable part of the light was absorbed by the glass and by food plants, the limit of light to which the larvae are sensitive must be taken as being close to 1 lux.

Experiments with *Acronycta rumicis*, set up on a different plan, led to similar conclusions. Short-day conditions were used in them also, but 12 hours of light of constant intensity (60-65 lux) were alternated with 12 hours of light reduced to a varying extent, down to total darkness. When the light was below sensitivity-level, the short-day effect and diapause in all pupae were induced. The results of these experiments showed that when the intensity of light during the 'dark' period was 5 lux or more diapause was not induced, just as with continuous illumination of high intensity. The effect of the light-rhythm was weakly shown only when the light in the 'dark' period was below 2-3 lux, but in these conditions diapause was observed in only 10·7% of the pupae. Consequently, to obtain the full photoperiodic effect it is necessary that the intensity of light during the 'dark' period of the 24 hours should be below 2-3 lux.

The effectiveness of weak light has also been noted for other species studied. WAY and HOPKINS (1950), in experiments with *Polia* (*Diataraxia*) *oleracea*, found that a change in the light intensity during the light part of the day from 220 foot-candles (2,367 lux) to 1 foot-candle (10·8 lux) did not affect the photoperiodic reaction. Consequently the limit for this species lies considerably below 10 lux. According to DICKSON (1949), external light of 3 foot-candles (32 lux) proved to be adequate for photoperiodic reaction in larvae of the fruit moth *Laspeyresia molesta*, which lives inside fruit. With 12-hour periodic illumination of lower intensity development proceeded without diapause, as in total darkness. If one considers the low translucency of the tissues of an apple, the limit of sensitivity of the larvae must actually be close to 1 lux, i.e. close to the limit found in free-living species. The limit for the spider mite *Metatetranychus ulmi* is approximately 10 lux (LEES, 1953a).

Very high sensitivity has been discovered in the Colorado Beetle (DE WILDE and BONGA, 1958). The first signs of photoperiodic reaction are observed in it with light of even 0·1 lux. The reaction increases with increase in light intensity up to 5 lux, at which point it reaches its full value, and further increases in light intensity do not affect it. A similar limit has been found in the silkworm (KOGURE, 1933). Still higher sensitivity has been found in larvae of the midge *Metriocnemus knabi*, which in experimental conditions reacted to light of intensity 0·0025 foot-candles, i.e. about 0·02 lux (PARIS and JENNER, 1959).

We considered it important to determine not only the threshold of light intensity necessary for photoperiodic reaction but also the effect of light intensity on critical day-length. For that purpose larvae of the Belgorod form of *Acronycta rumicis* were reared by us at a temperature of 22° in varying day-length conditions, from 12 hours of light to continuous light with one-hour intervals of darkness. The light source was a 220-watt electric lamp. During the light period the light intensity was regulated by varying the distance from the lamp and using a gauze screen. In three parallel series of experiments the light intensity was 15-20, 60-65, and 300-320 lux. The results of these experiments showed that, regardless of the intensity, diapause was not induced with 17 hours or more of light per day, but with 15 hours or less all pupae entered diapause. At the critical photoperiod—16 hours of light—continuous development was observed in a small percentage of the pupae in all the series, without any regular relation to the intensity of the light. Thus the critical day-length did not change. Neither were any noticeable differences observed in critical day-length for different species in numerous experiments made in natural and electric lighting with intensity of some tens of lux. Therefore the data from laboratory experiments with artificial light are fully applicable to the analysis of development in natural conditions.

A low light threshold is characteristic of photoperiodic reactions not only in insects but also in other organisms. For the majority of plants, light of intensity from one to several tens of lux is physiologically effective, but some species react even to light of intensity 0·1 to 0·5 lux (SAMYGIN, 1946). Similar data exist also for mammals. High sensitivity has an undoubted adaptational significance, as it modifies the effect on the photoperiodic reaction caused by casual wide fluctuations in daylight, which are constantly observed in nature as a result of weather conditions.

The level of illumination accepted by organisms as 'daylight' must be higher than the intensity of moonlight, as only in that case could the photoperiodic reaction retain its biological significance as a seasonal regulator of vital phenomena. It is known that the maximum light during the period of full moon does not exceed 0·25 lux, and dispersed moonlight is even weaker (SHARONOV, 1945). When one considers the sensitivity to light and the living conditions of the majority of insects, it is evident that moonlight cannot substantially affect their photoperiodic reactions. It is characteristic that very high sensitivity to light is found only in forms that live in concealment (*Metriocnemus knabi*), dwelling in places inaccessible to direct moonlight.

In evaluating the photoperiodic conditions of insect development in nature it is necessary to take into account not the statistical length of the day, calculated from sunrise to sunset, but the whole light portion of the 24 hours, including part of the twilight. For an approximation to the biologically-effective day we may take its length as including the so-called 'civil twilight' (when the sun is not more than 6°-7° below the horizon), when light intensity exceeds 1-3 lux (SHARONOV, 1945). As the light changes very rapidly during twilight (twofold or threefold in five minutes), in practice one may ignore the small differences in the light-sensitivity thresholds of species. From an ecological point of view it is much more important to consider the amount of illumination in actual habitats, which (particularly in the case of species that live in concealment) may differ considerably from the amount on exposed surfaces; but there are no data on this subject in the literature.

7. The significance of the spectral composition of light

The first investigations in this field, made by KOGURE (1933) on a bivoltine race of silkworms, showed that different parts of the spectrum differ in their photoperiodic activity. From eggs continuously irradiated at a temperature of 15° with orange-yellow and red light (over 5,500 Å) adults were obtained which laid eggs, most of which developed, with from 3% to 8% undergoing diapause—a result coinciding with that obtained in conditions of total darkness. Under the influence of blue-violet rays (3,500 to 5,100 Å) of approximately the same energy, adults were obtained which laid 98% diapausing eggs. The same result was obtained by irradiating younger larvae.

In the experiments of DICKSON (1949) with the Oriental Fruit Moth *Laspeyresia molesta*, the effects on larvae of different parts of the spectrum, with short photoperiods (12 hours of darkness and 12 hours of light), were compared. The results showed clearly that long-wave light from approximately 4,000 to 5,800 Å—i.e. the whole range from violet to yellow—exerted a strong effect, inducing, as in nature, typical photoperiodic reaction and a high percentage (87% to 99%) of diapausing prepupae. Red light (6,600 Å) had much less effect, inducing diapause in only 20% of the larvae. Ultraviolet light (3,600 Å) and infrared light (14,000 Å) were ineffective and resulted in non-diapause development, just as did total darkness.

For the mite *Metatetranychus ulmi*, according to LEES (1953a), the range from blue-green to near ultraviolet light (3,650 to 5,000 Å) has photoperiodic effect, with maximum sensitivity being shown to blue light of wave-length about 4,250 Å. The whole range of the spectrum with wave-lengths over 5,300 Å, from yellow to infrared, had the same photoperiodic effect as darkness.

Therefore all these species are sensitive, in their photoperiodic reaction, to only the short-wave part of the spectrum, and in this respect are opposite in reaction to plants and vertebrates.

Studies by GEISPITS (1957), however, made on several long-day Lepidoptera, disclosed great differences in the reactions of species to long wavelengths (Table 8). In her experiments larvae received daily 9 hours of white light and 15 hours of light coming through a filter with a narrow spectral range of translucency. Sensitivity to the filtered light would be shown by a reaction the same as that to continuous illumination; insensitivity would be shown by a short-day effect, i.e. by induction of diapause.

In the Pine Moth *Dendrolimus pini*, as in the preceding species, sensitivity to the short-wave part of the spectrum is clearly shown. With alternation of white and violet light, as in experiments with continuous light, diapause did not occur. Green light produced a weaker reaction and induced diapause in some of the larvae.

TABLE 8

The dependence of the photoperiodic reaction in larvae of different species of Lepidoptera on the spectral composition of the light (after Geispits, 1957)

Daily light rhythm (hours)	Region of maximum filter-passage (Å)	% of diapausing larvae		
		Dendrolimus pini	*Pieris brassicae*	*Acronycta rumicis*
White 9, red 15	6550	100	92·5	0
White 9, orange 15	5850	100	—	—
White 9, green 15	5300	15	11·3	0
White 9, violet 15	4070	0	65·7	0
White 9, darkness 15	—	100	100	100
Continuous white light 24	—	0	0	0

With red and orange light all larvae entered diapause, and thus the long-wave part of the spectrum above 5,850 Å is taken by the Pine Moth to be equivalent to darkness. Red light was also without effect on *Pieris brassicae*, which species is most sensitive to green light, much less so to violet.

The noctuid *Acronycta rumicis* is exceptional in its reaction to the spectrum. In all experiments with light filters it developed without diapause, as in continuous white light. That shows that *Acronycta rumicis*, unlike other species studied, is sensitive to the whole range of visible light, including red. A similar type of reaction was found by DE WILDE and BONGA (1958) in the Colorado Beetle *Leptinotarsa decemlineata*. For it the whole long-wave range of the spectrum from 4,230 to 6,750 Å, i.e. from violet to red, proved to have photoperiodic effect. Only infrared irradiation above 7,000 Å induced no reaction.

It is interesting to evaluate the ecological significance of the varying reactions of insects to the spectral composition of light. The high photoperiodic effect of the blue-green part of the spectrum on the majority of insects may be most simply explained by reference to their living conditions. Species living among dense vegetation, especially those living under forest canopy or within plant tissues, are subject to the action of light filtered through green leaves and almost completely deprived of rays from the red part of the spectrum. Probably it is on that account that the photoperiodic reactions of plants and of insects towards the spectrum are in most cases complementary. Long-wave red-orange light exerts the greatest influence on plants, as is well known, and short-wave blue-green light on insects. It is more difficult to offer a biological explanation for the effect of red light on some species. Larvae of *Acronycta rumicis* and of the beetle *Leptinotarsa decemlineata* belong to photo-positive species that avoid shade and dense vegetation. The ecological differences between these species and Cabbage White Butterflies, Pine Moths, and other species not sensitive to red light are, however, not great enough to explain the observed differences in reaction to the spectrum. Further comparative studies in this field are required.

8. The stages of development sensitive to photoperiod

The faculty of reacting to day-length is shown by insects only in definite stages of their life cycle, whereas other stages in their ontogenesis are usually neutral. Photoperiodic conditions during the sensitive period determine the nature of the physiological processes which later lead to diapause or other changes in development, independently of the subsequent light conditions. Thus photoperiodic reaction in insects is based on an irreversible after-effect of the photoperiod, which plays the role only of a trigger or signalling stimulus.

A few described cases of changes in reaction under the influence of subsequent light conditions do not contradict the above statement. For instance, parthenogenetic females of the aphid *Megoura viciae*, with alternation in the light conditions, may produce either parthenogenetic or sexual offspring. Determination of the form of the offspring occurs at an early stage of development of the embryo while still in the maternal body. Since formation of the embryo takes place gradually during the life of the mother, if the light conditions are changed the form of the offspring also changes (LEES, 1959b). Apparently similar phenomena occur in the mite *Metatetranychus ulmi*, females of which may lay diapausing eggs and active eggs in succession, according to the light conditions of the deutonymph and the imago (LEES, 1953a).

Insects may be photoperiod-sensitive at different stages of

ontogenesis, but such stages are strictly defined for each species. The differences among species in the sensitive and diapause stages are illustrated by selected examples in Table 9. In most cases the sensitive period immediately precedes the diapause stage, but in the Grape Berry Moth *Polychrosis botrana* (Komarova, 1949) and the sawfly *Lygaeonematus compressicornis* there is a considerable interval between these stages. The interval is especially great in the silkworm, in which diapause in the eggs of the daughter generation is determined by the developmental conditions of the eggs of the maternal generation (Kogure, 1933), i.e. the interval between the sensitive and diapause stages constitutes an entire ontogenetic cycle. It is difficult to give a general physiological explanation of such specific peculiarities. It is fully evident that the development of photoperiod-sensitivity during a certain stage, like the whole of the seasonal cycle, is determined by the particular features of the ecology of a species.

From the data in Table 9 it is seen that sensitivity to light

Table 9

The stages of insect development sensitive to photoperiodic conditions

Species	Diapausing stages	Sensitive stages
Bombyx mori	Egg	Embryo of maternal generation after blastokinesis
Pandemis ribeana	Larva, instar III	Larva, instars I and II
Dendrolimus pini	Larva, all instars	Whole period of larval development
Agrotis C-nigrum	Larva, instars III and IV	Larva, instars I to III
Loxostege sticticalis	Prepupa	Late larval stages
Lygaeonematus compressicornis	do.	Embryo
Acronycta megacephala	Pupa	Late larval stages
Smerinthus populi	do.	do. do.
Polychrosis botrana	do.	Embryo and larva, instar I
Chrysomela fastuosa	Imago	Imago
Haltica saliceti	do.	do.
Leptinotarsa decemlineata	do.	Larva and imago
Culex pipiens	do.	do. do.
Anopheles maculipennis	do.	do. do.

rhythm is found in all the principal stages of metamorphosis except the pupal stage. As a general rule, the greatest sensitivity to photoperiodic conditions is shown by the larvae. Photoperiod-sensitivity is much more rarely found in the imago; it has been observed in cases where the adult insect is characterized by an intensive and complete feeding habit (e.g. leaf-eaters, blood-sucking mosquitoes). Such correspondence of the sensitive period with feeding stages may be explained by the fact that preparation for diapause is linked with the accumulation of reserve food supplies, which provide for metabolism during the subsequent long resting period. It is not by accident that in those rare cases where sensitivity to light conditions is found during the embryonic period (*Bombyx mori*, *Polychrosis botrana*, *Lygaeonematus compressicornis*) the effect is shown during the later stages of the cycle (prepupa, pupa) or even in succeeding generations, i.e. after the period of larval feeding. In such cases, evidently, only the primary hormonal stimulus to diapause arises during the embryonic period, and preparation for diapause itself exists throughout larval development, in spite of the neutral reaction of the larva to the light conditions.

In several of the species studied photoperiod-sensitivity is not restricted to a single stage of metamorphosis. For instance, the blood-sucking mosquitoes *Anopheles maculipennis* and *Culex pipiens*, and also the Colorado Beetle *Leptinotarsa decemlineata*, react to the daily light rhythm not only in the imaginal but also in the larval stage (DANILEVSKII and GLINYANAYA, 1958; VINOGRADOVA, 1958; GORYSHIN, 1958a). That is found to a smaller extent in *Bombyx mori* and *Polychrosis botrana*, in which the first two larval instars, as well as the embryonic stage, react to light conditions.

Sensitivity to light during the larval instars may vary with age. The nature of such variations, in view of their ecological importance, has been studied by a number of authors. DICKSON (1949), by transferring larvae of *Laspeyresia molesta* through definite time-intervals from short to long days, and in parallel experiments from long to short days, discovered that abrupt age-changes in sensitivity do not occur in larvae of that species, but that the younger instars are much more sensitive than the older to the light conditions. On the other hand, for *Polia oleracea* (WAY and HOPKINS, 1950) and *Pyrausta nubilalis* (MUTCHMOR and BECKEL, 1959) it has been shown that diapause is determined by the light conditions operating from the moult in the final instar. Short-day conditions have no effect on younger instars. Increased sensitivity in the older instars is observed also in *Antheraea pernyi* (TANAKA, 1950a, 1950b; BELOV, 1951). In *Barathra brassicae* sensitivity remains uniform throughout larval development, and the percentage of diapausing larvae increases in proportion to the duration of action of the short day (MASAKI, 1957b).

The problem of sensitive periods is complicated by the fact that the effect produced is determined not only by the instars on which the light conditions operate but also by the number of photoperiodic impulses. That is clearly demonstrated by the experiments of GEISPITS (1949, 1953) with *Dendrolimus pini*, in which the action of the short day can induce diapause at any larval stage. In such cases diapause always begins 30 to 35 days after the larva is placed in short-day conditions (Table 10). Thus photoperiod-sensitivity remains unchanged during the whole period of larval development, but the effect is determined by the number of short days experienced. The data in Table 11 show that in fact diapause is predetermined after 20 short photoperiods. In these experiments larvae were kept in short-day conditions for different periods from the moment of emergence from the egg, and later were transferred to conditions of continuous illumination.

TABLE 10

The effect of a 12-hour day on the onset of diapause in *Dendrolimus pini* larvae (after Geispits, 1949)

Beginning of short-day action	No. of short days until onset of diapause	Diapausing larvae		
		%	Instar	Average weight (mg)
Egg-laying	35·5 (32-39)	100	II	48
Instar I	30·0 (30-30)	100	III	107
Instar III	30·7 (30-33)	100	IV	351
Instar IV	30·3 (30-31)	100	V	666
Instar V	36·1 (31-48)	100	VI	1731
Continuous light	—	0	—	—

TABLE 11

The minimum number of short-day impulses required for the induction of diapause in *Dendrolimus pini* larvae. Temperature 20°

Pattern of experiment	Diapausing larvae			Time of onset of diapause (days)
	No. of larvae in experiment	%	Instar	
Continuous light	50	0·0	—	—
Constant short days (12 hrs.)	50	96·0	II	32-39
15 short days	30	0·0	—	—
20 ,, ,,	12	75·0	II	34-39
25 ,, ,,	35	97·2	II	34-39
28 ,, ,,	15	93·4	II	33-36
30 ,, ,,	21	95·3	II	29-39

Because of the importance for the reaction of the number of photoperiods experienced, it is possible to arrange a different treatment of the experimental data, whereby the sensitivity of different stages may be evaluated without taking account of their duration. The decisive role of the older instars, established for a number of species, may to a considerable extent be explained by the fact that they are of longer duration than the younger instars.

The relative roles of age and number of photoperiods experienced are clearly seen from experiments with *Pieris brassicae* and *Acronycta rumicis*. In both species, action of the short day on each of the younger instars separately did not induce diapause. Only when it acted on the last instar was partial diapause observed. The impression was created that the last instar in these species is the one most sensitive to light. This is indeed so for *Acronycta rumicis*. From the data in Table 12 it follows that during the first five days of development the larvae show absolutely no reaction to the light conditions, but later their sensitivity progressively increases. To obtain full diapause, not fewer than 15 short days are necessary during the older instars.

Analysis of the data obtained for *Pieris brassicae* leads to different conclusions. From Table 13 it is seen that the sensitivity of the larvae to light remains unchanged throughout their whole period of development. The more noticeable role of the fifth

TABLE 12

The sensitivity of *Acronycta rumicis* larvae to the action of short days at different periods of development. Temperature 21°
(from data of K. F. Geispits)

No. of experiment	Days of development					% of diapausing pupae
	5	10	15	20	25	
1	——	······	······	······	······	0·0
2	——	——	······	······	······	2·7
3	——	——	——	······	······	17·3
4	——	——	——	——	······	55·6
5	······	······	······	······	——	21·4
6	······	······	······	——	——	78·6
7	······	······	——	——	——	98·6
8	······	——	——	——	——	100·0
9	——	——	······	——	——	95·0
10	——	——	······	······	——	31·2
11	······	······	······	······	······	0·0
12	——	——	——	——	——	100·0

Note. Solid lines denote short days (12 hours), and dotted lines continuous light.

instar is due merely to its longer duration. If the first instars are exposed to light action of the same duration, the result obtained is similar (experiments 1 and 6; 2 and 5; etc.). At any period of larval development 10 to 11 short days are required to induce diapause in all larvae.

The number of photoperiods required to produce an effect varies according to the species. For *Dendrolimus pini* not fewer than 20 photoperiods are required, for *Acronycta rumicis* 15, for *Pieris brassicae* 11, and for *Loxostege sticticalis* only 7-8 are sufficient. For total elimination of diapause in *Araschnia levana*, whose larvae develop in natural short-day conditions, 5 to 6 days

TABLE 13

The sensitivity of *Pieris brassicae* larvae to the action of short days at different periods of development. Temperature 18°-19°

No. of experiment	Days of development of larvae, and instars (days 5, 10, 15, 20)					% of diapausing pupae
	L_{I}	L_{II}	L_{III}	L_{IV}	L_{V}	
1	———	———	·······	·······	·······	30·4
2	———	———	———	·······	·······	81·5
3	———	———	———	———	———	100·0
4	·······	·······	———	———	———	100·0
5	·······	·······	·······	———	———	100·0
6	·······	·······	·······	·······	———	38·5
7	·······	·······	·······	·······	·······	0·0
8	———	———	———	———	———	100·0

Note. Solid lines denote short days (12 hours), and dotted lines continuous light. L_{I-V}—larval instars.

of continuous illumination acting on the last two instars proved sufficient, but a partial effect was observed after only 3 days (DANILEVSKII, 1948).

Data set forth in the following chapters show that the number of photoperiodic impulses required to induce diapause may vary considerably under the influence of temperature and nutrition. In other words, sensitivity to photoperiodism depends on external conditions. This fact, no doubt, has substantial importance in the regulation of the seasonal cycle in nature.

9. Photoperiodic receptors

The problem of determining which organs receive photoperiodic stimuli is very difficult to solve experimentally. The literature in this field is still very limited and the conclusions are contradictory.

The first data were obtained by the Japanese investigator

TANAKA (1950c) and by BELOV (1951). These two authors worked independently by similar methods and on the same subject—the Chinese Oak Silkworm *Antheraea pernyi*. In order to discover the role of the visual organs of the larvae in receiving photoperiodic stimuli, Tanaka covered the surface of the eyes (ocelli) with opaque lacquer or burned out the ocelli during the sensitive period (fourth instar) by thermocautery.

If light is received by the ocelli, then it was to be expected that the blinded larvae would in any conditions produce only non-diapausing pupae, as happens in normal larval development in total darkness. But it was found that the blinded larvae retained the photoperiodic reaction, and in short-day conditions produced diapausing pupae. From these experiments the conclusion was drawn that photoperiodic stimuli are received not by the visual organs but by some other special receptors.

BELOV (1951), in similar experiments with blacking-out and destroying the surface of the ocelli of larvae, came to the same conclusion. In further experiments an attempt was made to determine the precise nature of the photoperiodic receptors. According to the data so obtained, in different light conditions substantial changes are observed in the form and dimensions of the flask-shaped epidermal sensillae (trichoid sensillae) on the backs of the larvae. After mechanical removal of these sensillae, elimination of normal photoperiodic reaction was observed. Belov concluded from this observation that the trichoid sensillae play a leading part in receiving photoperiodic stimuli. This suggestion, however, is rather improbable, the more so since our experiments with *Antheraea pernyi* have not confirmed the changes in form of the trichoid sensillae with varying duration of daylight as described by Belov. But the possibility of epidermal reception is not excluded. Diffuse epidermal sensitivity to light was observed long ago in larvae of other species (WIGGLESWORTH, 1939).

The investigations of DE WILDE (1958), carried out on *Leptinotarsa decemlineata*, gave results similar to those obtained for *Antheraea pernyi*. Beetles blinded by diathermic cautery or by covering the surface of the eyes with black lacquer reacted normally to the light rhythm. With a temperature of 25° and a long day (20 hours of light) they matured, showing no decrease in fertility as compared with controls. With a short 10-hour day they commenced diapause and burrowed into the soil on the same dates as normal beetles. De Wilde therefore concluded that the visual organs do not play a substantial role in photoperiodic reaction.

Geispits (1957), working with *Dendrolimus pini* larvae, came to a different conclusion. In her first experiments she checked the photoperiodic reaction in larvae in which the surface of the ocelli had been carefully covered with opaque lacquer. Such larvae were raised in short-day (9-hour) conditions, i.e. in conditions that necessarily induced diapause. The controls were larvae with undamaged ocelli, kept in short-day conditions and in total darkness, which induces development without diapause. The results obtained showed that in short-day conditions diapause developed in all the blinded larvae, but 20 days later than in normal larvae. In total darkness development proceeded without interruption. These data agree basically with those obtained by the preceding authors, but still point to some participation by the visual apparatus in photoperiodic reaction.

Further studies disclosed that the head capsule of larvae can be easily penetrated even by light of low intensity, and thus that blacking out the surface of the ocellus with opaque lacquer does not ensure complete isolation of the visual receptors themselves from light. Therefore blinding by that method is inadequate for solving the question of the part taken by the eyes in the photoperiodic reaction of insects.

Geispits adopted another method to locate the photoperiodic receptors. Rearing larvae in a chamber with constant light, she covered the heads of one test group of larvae for 12 hours daily with opaque caps tightly attached to the region of the first thoracic segment. A second group had the body isolated from light with opaque coverings, leaving the head free, also for 12 hours daily. The controls were larvae kept in 12-hour and continuous light conditions. Pine Moth larvae easily survived the periodic fasting inevitable with this method, and they retained the photoperiodic reaction (Danilevskii, 1956).

The results of these experiments (Table 14) show that the regular action of a short photoperiod on the head region only (experiment 1) induced normal diapause in all larvae, just as in the control group raised in short-day conditions (experiment 2). In contrast, larvae whose bodies were periodically darkened but

TABLE 14

The reaction of *Dendrolimus pini* larvae to the photoperiodic action on different parts of the body (after Geispits, 1956)

No. of experiment	No. of larvae in experiment	Daily rhythm of illumination of parts of the body (hours)		% dia-pausing
		head	body	
1	12	12	24	100
2 (control)	47	12	12	100
3	12	24	12	0
4 (control)	43	24	24	0

whose heads remained illuminated (experiment 3) developed without interruption, just as did the controls in continuous light (experiment 4). This experiment, remarkable for its simplicity and conclusiveness, shows that in the Pine Moth the organs of photoperiodic reception are located in the head region.

Geispits considers it most probable that the eyes (ocelli) of larvae serve as the receptive apparatus. A weighty argument in favour of this is provided by experiments that have proved the great similarity in the effects of different parts of the spectrum with regard to such independent phenomena as photoperiodic reaction and phototaxis. The similarity stands out with particular clearness when different species are compared. As shown above (see Table 8), for Pine Moth larvae (as for the majority of other species) the violet and blue-green part of the spectrum is photoperiodically active, whereas orange and red rays are similar to darkness in their effect. But for *Acronycta rumicis* red light also is effective. The same differences between these species are observed in phototaxis to monochromatic light.

When illuminated with white, violet, or blue light, Pine Moth larvae move directly towards the source of illumination, selecting the required direction quickly and without searching for it. Less assured movements are observed in green and especially in orange light. When illuminated by red rays the larvae lose their orientation and move haphazardly, as in total darkness. Larvae of *Acronycta rumicis* clearly distinguish all regions of the visible spectrum, including red light, in which they make fully oriented movements. According to the observations of N. I. Goryshin and G. F. Tsvetaeva (unpublished data), the intensity thresholds of received light for photoperiodic reaction and for phototaxis are close together. In both cases they are about 1 lux. On the other hand, flashing lights of varying frequency show somewhat different effects on these phenomena.

Available experimental data are still inadequate for a final solution of the problem of the nature and precise location of the photoperiodic receptors, but participation by the visual organs in one form or another is almost beyond doubt. It is characteristic that even the embryonic photoperiod-sensitivity of *Bombyx mori* appears in the late stages after blastokinesis, when the nervous system of the larva is formed and the ocellar buds are pigmented.

Other means of reception, however, are also available. With regard to vertebrates, for which the leading role of the eyes in photoperiodic reception has been demonstrated in a large number of studies, there are also indications of skin sensitivity to photoperiod (IVANOVA, 1936). Particularly interesting is the work of Benoit and his collaborators (BENOIT, 1950), which shows the possibility of stimulating sexual maturation in blinded ducks by illuminating a region of the hypophysis or of the hypothalamus with a narrow pencil of light. By analogy with these findings, it is very probable that in insects photoperiodic stimuli may be received not only through the visual apparatus, but also directly by the neurosecretory centres of the brain.

Chapter III

THE RELATION OF NUTRITIONAL AND LIGHT FACTORS IN REGULATING DIAPAUSE

In nature, seasonal changes in day-length are accompanied by changes in other ecological factors that have independent effects on the physiological state of insects. It is therefore necessary to evaluate the extent to which these additional external influences are reflected in the photoperiodic reactions that regulate development and the onset of diapause in insects. The nutritional factor presents special interest in this respect, as the process of preparation for diapause and for a long resting period is always accompanied by accumulation within the organism of special food reserves, and often by profound internal reconstruction linked with metabolism.

Many investigations have been devoted to the problem of the dependence of diapause on nutrition. After the works of Steinberg and Kamensky (1936), Zolotarev (1938, 1940a, 1940b), and Squire (1939, 1940) had appeared in ecological literature, it was considered as proved that seasonal and age changes in the chemistry of food plants constitute one of the chief factors regulating the annual developmental cycles of insects.

Many authors resorted to this explanation in cases where the initiation of diapause could not be attributed to the effect of temperature conditions. Aristov (1932), Garlick (1948), and Vasil'ev (1951) held that the onset of diapause in the Codling Moth is induced by eating ripe fruit. In the opinion of Kozhanchikov (1948a), in many *Acronyctinae* diapause depends mainly on the qualitative composition of the diet. Grison (1947) found that the feeding of *Euproctis similis* larvae on young leaves warded off diapause in them. The works of Larchenko (1955, 1956, 1958a), dealing mostly with the Colorado Beetle, were also devoted to proving a similar dependence on food. Many data exist showing the influence of the composition of their diet on the seasonal cycle of aphids.

Because of the well-established fact of the leading role of diet in regulating seasonal development in insects, the opinion has even been expressed that day-length affects insects not directly but indirectly, by changing the composition of food plants or the normal rhythm of feeding and assimilating food. MARCOVITCH (1924) admits that possibility with regard to aphids.

Experimental data now available enable us to examine the nature of the interaction of light and food conditions and to estimate the relative part of these factors in regulating diapause.

1. The independence of photoperiodic reactions in insects and in their food plants

The questions of the independent nature of the reception of photoperiodic stimuli by insects, and of the relation between the photoperiodic reactions of phytophagous species and of their food plants, are of the greatest importance. They have therefore been specially analysed in a number of experimental investigations. WAY and HOPKINS (1950), in experiments with *Polia oleracea*, showed that when larvae were fed in long-day (12-hour) conditions with cabbage leaves grown in short-day (8- to 12-hour) conditions, diapause was not induced. In the converse experiment, when larvae were subjected to short-day conditions and their food plants grown in long-day conditions, only diapausing pupae were produced. Thus diapause in *Polia oleracea* does not depend on the photoperiodic conditions in which its food plants grow, but the photoperiodic effect is produced directly on the larvae. Similar results were obtained for diapause in *Leptinotarsa decemlineata* (JERMI and SARINGER, 1955; WĘGOREK, 1959b) and in the seasonal forms of the jassid *Euscelis plebejus* (MÜLLER, 1957b). The independent nature of the long-day reaction and its lack of connection with photoperiodic reaction in plants were also proved by the experiments of LEES (1953a) with the mite *Metatetranychus ulmi*. Direct reception of photoperiod has therefore been established for widely-differing phytophagous species.

Only in the recent work of HUGHES (1960) have data been obtained indicating the possibility of receiving photoperiod stimuli through food plants. According to his observations larvae of the Cabbage-root Fly *Hylemyia brassicae* developing on turnip roots in the soil produced active pupae in long-day conditions and only diapausing pupae in short-day conditions. When the soil surface around food plants was covered with opaque material the results of the experiment were only slightly affected. The percentage of short-day diapausing pupae fell somewhat if before the experiment the food plants were subjected to long-day light action. These findings led Hughes to the conclusion that development of the Cabbage-root Fly is determined by chemical changes which take place in food plants under the influence of long days. This conclusion, however, cannot be held to be fully proved. The investigations of Sh. M. Zabirov, made in our laboratory independently of the work of Hughes, showed that in the Cabbage-root Fly a clear photoperiodic reaction is displayed also when larvae are fed on small parts of tubers outside the soil; in this case development in long-day (18-hour) conditions proceeds without diapause, and in short-day conditions all pupae enter diapause. Thus the larvae are capable of receiving photoperiodic stimuli directly. The acceptability of Hughes' conclusions is diminished also by the fact that, according to his data, the turnip tubers used in his experiments allowed about 0·6% of the light falling on their surface to pass through, which may have affected the results of his experiments.

Many data exist at present indicating that photoperiodic reaction is not peculiar only to insects that feed on living plants. It is also clearly exhibited in carnivorous insects—predators (*Chrysopa* sp.), internal parasites (*Apanteles glomeratus* and *A. spurius*), and blood-sucking insects (*Anopheles maculipennis* and *Culex pipiens*). The light conditions affect insects' development even when they feed on dead substrate or simple carbohydrates. Thus a definite photoperiodic reaction is observed in larvae of the pyralid *Plodia interpunctella*, which feeds on dried fruits. Finally, a normal photoperiodic reaction has been obtained for *Pyrausta nubilalis* when the larvae are fed on synthetic food material (MUTCHMOR and BECKEL, 1959).

We must also point out that in short-day (9 hours of light) conditions larvae of *Dendrolimus pini*, undergoing diapause and not feeding, remain in a resting state for an average of 26 days. With long-day conditions and the same temperature full reactivation takes place on the 17th day (GEISPITS, 1949). In this case we have a special type of photoperiodic reaction, which occurs in the complete absence of feeding. The independent nature of the photoperiodic reaction is perhaps more clearly illustrated by the silkworm, in which sensitivity to the light conditions is displayed in the egg stage.

2. The relation of photoperiodic reaction to the daily rhythm of activity

The effect of day-length on the sexual cycle of birds and mammals is sometimes looked upon as a result of changes in their daily activity and feeding periodicity. The possibility of a similar mechanism of action affecting insects also should not be rejected without special investigation. WAY, HOPKINS and SMITH (1949) have pointed out the possible dependence of diapause on changes in feeding rhythm with varying light. The data of ANDRIANOVA (1948) are also in favour of this view: she observed in larvae of the Chinese Oak Silkworm (*Antheraea pernyi*) a definite daily rhythm of growth, linked with changes in light intensity and with the alternation of day and night. A daily rhythm in respiratory metabolism is known to exist in many insects.

Since in the majority of insects the daily rhythm of activity is well expressed, we considered it of interest to discover what relation exists between it and photoperiodic reaction. According to the investigations made by K. F. Geispits in our laboratory, the daily rhythm of growth in conditions of constant temperature and light rhythms is specific for each species. In a univoltine race of *Antheraea pernyi*, with natural light, maximum growth was observed between 10 a.m. and 2 p.m. and during the evening hours. At night, from 2 to 10 a.m., growth is very slow. In total darkness the rhythm is much smoothed down. A quite different type of growth is characteristic of *Barathra brassicae*. Increase in the weight of larvae of this species takes place only during the evening and night hours, whereas during the daytime there is a considerable fall in weight (Fig. 13).

In connection with these data the daily rhythm of feeding of several species with different types of daily activity was investigated. Experiments were made at constant temperature. The feeding rhythm of larvae was registered by means of special apparatus, which automatically recorded the sounds of leaf-eating.

The receiving part of the apparatus—a sensitive piezomicrophone with a microphone amplifier—was placed in a soundproof chamber with the insects. In analysing the sounds, the duration of periods of eating was calculated in minutes for each hour of the day. In this way the feeding rhythms of *Pieris brassicae*, *Antheraea pernyi*, *Acronycta rumicis*, *Dendrolimus pini*, and *Barathra brassicae* were studied.

At the same time experiments were made on the effects of day-length on the development cycle of the above species.

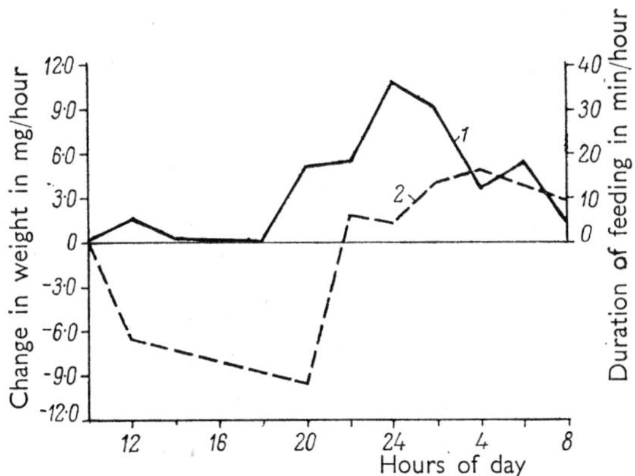

FIG. 13. The daily course of feeding and growth of *Barathra brassicae* larvae at a temperature of 20° in natural illumination (Leningrad, beginning of August).

Curves: 1, intensity of feeding; 2, change in weight.

We may divide the species studied into three groups, according to the type of daily rhythm of activity and feeding:

(1) Species with a clear preponderance of activity and feeding in the light hours of the day—*Pieris brassicae* and *Dendrolimus pini*. In these species feeding is usually not completely suspended during the dark part of the day, but is markedly reduced. Pine Moth larvae in photothermostatic conditions, with a temperature of 25° and a 14-hour day, fed during the light part of the day for approximately 11·7 (7-17) minutes per hour, and during the dark part for 4·2 (1-8) minutes per hour.

(2) Species with typical nocturnal behaviour, whose feeding in alternating light conditions takes place exclusively during the

dark part of the day. This type of behaviour is characteristic of *Barathra brassicae* (Fig. 13).

(3) Species not manifesting a definite dependence on light conditions, e.g. larvae of *Acronycta rumicis* and the 'gor'kovskii' univoltine race of *Antheraea pernyi.* Feeding by such forms continues with approximately uniform intensity throughout the 24 hours. Thus larvae of the Chinese Oak Silkworm feed, on an average, for 24 minutes per hour during the daytime and 23 minutes per hour at night.

TABLE 15

The type of daily rhythm of feeding and the photoperiodic reaction

Species	Type of daily activity	% of diapausing individuals	
		Short day (8-12 hours of light)	Long day (18-24 hours of light)
Dendrolimus pini	Mainly diurnal feeding	100·0	0·0
Pieris brassicae	do.	100·0	0·0
Acronycta rumicis	Feeding at any time	100·0	0·0
Antheraea pernyi (gor'kovskii univoltine race)	do.	5·0	60·0
Barathra brassicae	Nocturnal feeding	100·0	0·0

In Table 15 we show the results of investigations of photoperiodic reaction in species with different types of daily activity. The photoperiodic reaction of the majority of species proved to be uniform even with different types of daily activity. The nocturnal larvae of *Barathra brassicae,* like the diurnal larvae of *Pieris brassicae,* produced diapausing pupae when developing in short-day conditions, but in long-day conditions developed without diapause. On the other hand, species with similar types of behaviour may have different types of photoperiodic reaction. That is seen by comparing *Acronycta rumicis* with the univoltine race of *Antheraea pernyi.* In the latter pupal diapause is induced by long days, whereas in *Acronycta rumicis* it is induced by short days. Thus there is no connection between the type of daily activity and photoperiodic reaction.

In addition to the above observations, special experiments on disturbance of the natural daily feeding rhythm were made with Pine Moth larvae. The experimental larvae, produced from eggs of a single brood, were given food for only 12 hours a day. Two groups of larvae were kept in 12-hour-day conditions, but the feeding period for one of them coincided with the light half of the day and for the other with the dark half; a third group, also

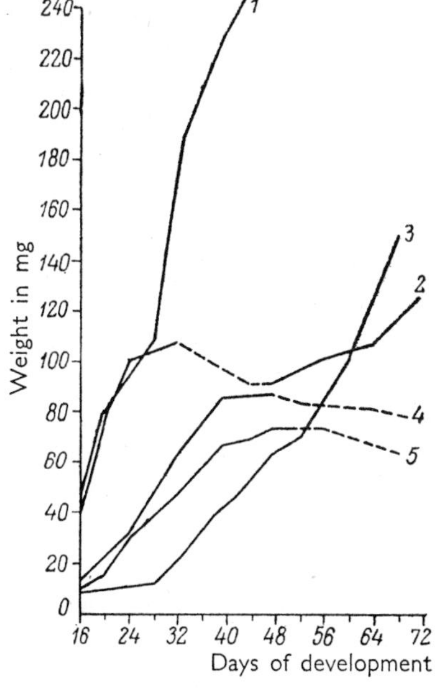

FIG. 14

Growth and diapause in *Dendrolimus pini* larvae with different daily conditions of light and feeding.

1. Constant food with continuous light.
2. Constant food with short (12-hour) day.
3. 12 hours of food per day with continuous light.
4. 12 hours of food in the dark period of a short day.
5. 12 hours of food in the light period of a short day.

——, active development
– – –, diapause

feeding only 12 hours a day, was kept in 24-hour light. Controls were groups of larvae receiving food continuously in 24-hour-day and 12-hour-day light conditions. All the experiments were carried out simultaneously in photothermostatic conditions at a temperature of 20° (Fig. 14). With interrupted feeding the larvae developed much more slowly than the controls; but in spite of the delay in growth, the experimental larvae retained the type of photoperiodic reaction normal for the species. In the short 12-hour-day conditions all larvae, regardless of their feeding conditions, entered diapause on reaching the fourth instar. Larvae reared in 24-hour light, both those feeding only 12 hours a day and those receiving food continuously, developed without diapause. Thus the onset of diapause proves to have no connection with the amount of food received or the feeding rhythm.

It must be noted, however, that feeding conditions were reflected in the duration of the pre-diapause preparatory period. Normally diapause in the Pine Moth comes on 30 days after the short day begins to take effect (GEISPITS, 1949, 1953), which was also observed in our experiment in the control larvae which received food continuously. Larvae feeding 12 hours a day entered diapause only on the 48th to the 56th day, but at the same age as the controls. This shows that the onset of diapause is linked not only with a definite number of short photoperiods but also with the passing in such conditions of a definite stage of development required for the physiological reconstruction of the organism and the accumulation of food reserves. As the accumulation of food reserves depends on the amount of food consumed, this probably explains the delay in onset of diapause in the experimental larvae.

From all of the above experiments it is concluded that adaptations of the seasonal cycle of insects to changes in the daily periodicity of light on the one hand, and the daily rhythm of their behaviour and activity on the other hand, evolved independently of each other, and are phenomena quite independent in their biological and physiological aspects.

3. The role of seasonal changes in food plants in regulating diapause

The unique nature of the photoperiodic reaction in insects and its independence of periodicity in behaviour and feeding still do not exclude the possibility of initiation of diapause by seasonal and growth changes in food plants as well as by light conditions.

The rearing of different species of Lepidoptera (*Dendrolimus pini*, *Acronycta rumicis*, *Pandemis ribeana*, *Agrotis C-nigrum*) throughout the year in constant temperature and varying photoperiodic conditions demonstrated the leading role of long days in initiating diapause. Artificial variations in the duration of daylight easily succeeded in inducing typical diapause in spring and summer, during the active vegetative period, or averting its onset in autumn and winter, when the vegetative period of food plants has come to an end and when insects in a natural environment obligatorily enter diapause.

The absence in these experiments of effects due to food plants requires us to re-examine the evidence that originally led us to look upon seasonal changes in the composition of food plants as an important regulator of the cycle of development and diapause in insects.

In the detailed work of STEINBERG and KAMENSKY (1936) it was shown experimentally that in the Beet Webworm *Loxostege sticticalis*, in conditions of constant temperature (25°) and humidity, regular fluctuations in the percentage of diapausing larvae were observed. In winter (from the end of September until April) all larvae entered diapause. With the arrival of spring the percentage of diapausing larvae fell sharply, reaching a minimum in mid-summer. After carefully analysing the experimental data, the authors came to the conclusion that diapause commenced when the larvae ate plants (beets) that had developed in unfavourable conditions. But the light conditions in these experiments were not studied. Moreover, when we compare the curve of seasonal fluctuations in the percentage of diapausing larvae as given in the work of Steinberg and Kamensky with fluctuations in day-length in Leningrad, where the investigations were made, we are readily convinced of the close relation between these phenomena. We therefore made a special study of the reaction of Beet Webworm larvae to changes in photoperiodic conditions.

The material was obtained in the laboratory from adult moths collected in Belgorod province. Experiments in natural lighting conditions confirmed the seasonal nature of the onset of diapause in constant temperature (22°-23°): all larvae developing in early June pupated, and entered diapause in September (Table 16). But artificial changes in illumination enabled us to change the course of the reaction completely. July larvae raised in shortened periods of daylight (8 hours of light per day) produced only diapausing prepupae; on the other hand, in September—when the food plants (*Chenopodium album*) had died off—we obtained full pupation of the larvae when the day was lengthened with artificial light.

In order to exclude any possible effect due to living plant food, in July we made an experiment in feeding larvae on artificial

TABLE 16

The effect of light conditions in varying the numbers of diapausing prepupae of *Loxostege sticticalis*. Food—pigweed (*Chenopodium album*).
Temperature 22°-23°

Light conditions	% of diapausing prepupae	
	July	September
Natural light (50° N.)	0·0	100·0
Long day (20 hours of light)	0·0	0·0
Short day (8 hours of light)	100·0	100·0

food—soaked rye bread. Control larvae from the same brood received natural food (*Chenopodium album*). The growth rate of larvae on artificial food was much slower than normal; their final size and weight were much reduced, and about 80% of the larvae died during development. The survivors, however, displayed the same photoperiodic reaction as the controls, i.e. they all entered diapause in short-day and pupated in long-day conditions.

These data lead to the conclusion that the main factor determining the seasonal onset of diapause in the Beet Webworm in constant temperature is fluctuations in day-length, and not changes in the biochemical composition of food plants. ANDRIANOVA (1948) and BELOV (1951) came to a similar conclusion with regard to the work of ZOLOTAREV and his colleagues (1938, 1940a, 1940b) on the Chinese Oak Silkworm *Antheraea pernyi*. By precise experiments these authors showed that the seasonal nature of onset of diapause in the multivoltine form of the Chinese Oak Silkworm is due not to changes in the biochemical composition of the food, as Zolotarev supposed, but to the light conditions. Checking experiments proved that my first views on this subject (DANILEVSKII, 1947) were wrong.

One of the best indications of the dependence of diapause on diet appeared to be the data obtained by SQUIRE (1939, 1940) for *Platyedra gossypiella*. He found that the percentage of diapausing larvae increased with the ripening of cotton seeds in direct proportion to the decrease of their water content and the increase of their fat content.

When larvae were reared in an artificial environment, however, no clear dependence of diapause on the fat content of the food was discovered (VANDERZANT and REISER, 1956a, 1956b). It is possible that even in this case diapause is determined by the light conditions, since even the insignificant changes in day-length observed in tropical countries are capable of regulating the onset of diapause in insects.

Also worthy of examination are the works of LARCHENKO (1955, 1958a) on the dependence of diapause in the Colorado Beetle on the food supply. The timing of diapause in late summer is explained by Larchenko as being due merely to the effect of growth changes in the biochemical composition of potato leaves. She attributes decisive significance to the fat and protein content of the leaves—the 'lipocytaric coefficient', which increases as the plant grows. Confirmation of the role of food in inducing diapause is seen by Larchenko in the fact that the values of the lipocytaric coefficient in potato leaves in autumn and in the tissues of beetles in diapause prove to be very similar.

The special biochemical investigations of WĘGOREK (1959b), however, did not confirm the correlation between the seasonal changes in the fat and protein contents in potato leaves and the onset of diapause in Colorado Beetles. It must be remembered that Larchenko's experiments were made during the active period with natural lighting, and therefore in the results obtained one cannot separate the effects of food from those of seasonal changes in day-length. Besides, the investigations of other authors, in which the complex of external conditions was properly taken into account (DE WILDE, 1954, 1955; JERMI and SARINGER, 1955; GORYSHIN, 1956, 1958a), clearly point to the importance of photoperiodic reaction in initiation of diapause in the Colorado Beetle. Particularly convincing in this respect are the results of Goryshin, in which it is demonstrated that by artificially regulating the duration of light one can at will induce or avert diapause, regardless of the time of year or the nature of the plant food. Development of larvae and beetles in day-lengths below 16 hours always induces diapause, whereas with longer days (17-18 hours) the beetles develop and mature normally, and only a few individuals enter diapause. It was also observed in Goryshin's experiments that with development in long-day conditions a diet of young plants somewhat accelerated the maturing of *Leptinotarsa decemlineata* as compared with a diet of old plants

(Fig. 15); but in short-day conditions diapause appeared inevitably with any diet. Similar results were obtained by feeding larvae with varieties of potato that were in different degrees resistant to Colorado Beetles.

The majority of other statements in the literature on the effect of diet on diapause in insects are based on fragmentary data or logical deductions. In many cases one may suspect that the operative factor was the neglected light conditions. Thus the widespread view of the dependence of diapause in the Codling Moth on diet has not been confirmed. DICKSON (1949) observed in experimental conditions a clear photoperiodic reaction, regulating diapause, in this species. SHEL'DESHOVA (1956) discovered that in natural conditions the chief factor determining the complex annual cycle of the Pear Moth is seasonal variations in day-length. In present-day literature on species living in temperate latitudes we have not a single proved instance in which diet was the principal factor in inducing diapause.

The opposite conclusion, to which analysis of published material has led us, does not fully solve the problems raised by the work of STEINBERG and KAMENSKY (1936) and ZOLOTAREV (1938, 1940a, 1940b). Fairly precise observations still indicate that diet may affect the induction of diapause. That is seen from the above-cited experiments of Goryshin with Colorado Beetles (see Fig. 15). We shall present a few more facts.

In the experiments of LEES (1953a), the Red Spider Mite *Metatetranychus ulmi* developed without diapause at a temperature of 15° and with a long day (16 hours), but with a short day (8 hours) 94% to 95% of the females laid wintering eggs. When they were fed on old yellowing leaves the tendency to diapause increased sharply: with a 16-hour day 80% entered diapause, and with an 8-hour day 100%. Even at a high temperature and with a long (16-hour) day there was a small percentage (12%) entering diapause among those fed on old leaves. A periodic short fast increased the tendency to diapause.

According to my observations on the Lower Volga steppes, larvae of the Beet Webworm from a single brood, kept in early August in strictly parallel conditions, developed without diapause when fed on pigweed (*Chenopodium album*), but when fed on wormwood (*Artemisia incana*) an overwhelming majority of them entered diapause.

With simultaneous feeding of *Antheraea pernyi* larvae on oak and birch the numbers of diapausing pupae were often different, the number being usually lower on oak than on other tree species. In the experiments of GEISPITS (1953) on the Satin Moth *Leucoma salicis* in uniform light conditions—20 hours of light per day—a smaller percentage of diapausing larvae was observed when they

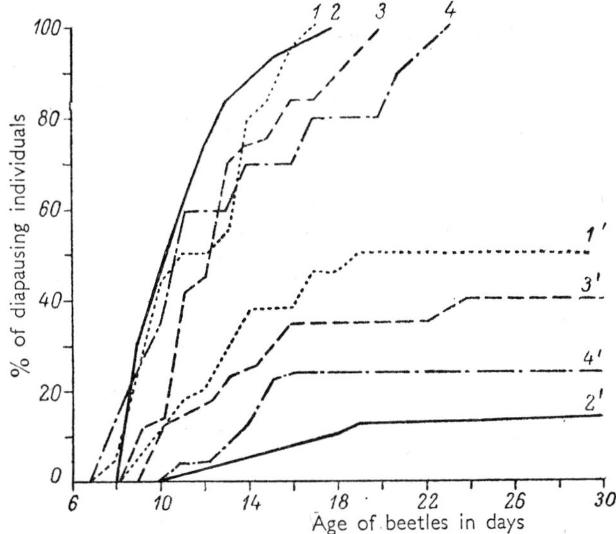

FIG. 15. The dates of onset of diapause in the beetle *Leptinotarsa decemlineata* reared on different kinds of food in short-day and long-day conditions. Temperature 25° (from Goryshin, 1958).

1 to 4, short-day series; 1′ to 4′, long-day series. Food: 1, 1′, old potato plants of the Akkerzegen variety; 2, 2′, flowering plants of the Akkerzegen variety; 3, 3′, hybrids between cultivated and wild potatoes; 4, 4′, wild species of potato, *Solanum gibberulosum*.

were fed on young poplar leaves than when they were fed on old ones.

Study of the joint action of light and diet helps us to discuss the mass of contradictory evidence and to evaluate the role of diet in regulating diapause.

GORYSHIN (1953, 1958b), in experiments with *Chloridea obsoleta*, observed that with extreme variations in light—short and long days—no effect from differences in food was manifest. In the threshold region of photoperiods, however, such effects were clearly seen. On diets of cotton seedcases and tomatoes the critical photoperiod was an hour less than on a diet of cotton leaves (Fig. 16). Such differences in critical day-length are of great ecological importance, affecting the dates of onset of diapause in nature.

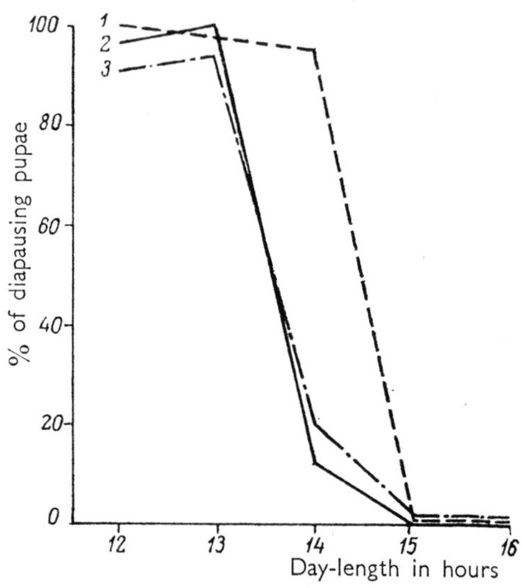

FIG. 16. Changes in the photoperiodic reaction of *Chloridea obsoleta* larvae under the influence of different diets. Temperature 25° (after Goryshin, 1958).

1, diet of cotton leaves; 2, of cotton seedcases; 3, of tomatoes.

Similar results were obtained in studies of photoperiodic reaction in the Mallow Moth *Gelechia malvella*. Diapause in this species, according to BABAYAN (1958) and MKRTUMYAN (1958), is determined by changes in the larval diet. When fed in summer on blossoms and buds of cotton and wild mallow the larvae pupated without delay; but by autumn, with a change to a diet of ripe seeds of *Althaea taurinensis* and cotton seedcases, diapause occurred. But, as is seen from data collected by I. A. KUZNETSOVA (Fig. 17), the chief factor regulating onset of diapause in the Mallow Moth is still the change in day-length. Even with high temperature (about 27°) shortening of the day in the experiments induced diapause on any diet, but the critical threshold of reaction varied according to the species of food plant. Thus feeding the larvae on fruits of *Alcea rosea* and *Althaea taurinensis* increased the tendency to diapause, and the critical threshold of reaction was raised approximately an hour above that observed on a cotton diet. Moreover, feeding the larvae on autumn food—cotton seedcases and ripe seeds—produced no noticeable change in photoperiodic reaction as compared with that observed on a diet of buds and blossoms. These experimental data confirm observations made in the field in the Nakhichevan ASSR. Diapause of the Mallow Moth occurred much earlier on *Althaea taurinensis* than on cotton (Fig. 18). On *Althaea* 50% of diapausing larvae were observed in the field about August 1, with a long day of 14 hours 20 minutes exclusive of twilight, but on cotton the same percentage was found only towards the end of that month, when the day had shortened to 13 hours 20 minutes.

It is of interest to note that, besides the changes in photoperiodic reaction due to aging of the leaves, the moisture conditions in the plant food also affect it. Thus the mite *Tetranychus urticae*, when developing on aspidistra at a temperature of 18° in an experiment with abundant watering of the plants, almost never entered diapause in any light conditions. In parallel experiments made on plants that were not watered, the reaction to the light conditions was markedly different, and in short-day conditions the great majority of the larvae entered diapause (Fig. 19).

Thus the effect of diet on diapause proves to be closely linked with that of light, and is expressed in variation of the norm of photoperiodic reaction. In the cases studied, the effect of diet was noticeable only in the region of critical photoperiods. A typical long or short day exerted such powerful influence on development that it completely swamped the effect of diet. This explains why at the end of summer, when for most insects day-length is near the critical point, the effect of dietary variations on diapause is more clearly displayed. At the beginning of summer when the day is long, as in autumn when it is short, it is difficult or impossible to detect the influence of diet.

The minor role of diet, as compared with that of light conditions, in regulating diapause is apparently due to the different degrees of variability of these two factors. Changes in the bio-

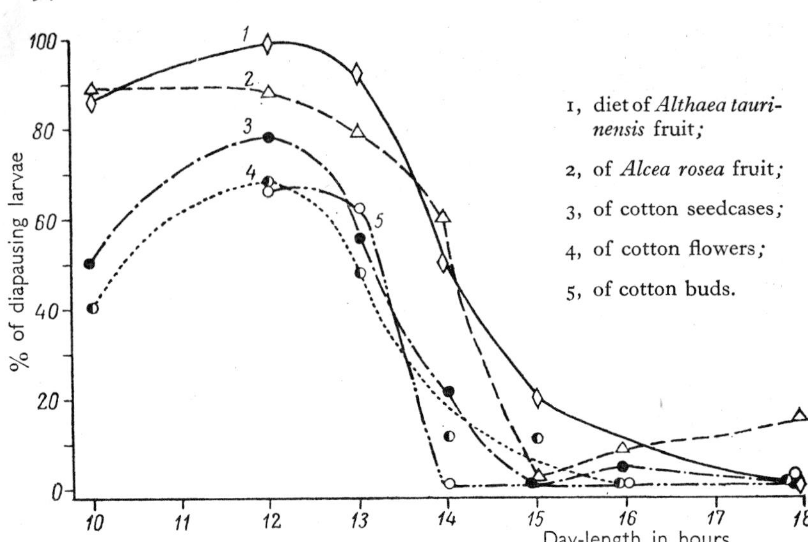

FIG. 17. Changes in the photoperiodic reaction of *Gelechia malvella* larvae under the influence of different diets (from data of I. A. Kuznetsova).

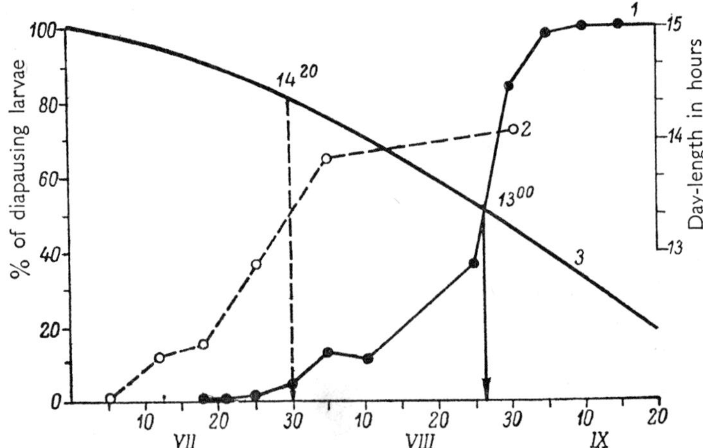

FIG. 18. Changes in the appearance of diapausing larvae of *Gelechia malvella* in natural conditions in Norashen in 1958 (from data of I. A. Kuznetsova).

1, developing on cotton plants; 2, on *Althaea taurinensis*; 3, day-length in hours; arrows—critical day-length.

chemical composition of food during the season, regardless of their known regularity, depend to a great extent on the species and age of the plants and also on fluctuations in weather conditions. The nutritional factor thus cannot serve as a safe regulator of an adaptation so vitally important as diapause. One may expect an increase in the relative importance of diet only in monophagous, especially sedentary, insects, as dietary habits such as theirs preclude variation in the species of their food plants.

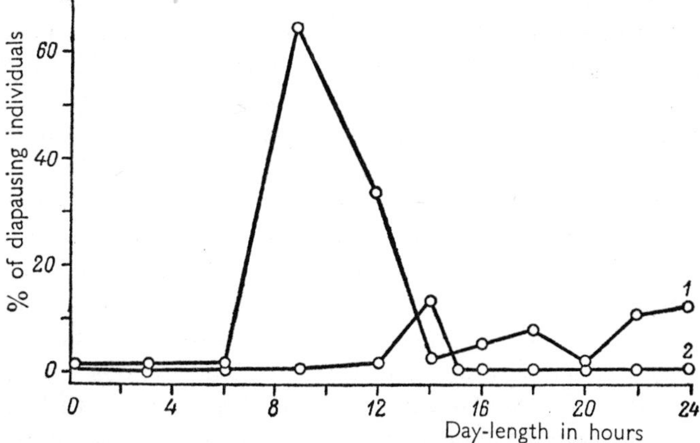

FIG. 19. Changes in the photoperiodic reaction of the mite *Tetranychus urticae* with different amounts of moisture in the food plant (*Aspidistra*). Temperature 18° (Geispits, 1960).

1, percentage of diapausing females on unwatered plants; 2, on well-watered plants.

Data in the literature stressing the great influence of diet on the cyclomorphoses and diapause of aphids and spider mites seem to confirm the above view. It is interesting to note that the interaction of light and diet, observed in the above-described experiments of Goryshin, permit wide variations in the relative roles of these factors. One can well imagine cases in which the photoperiodic reaction of a species is so much changed as the result of a difference in food that diet becomes the principal factor regulating the onset of diapause in natural conditions; but up to the present such cases have not been experimentally proved to exist.

4. The significance of endogenous nutrition in the physiological mechanism of diapause

The question of the role of reserve food deposits in the physiological mechanism of diapause is closely linked with the question of diet as an ecological factor regulating diapause.

The onset of diapause is always accompanied by accumulation in the tissues of reserve deposits that make prolonged fasting possible. Several authors therefore ascribe basic importance to the conditions of endogenous nutrition in the physiological mechanism of diapause. The view of the major role of endogenous nutrition has been most definitely developed by ANDREWARTHA (1952) in his hypothesis of 'food mobilization', and also in the concepts of LARCHENKO (1956), which are close to those of Andrewartha.

Andrewartha assumes that the immediate cause of a halt in development in the form of diapause is a temporary shortage or absence of hormones necessary for growth. The external factors regulating the onset and breaking of diapause act indirectly on the endocrine system, through the medium of tissues connected with accumulation of food reserves for endogenous nutrition. The activity of the endocrine system is stimulated by the arrival of easily-assimilated food material formed by the breakdown of the reserve deposits in fatty tissues or yolk.

In ecological conditions that permit non-diapause development, food reserves are deposited in the organism in an easily-mobilized form. In conditions causing diapause the reserves are laid down in a stable form, as a consequence of which these materials become unavailable for immediate use, and the activity of the endocrine system, deprived of its necessary nutriment, comes to a halt. The author suggests that one of the chief causes determining the form of the deposits is the qualitative nature of the food intake. Conversion of the stable food reserves into mobilized and assimilable material takes place during diapause under the influence of low temperature. This also causes the phenomenon of reactivation.

In Larchenko's opinion, diapause is also connected with the nature of the reserve deposits. The immediate cause of diapause is formation in fatty tissue or yolk of a special type of reserve deposit in the form of dense fat-protein granules, giving simultaneous fat and protein reactions. Because of the great stability and slow dissolution of these granules the entrance of food material into the lymph is impeded, which leads to a sharp decrease in metabolic activity, cessation of growth, increased resistance to unfavourable conditions, and a number of other phenomena characteristic of diapause. Development does not recommence until the advent of suitable conditions for conversion of the dense fat-protein granules into a dissociated state. Separation of free fat takes place slowly throughout the whole diapause period.

The chief difference between the views of Larchenko and of Andrewartha is that the former disregards entirely the role of hormonal regulation of diapause, and associates the stability and lack of assimilation of the reserves with their definite form of fat-protein granules. Larchenko considers that food conditions are the basic external cause of formation of these reserves. A shortcoming of both hypotheses is their inadequate foundation on experimental data.

Above all, there is no confirmation of the suggestion that the quality and quantity of the reserves deposited in fatty tissue are predominantly dependent on the food assimilated. For instance, when the mosquitoes *Culex pipiens* and *Anopheles maculipennis* were fed on the same sugar solution in short-day (12-hour) conditions that induced diapause, rapid deposit of large quantities of fat took place, whereas in long-day conditions fat accumulation was much slower (DANILEVSKII and GLINYANAYA, 1958; VINOGRADOVA, 1958). KUZNETSOVA (1955) studied the structure of fatty tissue in several species of Lepidoptera and in the leaf-eater *Haltica saliceti* during development in different light conditions. Her data show great differences in structure and quantity of the fat reserves in the active and in the diapause stages, in spite of the identical diet.

Thus the nature of the accumulation and structure of the food reserves proves to be dependent, not on the nature of the food eaten, but on light conditions during the developmental period. The leading role is played not by the composition of the food intake but by the method of its assimilation, which is controlled by external conditions, probably acting through the hormone system.

It is also easy to point out the lack of foundation for Larchenko's theory, which attributes diapause exclusively to the formation of fat-protein granules in fatty tissue. On this theory she would be forced to deny the possibility of imaginal and larval diapause in insects with incomplete metamorphosis, and even in the bug investigated by herself, *Eurygaster integriceps*, merely on the grounds that only free fat is deposited in the fatty tissues of these insects. Moreover, the existence of typical seasonal diapause has been experimentally proved in the nymph of the carnivorous bug *Reduvius personatus* (READIO, 1931), in the imago of *Acrydium arenosum* (SABROSKY, LARSEN and NABOURS, 1933), and in the imago of the jassid *Stenocranus minutus* (MÜLLER, 1957a). Finally, typical imaginal diapause is well known to exist in the bug *Eurygaster integriceps*. There is no doubt that with special investigation diapause will be found in the majority of Holometabola, which hibernate in the larval or imaginal phase.

On the other hand, one should on no account give the name of diapause (as Larchenko does) to temporary cessation of maturation in female Beet Webworms directly induced by insufficiency of moisture, merely because at such times breakdown of the fat-protein deposits does not take place. There is no doubt that the fat-protein granules are not the only form in which food reserves for diapause are laid down. Kuznetsova has shown in the above-mentioned work that food reserves laid down for diapause in fatty tissue may differ greatly in form. Whereas in larvae of the Satin Moth *Leucoma salicis* fat-protein granules are well developed, in *Euproctis similis* they exist only in insignificant amounts, and in diapausing larvae of *Pandemis ribeana* and *Cosmotriche potatoria* they are not formed at all.

It is also not confirmed that resumption of development depends on the breakdown of these granules. Gradual change in fatty tissue during diapause, with liberation of fat, is observed only during hibernation at high temperatures. In normal conditions, with low temperatures, fatty tissue retains its diapausing appearance without external alteration until spring, although by midwinter the capacity for potential development of the organism has been fully restored. In the Satin Moth the fatty tissue retains the granules almost unchanged even after the larvae have emerged from their winter cocoons; they disappear only when feeding begins. Similar facts were established by TULESCHKOV (1935).

Thus it is not the breakdown of the granules that causes the end of diapause; on the contrary, they break down as a result of development recommencing.

Investigation of the structural changes that take place during the life cycle in different organs and tissues, especially in the 'tissues of internal environment', are no doubt of interest for understanding the physiology of diapause, but they are only its morphological symptoms and not its cause. Some of the above criticisms apply also to the views of Andrewartha. On the whole his 'concept of food mobilization', as remarked by LEES (1955), does not agree with data on the role of the endocrine system, and especially of the neuro-secretory cells of the brain, in regulation of development and diapause in insects. WILLIAMS' (1946, 1947) experiments with *Platysamia cecropia* showed that low temperatures leading to the end of pupal diapause have a direct reactivating effect on the brain tissues and not on the reserve deposits: the chilling of pupae with the brain removed, carried out after implantation of an unreactivated brain, leads to the end of diapause and the renewal of development. If the pupa is chilled before implantation development does not recommence. It follows that temperature has no reactivating effect on other tissues, including the food reserves.

Chapter IV

THE RELATION BETWEEN TEMPERATURE AND LIGHT CONDITIONS IN REGULATING DIAPAUSE

The relation between photoperiodism and temperature is one of the central and most complex questions in the problem of the ecological regulation of seasonal cycles and diapause in insects. Physiological adaptations to temperature and day-length are closely interrelated. In natural conditions it is not easy to separate and evaluate the ecological role of each of these factors, because in the course of days and seasons they fluctuate synchronously. This is one of the reasons why the role of photoperiodism in regulating the seasonal development long remained unnoticed, and temperature conditions were held to be the principal external factor determining the commencement of wintering phases.

In the literature there is a widely-held view that the state of winter rest—diapause—is a consequence of the development of preceding stages of the life cycle of insects at temperatures below a definite level for a given species, and that at higher temperatures development proceeds without interruption. Hence 'temperature thresholds' for the onset of diapause have been established for many insect species.

The effects of temperature on the onset of diapause have been described in other ways. Dawson (1931) in experiments with the silkworm moth *Telea polyphaemus* came to the conclusion that diapause is determined not by the average level of temperature but by the direction in which it changes. In gradually rising temperatures active pupae are obtained, and in falling temperatures diapausing pupae. A similar result was obtained by Chugunin (1939) with the Codling Moth. Kozhanchikov (1949) associated diapause in the silkworm *Antheraea pernyi* with the effects on the larvae of daily fluctuations in temperature. He pointed out the possibility of inducing diapause in pupae of the noctuid

Acronycta rumicis by the direct action of low temperature (KOZHANCHIKOV, 1948). Similar facts have been noted for the fruit moth *Laspeyresia molesta* (DICKSON, 1949).

A condition close to diapause may sometimes be induced by high sublethal temperatures, e.g. in pupae of the Tree-of-heaven Silkworm *Philosamia cynthia* (DANILEVSKII, 1940) and of the Cabbage-root Fly *Hylemyia brassicae* (KOZHANCHIKOV, 1939b). A unique form of dependence has been observed in the Wheat Sawfly *Cephus cinctus* (SALT, 1947; CHURCH, 1955a). In over-wintering, fully-reactivated larvae of this species it is possible, by means of temporary high temperature (35°), to re-induce a state of stable diapause, to break which a second prolonged chilling or natural over-wintering is required.

The above data show the wide variety of possible ways in which temperature may take part in regulating diapause. But since all these studies were made without taking into account the light conditions, it is necessary to discover to what extent the conclusions drawn from them agree with the hypothesis that diapause depends on day-length.

An organic connection between the photoperiodic and temperature reactions that regulate the seasonal development of insects has been noted in a number of studies, but special investigations in this important field are few. Available experimental data have recently been reviewed by DANILEVSKII and GORYSHIN (1960), on whose data and conclusions the following account is based.

1. The change in the temperature threshold of diapause under the influence of day-length

Investigation of the simultaneous action of temperature and photoperiodic conditions on insect development shows that the level of temperature inducing diapause varies greatly, according to the length of the day. That is clearly evident in the case of the Cabbage White Butterfly *Pieris brassicae*, for which special investigations (MAERCKS, 1934; KOZHANCHIKOV, 1936) have established a temperature threshold of 20° to 22°. Fig. 20 shows the fluctuation in percentages of Cabbage White Butterfly pupae in diapause according to the temperature and photoperiodic conditions in which the larvae develop (DANILEVSKII and GORYSHIN,

1960). When the larvae are reared in long-day conditions (24 hours of light per day) diapause is not induced even at a temperature of 12°. With a short day, on the contrary, the tendency to diapause is so strongly manifest that it can be overcome only by temperatures of the order of 30°. If the larvae are reared in total darkness the pupae do not enter diapause at temperatures above 20°, but at lower temperatures the percentage in diapause progressively increases, reaching 80% at 15°. Thus the temperature threshold for induction of diapause in this species varies in accordance with the photoperiodic conditions by more than 15°. It is thus quite impossible to speak of a constant threshold for inducing diapause in any species, in the sense used by earlier investigators.

Data very similar to those described for *Pieris brassicae* may be adduced for many other species studied in our laboratory, e.g. *Pieris rapae*, *Acronycta rumicis*, *Dendrolimus sibiricus*, and *D. pini*. Similar results have also been obtained by other authors for several species of insects and mites—*Polia* (*Diataraxia*) *oleracea* (WAY and HOPKINS, 1950); *Metatetranychus ulmi* (LEES, 1953a); *Apanteles glomeratus* (MASLENNIKOVA, 1958).

In the light of these data we can understand why the temperature thresholds for induction of diapause, as recorded in laboratory experiments by several authors—20°-22° for *Pieris brassicae* (MAERCKS, 1934; KOZHANCHIKOV, 1936); 17°-18° for *Loxostege sticticalis* (KOZHANCHIKOV, 1935b); 22°-24° for *Pyrausta nubilalis* (KOZHANCHIKOV, 1938b); 20° for *Chilo simplex* (FUKAYA, 1950); 25° for *Philosamia cynthia* (DANILEVSKII, 1940); etc.—were not found acceptable in field investigations and indeed were often contradicted by them.

Observations made on *Pieris brassicae* in the neighbourhood of Leningrad showed that the fluctuation of the temperature threshold for diapause under the influence of seasonal changes in day-length, as established by laboratory experiments, is fully manifested in natural conditions. In the first generation, larvae of which develop in the long days of June, diapausing pupae are never found, although the average temperature during that period is often below 15° and in some years remains even at the 12°-14° level. On the other hand, larvae of the autumn generation, developing in the short-day conditions that begin in September, always produce diapausing pupae even in cases where the temperature is higher than during the development of the first generation. In experiments made in a greenhouse with natural illumination, full diapause of second-generation pupae was observed in mid-September even with an average temperature of 20°-22°.

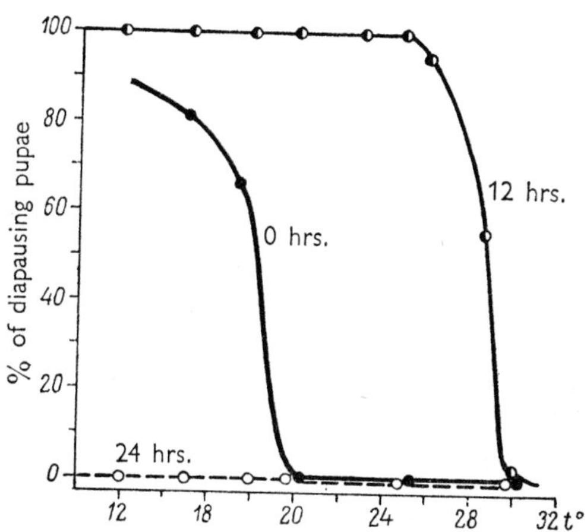

FIG. 20. The dependence of diapause in *Pieris brassicae* pupae on the temperature and light conditions during larval development.

24 hours, continuous light; 12 hours, short day; 0 hours, continuous darkness.

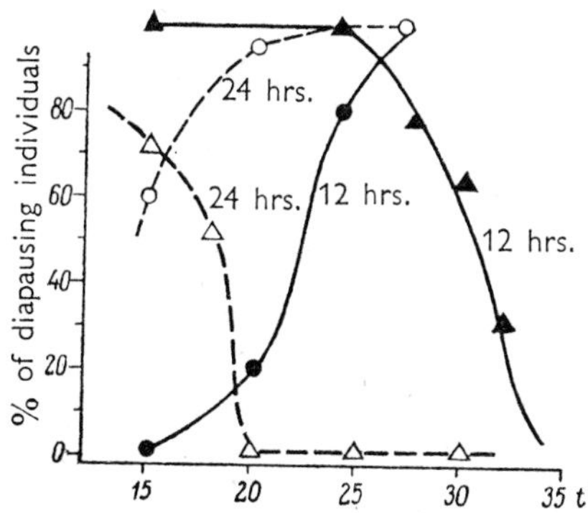

FIG. 21

The types of dependence of the photoperiodic reaction on temperature.

△, ▲: the percentage of diapausing pupae of *Acronycta rumicis* (Belgorod) when their larvae were reared in continuous light (24 hours) and short days (12 hours)

○, ●: the percentage of diapausing eggs of *Bombyx mori* when eggs of the maternal generation were incubated in long and short days.

2. The types of photothermal regulation of diapause

From the data presented in the last paragraph it is clear that diapause is induced by both the temperature and the light conditions, and it is therefore impossible to consider the action of either of these factors in isolation. Available experimental data, however, on the effect of photothermal conditions on insect development cannot be brought together into a single unified pattern. The observed interrelations bear a deeply-marked imprint of specific peculiarities.

The majority of polycyclic species with long-day reactions are characterized by the fact that higher temperatures and longer days produce in them development without diapause, whereas lowering the temperature and shortening the day induce diapause. Such a type of regulation of diapause has been described for *Polia oleracea* (Way and Hopkins, 1950) and *Metatetranychus ulmi* (Lees, 1953a). Characteristic examples are also the reactions of *Acronycta rumicis* (Fig. 21), *Pieris brassicae* (Fig. 20), and a number of other species.

The opposite type is seen in the silkworm. According to Kogure (1933), falling temperature and short days during the period of incubation of eggs of the maternal generation lead to continuous development, whereas a high temperature of incubation and long days induce diapause (Fig. 21). It is possible that such relationships will also be found in other short-day species.

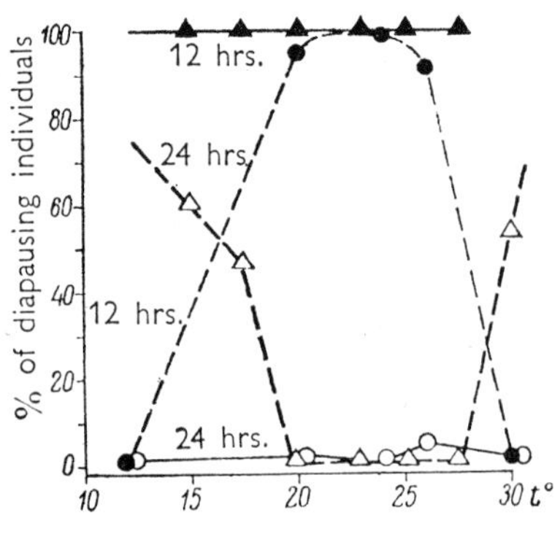

△, ▲: the percentage of diapausing individuals of *Spilosoma menthastri* when their larvae were reared in long (24 hours) and short (12 hours) days;

○, ●: similar data for *Laspeyresia molesta*.

Fig. 22. The types of dependence of the photoperiodic reaction on temperature.

A third type is illustrated by the reaction of the Oriental Fruit Moth *Laspeyresia molesta* (DICKSON, 1949), in which short-day action induces diapause only in medium temperatures (20°-26°). Higher or lower temperatures result in continuous development, regardless of the light conditions (Fig. 22). Similar results were obtained by KOMAROVA (1959) for the Cotton-boll Worm *Chloridea obsoleta* (Table 17).

TABLE 17

The effect of light and temperature conditions on the onset of diapause in *Chloridea obsoleta* pupae (after Komarova, 1959)

Temp. during devt. of larvae (°)	Long day (18 hours of light)		Short day (10 hours of light)		
	Pupae obtained	% dia-pausing	Pupae obtained	% dia-pausing	Average duration of diapause (days)
29·5	28	0	47	6·4	80·5 (84-77)
25·2	31	0	45	62·2	68·7 (106-32)
23·1	48	0	52	94·2	55·2 (142-32)
19·6	22	0	24	33·2	41·0 (38-44)

An inverse relationship has been found in *Spilosoma menthastri* (Fig. 22). In this case non-diapause development is limited by a narrow temperature range (20°-27°). A rise or fall in temperature induces diapause in *Spilosoma menthastri* even in long-day conditions (DANILEVSKII, 1957a).

Finally, the unique development-temperature relationship observed in the arctiid *Parasemia plantaginis* is worthy of note (Table 18). With low temperature (15°) the larvae display the usual long-day-type reaction, with general larval diapause in short-day (12-hour) conditions and continuous development in long-day (18- to 24-hour) conditions. A rise in temperature to 23°-24° induces an inverse photoperiodic reaction. In this case, with a short day development proceeds much more rapidly and uniformly than with a long day, which induces evident depression, brief interruptions in growth, and considerable mortality. In such conditions typical diapause frequently occurs in some of the larvae.

The above characteristic of *Parasemia plantaginis* is interesting because of its analogy with the reaction of several plants (*Euphorbia*

TABLE 18

The inversion of the photoperiodic reaction in *Parasemia plantaginis* larvae under the influence of temperature

Indicator of larval development	Temperature and photoperiod during larval development			
	15°		23°	
	12 hours	24 hours	12 hours	24 hours
Average weight on 40th day (mg)	4·0 (3-12)	21·6 (8-32)	184·8 (56-335)	81·1 (19-202)
% diapausing	100	0	0	0
% pupating on 50th day	0	0	94·1	20·0
Duration of development (days)	—	—	49 (42-56)	57 (44-65)
Mortality (%)	5·0	6·2	5·9	55·0

pulcherrima, *Ipomoea purpurea*, *Xanthium pensylvanicum*), in which changes in temperature can also induce inversion of photoperiodic reaction (SAMYGIN, 1946). Such cases indicate the conditional nature of a division of species into short-day and long-day groups.

3. The optimum temperature for photoperiodic reaction

In entomological literature there is a widely-held view that diapause is induced by conditions unfavourable for growth. A number of investigations have been devoted to the experimental basis for this point of view. MAERCKS (1934), after studying the cycle of *Pieris brassicae*, concluded that diapause is a function of non-optimal temperature and other harmful factors. KOZHANCHIKOV (1935a, 1937a) also regarded diapause as a form of reaction of the organism to growth in unfavourable temperature conditions. In the work of COUSIN (1932) diapause is defined as a direct result of unfavourable influences. Such a point of view is not far from that put forward by SIMMONDS (1948), who is inclined to consider diapause as being in general a pathological phenomenon.

The results of investigations of photoperiodic reactions in

insects do not agree with such views and compel us to re-examine the question of the relationship between conditions inducing diapause and temperature norms required for growth and development.

Analysis of available experimental data indicates that, with all the complexity and variability of its relationship with temperature, photoperiodic reaction—like other physiological processes—has a definite optimum temperature. As the temperature departs from this point in either direction the reaction to photoperiod gradually weakens until it disappears altogether. This is particularly clearly seen in *Laspeyresia molesta*, *Spilosoma menthastri*, and *Chloridea obsoleta* (Table 17), on which extreme temperatures, high and low, have similar effects. But with other types of photothermal relationships also one finds a similar law in operation, with this difference only—that the disappearance of reaction to light in the vicinity of the high and low limits is induced by different causes. Thus in species of the ordinary long-day type high temperatures suppress the photoperiodic reaction, enabling continuous development to take place even in short-day conditions. In low temperatures also photoperiodic reaction disappears, and diapause is induced in any light conditions.

Fig. 23 presents examples of changes in the intensity of photoperiodic reaction in different species in accordance with the temperature conditions in which the stages sensitive to the light conditions developed. The percentage of individuals reacting to day-length is taken as the indicator of intensity. As is seen from these data, the optimum temperature for photoperiodic reaction varies greatly in different species. In the mite *Metatetranychus ulmi* (LEES, 1953a) it lies at 13°-18°. In the Leningrad population of *Acronycta rumicis* the photoperiodic effect is manifested in a narrow range of high temperatures (25°-28°). There is a much wider temperature range for optimum reaction in *Pieris brassicae* (12°-26°), the lower limit not having been reached in the experiments.

The above features are of great importance in the biology of a species, indicating the relative roles of temperature and light conditions in regulating the seasonal cycle. The wider the range of optimum temperatures for photoperiodic reaction, the greater relatively is the role played by light conditions in a natural environment. Where the thermal range is narrow, the temperature conditions may acquire predominant importance in regulating diapause. Table 19 compares temperature norms for photoperiodic reaction in the insect species under study with indicators of their temperature requirements during the period of growth and development. From these data it follows that the optimum for photoperiodic reaction always lies within the temperature range that is entirely favourable for the growth and development of the stages sensitive to day-length.

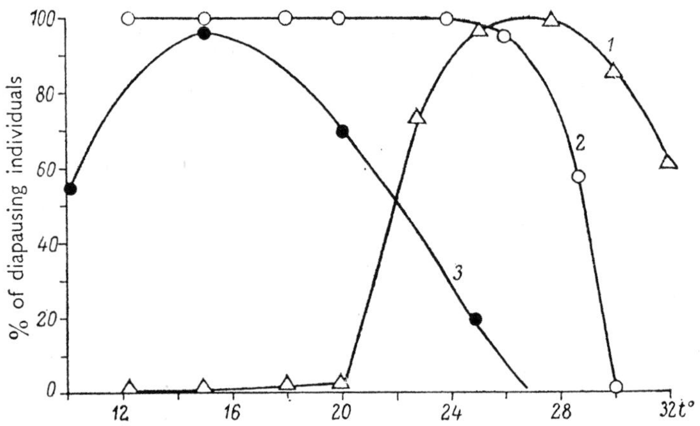

FIG. 23. The temperature optima for the photoperiodic reaction in different species.

1, *Acronycta rumicis* (Leningrad); 2, *Pieris brassicae*; 3, *Metatetranychus ulmi*.

From the ecological point of view the fact that the photoperiodic reaction that induces diapause corresponds in time with optimum temperatures for growth is fully explainable. Only in this case does change in day-length, as a permanent signal of the approach of unfavourable conditions, acquire an ecological meaning and precedence over other factors that regulate the seasonal cycle of insect development. Physiological preparation for diapause, accompanied by intensified accumulation of food reserves, also takes place readily in conditions favourable for growth.

Thus the widespread view that diapause is caused by temperature conditions unfavourable for growth proves to be mistaken. Diapause must be regarded as an adaptation to survival

TABLE 19

The temperature norms of the photoperiodic reaction and the development of sensitive stages

Name of species	Population	Temperature norms (°)			
		Development of larvae		Photoperiodic reaction	
		Limits	Optimum	Limits	Optimum
Pieris brassicae	Leningrad	10-31	16-26	12-29-30	12-25
Pieris napi	do.	10-32	16-26	12-29-30	18-25
Dendrolimus pini	White Russia	6-32	15-25	10-30	12-27
Dendrolimus sibiricus	Tomsk province	6-30	15-25	10-28	12-27
Antheraea pernyi	North China	8-32	16-26	14-28	—
Acronycta rumicis	Leningrad	10-34	15-30	12-30	25-28
Polia oleracea	England	10-34	15-30	12-30	—
Barathra brassicae	Sumy province	8-32	15-26	15-30	18-25
Chloridea obsoleta	Northern Caucasus	17-36	22-32	19-30	19-27
Spilosoma menthastri	Sukhumi	10-31	17-25	20-30	20-28
Loxostege sticticalis	Ukraine	12-36	20-32	18-30-32	20-27
Laspeyresia molesta	California	8-32	—	12-26	20-26
Leptinotarsa decemlineata	DDR (East Germany)	12-33	—	18-30	20-30

in conditions unfavourable for growth and not as a consequence of them.

The biological significance of the temperature limits of photoperiodic reaction must be further evaluated. We have discussed above the fact that high temperature depresses photoperiodic reaction in the majority of the long-day species studied and leads to the absence of diapause in any light conditions. Such suppression is most often observed in the zone of sublethal temperatures, and therefore it may be looked upon as an indicator of the breakdown of processes of normal development. This is particularly clearly seen in *Pieris brassicae*, *Pieris rapae*, *Polia oleracea*, and *Acronycta rumicis*. The upper threshold of photoperiodic reaction in the southern species *Laspeyresia molesta* and *Chloridea obsoleta* lies somewhat below the sublethal zone, but in that case it is found beyond the limits of temperatures optimal for growth.

In a natural environment such high temperatures, preventing the onset of diapause, occur only in summer, when day-length is at a maximum and acts on development in the same direction. Consequently for species in temperate latitudes the suppression of photoperiodic reaction by high temperatures is deprived of ecological significance and is not a special adaptation to seasonal conditions. Probably it is merely an inadequate result of the generally-stimulating action of high temperature, which, owing to its similarity to the long-day effect, is ecologically neutral and therefore is not eliminated by natural selection. For species whose range extends into tropical and subtropical countries the suppression of photoperiodic reaction by high temperature may serve as an adaptation to continuous development in the short days of summer in these latitudes.

The lower temperature limit of photoperiodic reaction is of great ecological importance for species in temperate climates. Low temperature—simultaneously with the short day, which also induces diapause—causes preparation for hibernation. This doubtless is an adaptation to the cold autumn conditions of northern regions.

It is of interest that in the southern species *Laspeyresia molesta* and *Chloridea obsoleta* the reaction to low temperature differs substantially from the usual type, in that low temperature does not

TABLE

The effect of short days (12 hours of light) on the onset of diapause

Indicator of larval development	10°	12·5°	15°	17·5°
No. of larvae in experiment	16	18	25	22
% diapausing	100	100	100	100
Diapausing instar	II-III	II-III	II-III	II-III
Average weight at onset of diapause	63·2	62·2	70·2	83·7
No. of days until onset of diapause	64·6 (58-71)	62·1 (42-83)	42·6 (39-55)	37·7 (34-46)
Duration of diapause (days)	50·5 (28-66)	39·2 (16-64)	25·6 (9-40)	25·9 (11-33)

induce diapause in them even with short days. KOMAROVA (1959) discovered that in natural conditions in Transcaucasia a large percentage of diapausing pupae was found only among the Cotton-boll Worms that had developed in early autumn at temperatures above 20°. At later dates the percentage of diapausing pupae decreases progressively with the fall in temperature. It is evident that such a reaction is the opposite of what one would expect in autumnal climatic conditions in temperate latitudes, and is probably due to the southern origin of the Cotton-boll Worm.

The number of photoperiodic impulses required to produce diapause is also linked with optimum temperature for reaction to day-length. In Pine Moth larvae diapause begins only after a definite minimum of short days have been experienced (GEISPITS, 1949, 1953). The number varies, however, under the influence of external conditions (Table 20).

The shortest duration of pre-diapause preparation (30 days) is observed at a temperature optimal for larval development (23°). Higher and lower temperatures check the onset of diapause, lengthening the period of preparation for it. The maximum period (over 60 days) is observed at 10°-12°, i.e. at the lower temperature limit for growth. From the data in Table 20 it follows that changes in the dates of commencement of diapause are due to the specific effect of temperature on photoperiodic reaction and have no direct connection with the rate of growth and development. Proof of that is found in the delay in the onset

20

in *Dendrolimus pini* larvae in different temperature conditions

20°	23°	25°	27°	30°	32°
15	20	24	17	19	27
100	100	95·8	98·3	21·0	0
III	III	III-IV	IV	IV-VI	—
107·1	97·8	164	176	224	—
36·3 (32-37)	30·1 (26-32)	37·3 (31-47)	38·9 (33-60)	33·1 (33-34)	—
23·1 (12-32)	16·6 (6-25)	12·7 (6-20)	10·5 (5-13)	1·2 (1-2)	—

of diapause caused by high temperatures, with simultaneous acceleration of development. Another indication that the dates when diapause begins are not dependent on the processes of growth and development is provided by the age and weight of diapausing larvae. With optimum temperature of 20°-23° diapause always began at the third instar, when the average weight of the larvae was about 100 mg. At lower temperatures it was observed in part in the second instar, at a weight of 60 to 70 mg. High temperature (27°-30°) caused a notable movement of the onset of diapause towards the later instars—the fourth, the fifth, and even the sixth, when the weight of the larvae reached 176-224 mg. Similar changes in photoperiodic reaction are observed in *Dendrolimus sibiricus*, but are less strongly marked.

From Table 20 it is seen that the duration of diapause of the Pine Moth depends on the temperature conditions in which it was initiated. With a short day and a temperature of 23° diapause lasts on an average about two weeks; at 10° the duration is tripled, being on an average 50 days. At high temperatures, on the other hand, it is greatly decreased, and at 30° only brief checks in growth are observed. But even in this case they are accompanied by all the symptoms of onset of diapause: absence of food from the intestine, elimination of special excreta, and movement of the larva into a resting-place. One may suppose that the duration of the resting period is connected not only with the conditions in which the diapausing larvae exist but also with the varying depth of diapause after it commences.

The extent to which the depth of diapause depends on the conditions in which its formation takes place is seen from the data of KOMAROVA (1959) for the Cotton-boll Worm (Table 17). The duration of diapause in pupae obtained at different temperatures and kept thereafter in uniform conditions proved to be variable. Pupae obtained at a temperature of 29° spent an average of 80·5 days in diapause, but the diapause period of pupae obtained at 19·6° was only 41 days. It is possible that these features determine the different dates of spring emergence of the adults in nature.

Up to the present little attention has been given to discovering the biological role of the duration of diapause. Probably it is of great importance, especially for tropical and subtropical species. Thus according to the investigations of Masaki the duration of diapause in *Barathra brassicae* (MASAKI, 1956a) and *Abraxas miranda* (MASAKI, 1958) varies greatly in accordance with the light conditions of preceding development. These qualitative variations in diapause ensure harmony between the phenology of the species mentioned and seasonal fluctuations in weather conditions in the subtropical climate of Japan. Similar data were obtained by NORRIS (1959) for the African locust *Nomadacris septemfasciata.*

4. The effect of constant temperature on critical day-length

Critical day-length, which determines the transition from long-day to short-day effect, is the chief indicator characterizing the ecological significance of photoperiodic reaction. It is generally understood to be a quantity constant for a species or for a definite geographical population. But since it is known that the calendar dates of onset of diapause in a natural environment are not quite constant, one must admit that critical day-length is dependent on other ecological conditions.

Experimental evidence of the influence of diet in this respect has been quoted in the preceding chapter; but it is still more important to discover how the critical threshold is dependent on temperature, since the temperature factor is subject to wide geographical and seasonal fluctuations and affects photoperiodic reaction more than other factors. This question has been investigated in *Acronycta rumicis*, *Chloridea obsoleta*, and *Leptinotarsa decemlineata* (GORYSHIN, 1955, 1958a, 1958b). Data have now been obtained for several other species of insects and spider mites.

Experimental data indicate that critical day-length depends on the temperature at which the development of light-sensitive stages takes place. A typical example is the southern form of *Acronycta rumicis*, in which the critical day-length varies in a regular manner, increasing by about $1\frac{1}{2}$ hours for each 5° of fall in temperature (Fig. 24). A similar movement of the critical threshold is also seen in other species. The degree and direction of change, however, depend to a great extent on the biological peculiarities of each species. This can be seen by comparing the reaction of *Chloridea obsoleta*—a polycyclic species with a tendency to non-diapause development—with that of *Leptinotarsa decemlineata*, in which a tendency to monocyclism is clearly shown (Fig. 25).

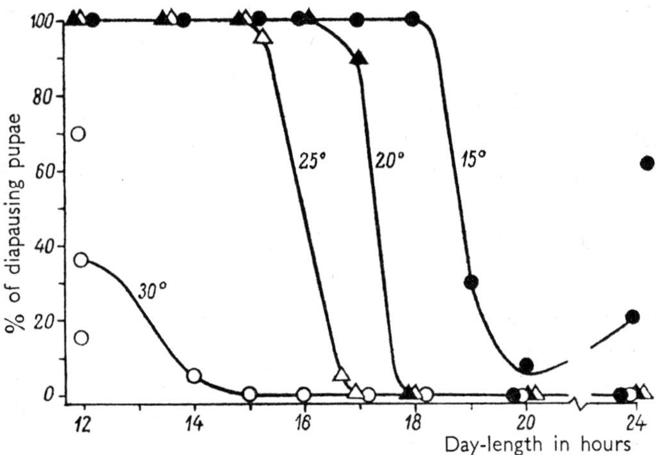

Fig. 24. Changes in the critical day-length under the influence of temperature during the period of larval development of the Belgorod population of *Acronycta rumicis*.

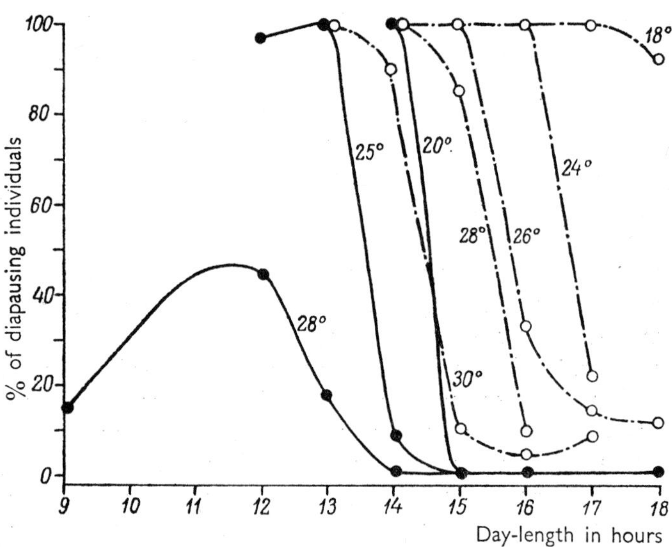

Fig. 25. Changes in the critical day-length under the influence of temperature during the period of larval development.

—— *Chloridea obsoleta*; –.– *Leptinotarsa decemlineata*.

An exception to the rule just given is the European form of *Pieris brassicae* (Fig. 26). In it the critical threshold remains practically unchanged through the whole range of normal occurrence of photoperiodic reaction from 12° to 26°, but with a further rise in temperature to 29°-30° the photoperiodic effect disappears altogether. It is to be noted that in this species differences in photoperiodic reaction between different geographical populations are smaller than in other species (DANILEVSKII, 1957a).

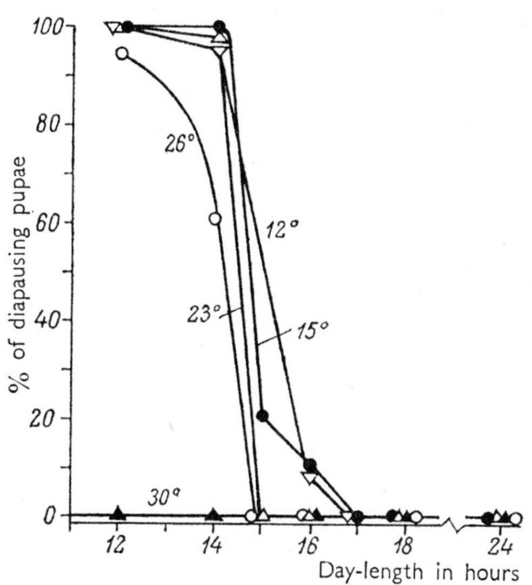

FIG. 26. The critical day-length for *Pieris brassicae* (Leningrad) at different temperatures during the period of larval development.

There is no doubt that changes in critical day-length under the influence of temperature have considerable ecological importance. The experimentally-discovered increases of 1 to 1½ hours in critical day-length with a fall of 5° in temperature are the equivalent of changes in natural day-length over a period of approximately 2 to 3 weeks. Phenological indicators regulated by the light conditions might fluctuate correspondingly under the influence of temperature. This explains why—regardless of the constancy of seasonal changes in day-length—the dates of onset of diapause in nature are subject to considerable variation from year to year, differing with temperature conditions. The observed dependence is important also as an adaptation to geographical variations in light and temperature conditions (GORYSHIN, 1955).

Parallel to the movement of critical day-length, an analogous process takes place in the zone of extremely short photoperiods. This is shown by an increase in the percentage of diapausing individuals occurring in total darkness when the temperature is lowered. This phenomenon, of course, has no adaptational significance, but it is worthy of note, as it shows once more how much the reaction to darkness depends on the value of critical day-length.

5. The effect of the temperature rhythm on photoperiodic reaction

All the above experimental data relate to the action of photoperiod in conditions of constant temperature. In natural conditions, however, the daily light rhythm is associated with more or less wide fluctuations of temperature. When the light and dark periods of the day commence, they are accompanied by a rise and a fall in temperature respectively. Study of the simultaneous action of the daily rhythms of light and temperature on the regulation of diapause is of fundamental interest. Only occasional facts relating to that question appear in the papers by DICKSON (1949) and LEES (1955). Fuller data have been obtained in our laboratory (DANILEVSKII and GLINYANAYA, 1950; GORYSHIN, 1955; DANILEVSKII and GORYSHIN, 1960).

Because of the great variety of possible combinations of light and temperature rhythms, experimental analysis of their effect on insects presents considerable complexity. Here we shall examine only a few of the simplest patterns.

In the first place we have to discover to what extent the critical day-length varies as a result of fluctuations in temperature that lie within the zone effective for development. Such fluctuations are most typical of the daily range of temperature during the vegetative period. An investigation of the role of the daily temperature rhythm was carried out by N. I. Goryshin on the Belgorod population of the noctuid *Acronycta rumicis*. In these experiments, groups of larvae were reared in different day-lengths with a constant 12-hour temperature rhythm, which ensured a uniform average temperature for each group. The pattern of experiments included two variants. In one of these 'day' was made to correspond with high temperature and 'night' with low, and in the other the reverse system was used.

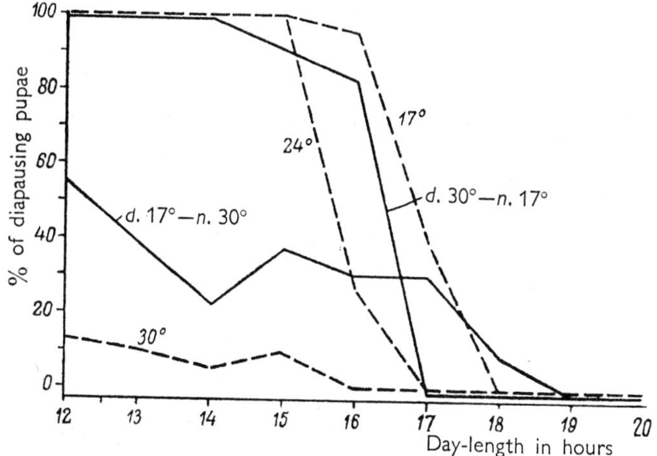

FIG. 27. The effect of a 12-hour rhythm of temperature on the photoperiodic reaction in *Acronycta rumicis* (Belgorod).

17°, 24°, 30°, controls at constant temperature; *d*.30°-*n*.17°, 30° by day, 17° by night; *d*.17°-*n*.30°, 17° by day, 30° by night.

Fig. 27 shows the results of an experiment in which the range of temperature fluctuation was from 17° to 30°. These temperatures correspond to the limits of the zone optimal for development of the Belgorod population of *Acronycta rumicis*. Control groups of larvae were reared in constant temperatures of 17°, 30°, and 24°. The last-mentioned corresponded to the average daily temperature for the experimental groups. With a normal daily temperature rhythm, in which night was cooler than day (Fig. 27, curve *d*.30°-*n*.17°), the critical day-length proved to be considerably higher than with a constant average temperature of 24° and approached that observed at 17°. A quite different result was obtained with the reverse system (Fig. 27, curve *d*.17°-*n*.30°), in which night was warmer than day. In these conditions the photoperiodic reaction was found to be upset, and even with a short day a large proportion of the pupae did not enter diapause; i.e. the result approached that obtained with a constant temperature of 30° (Fig. 27, curve 30°).

Similar data were obtained in an analogous experiment with

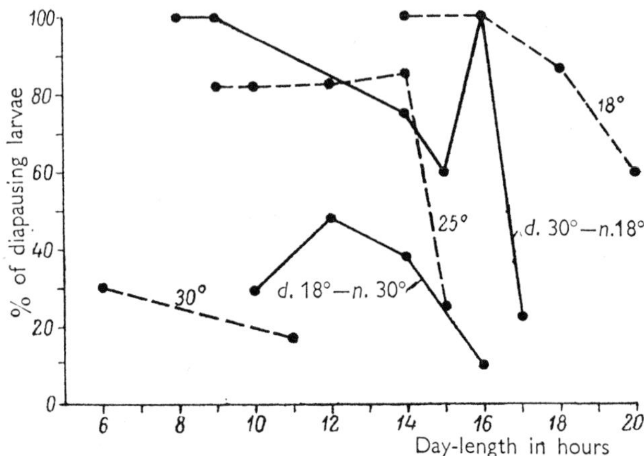

FIG. 28. The effect of a 12-hour rhythm of temperature on the photoperiodic reaction in the Armenian form of *Leucoma salicis*.

18°, 25°, 30°: controls at constant temperature; *d.*30°-*n.*18°: 30° by day, 18° by night; *d.*18°-*n.*30°: 18° by day, 30° by night.

12-hour fluctuations of temperature from 10° to 30°, where the lower temperature corresponded to the threshold for development. When the higher temperature coincided with the dark period of the day, even in short-day conditions development of the majority of the pupae was observed. When the temperature of 30° coincided with the light period the photoperiodic reaction remained normal, but the critical day-length was somewhat higher than with a constant temperature of 20°. Further experiments by N. I. Goryshin and T. Kind showed that the Armenian form of *Leucoma salicis* reacts to alternations in temperature in the same way as *Acronycta rumicis* (Fig. 28). But in the European form of *Pieris brassicae*—in which, unlike other species, critical day-length remains unchanged in temperatures from 25° to 12°—the reaction to alternations is somewhat different; low night temperatures produced no change in critical day-length, although high night temperatures suppressed diapause just as did constant high temperatures.

These data enable us to conclude that critical day-length depends on the level of night temperatures to a greater extent than on that of day temperatures. Results similar in principle were obtained by LEES (1955) in experiments on the effect of short days on diapause in the mite *Metatetranychus ulmi* with different temperature conditions. According to his data, with a constant temperature of 15° a short day (12 hours) induced the appearance of up to 100% of 'winter females' which laid diapausing eggs; at 20° the number of such females fell to an average of 70%, and at 25° to 21%. In short-day conditions and alternating temperatures the number of winter females proved to depend mainly on the temperature of the dark period. With a temperature of 25° by day and 15° by night there were 96% of winter females, and with these temperatures reversed, 53%.

The similarity of the results obtained with species so different in their biology and systematic position enables us to assume that here we are dealing with a general law. It is possible that the close dependence of photoperiodic effect on the temperature of the dark period has adaptational significance, since in nature night temperatures are as a rule more stable than day temperatures. It is evident that in natural conditions the average temperature during the 24 hours is not enough to determine the onset of diapause, and that it is probably more correct to take as a basic factor the temperature conditions during the night.

The above statement is supported by the results of an analysis of the conditions for diapause initiation in *Chloridea obsoleta*, made by N. I. Goryshin in the northern Caucasus (Fig. 29). Larvae that developed before August 20 (*a*), with day-length over 15 hours, produced only active pupae. The development of larvae that produced 50% of diapausing pupae (*b*) took place from August 17 to early September in days decreasing in length from 15 to 14 hours. Thus the critical day-length in nature may be taken as being 14 hours 30 minutes. This threshold is considerably higher than might have been expected from the average daily temperature, which at that time was about 25°. According to experimental data (Fig. 25) such a threshold is observed at a temperature of 20°, which corresponds to the level of night temperature in nature (Fig. 29, curve 5).

The dependence of photoperiodic reaction on sharp temporary fluctuations in temperature beyond the limits of temperatures effective for development and approaching the sublethal was investigated in the Belgorod form of *Acronycta rumicis* (DANILEVSKII and GLINYANAYA, 1950; GORYSHIN, 1955).

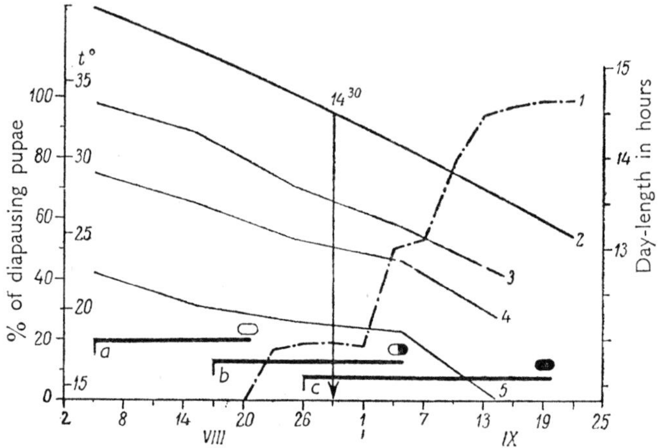

FIG. 29. The temperature and light conditions of development of *Chloridea obsoleta* in the northern Caucasus, 45°N. (from data of N. I. Goryshin).

1, changes in the numbers of diapausing pupae in field conditions (%); 2, day-length in hours; 3, average temperature within cotton plants over ten-day period, during daytime; 4, ditto, throughout 24 hours; 5, ditto, during night-time. *Horizontal lines*: the periods of development of larvae producing—*a*, non-diapausing pupae; *b*, 50%; *c*, 100% of diapausing pupae. 14 hours 30 minutes—critical day-length.

As is seen from the data in Table 21, daily 3-hour cooling even down to 0°, with continuous light and regular temperature of 26°-27°, did not induce diapause and did not injuriously affect development. In all cases only active pupae were obtained. But with rhythmic illumination such periodic cooling had a powerful effect. Thus with a constant temperature of 26°, a 3-hour period of light separating two 6-hour periods of darkness eliminated the effect of the latter, and the majority of pupae developed without diapause, as in continuous light. When that light interval was combined with cooling (Table 21, experiments 5-7) it proved to be ineffective, and all pupae that were obtained entered diapause.

TABLE 21

The effect of temperature on the sensitivity of *Acronycta rumicis* larvae to the action of light

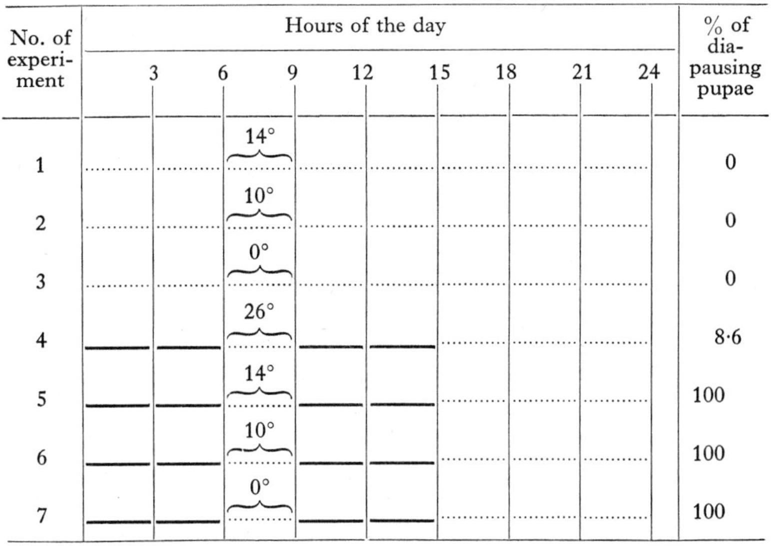

No. of experiment	Hours of the day								% of diapausing pupae
	3	6	9	12	15	18	21	24	
1	....	....	14°	....	....	....	....	....	0
2	....	....	10°	....	....	....	....	....	0
3	....	....	0°	....	....	....	....	....	0
4	———	———	26°	———	———	....	....	....	8·6
5	———	———	14°	———	———	....	....	....	100
6	———	———	10°	———	———	....	....	....	100
7	———	———	0°	———	———	....	....	....	100

Note. Solid lines denote the dark period of the day; dotted lines the light period.

In other words, with low temperature during the light interval the effects of the two dark periods fuse together and development proceeds in the usual short-day manner. The temperature threshold for acceptance of light stimulation proved to be unexpectedly high (14°).

A detailed investigation of the action of periodic severe cooling and overheating was also undertaken with *Acronycta rumicis* (GORYSHIN, 1955; DANILEVSKII and GORYSHIN, 1960). In these experiments a somewhat different photoperiodic pattern was used. As is seen from Table 22, in control experiments without cooling and with constant temperature of 25° a daily rhythm of 7 hours of darkness and 17 hours of light (experiment 1) is received as a long day, and development in these conditions proceeds without diapause. A rhythm of 10 hours of darkness and 14 hours of light (experiment 2) is received as a short day, and all pupae enter diapause. Daily 3-hour cooling during the dark period, both with the long day (experiments 3, 4) and with the short day (experiments 5, 6) do not make the reaction differ from that of the controls (experiments 1, 2). It proved to be a matter of indifference which part of the dark period coincided with the cooling. Since the low temperature halted active physiological processes, there was evidently no after-effect of the light interval during the period of darkness.

TABLE 22

The effect of periodic brief cooling on the photoperiodic reaction in *Acronycta rumicis* (Belgorod form)

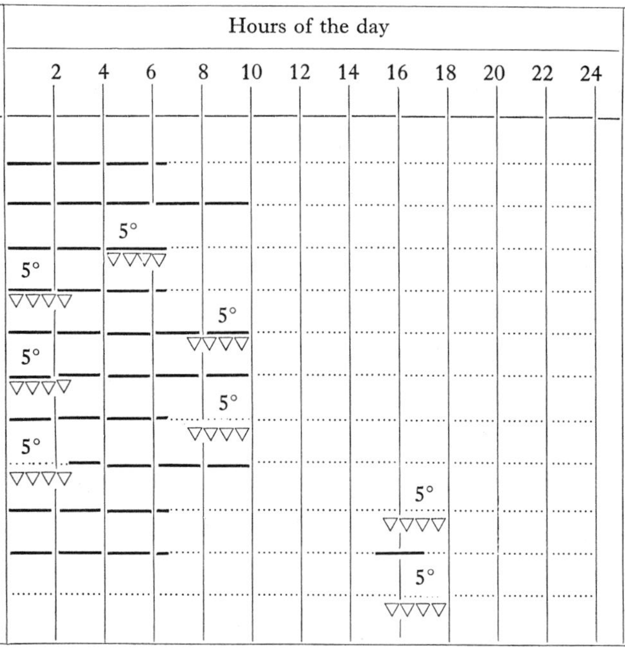

No. of experiment	Hours of the day: 2	4	6	8	10	12	14	16	18	20	22	24	% of diapausing pupae
1	—	—	—	- …	…	…	…	…	…	…	…	…	0
2	—	—	—	—	—	…	…	…	…	…	…	…	100
3	—	—	5° ▽▽▽▽	5° ▽▽▽▽ …	…	…	…	…	…	…	…	…	0
4	5° ▽▽▽▽	5° ▽▽▽▽ —	—	- …	…	…	…	…	…	…	…	…	0
5	—	—	—	— 5° ▽▽▽▽	5° ▽▽▽▽	…	…	…	…	…	…	…	100
6	5° ▽▽▽▽	5° ▽▽▽▽ —	—	—	—	…	…	…	…	…	…	…	100
7	—	—	—	- … 5° ▽▽▽▽	… 5° ▽▽▽▽	…	…	…	…	…	…	…	100
8	… 5° ▽▽▽▽	… 5° ▽▽▽▽ —	—	—	—	…	…	…	…	…	…	…	100
9	—	—	—	- …	…	…	…	… 5° ▽▽▽▽	… 5° ▽▽▽▽	…	…	…	0
10	—	—	—	- …	…	…	…	—	— …	…	…	…	0
11	…	…	…	…	…	…	…	… 5° ▽▽▽▽	… 5° ▽▽▽▽	…	…	…	0

Note. Solid lines denote the dark period of the day, dotted lines the light period. Rows of triangles denote the periods of cooling to 5°; for the rest of the day the temperature was 25°.

A quite different picture was obtained by cooling the larvae during the light period. If the cooling period was immediately adjacent to a 7-hour period of darkness, it had the same effect as the addition of 3 hours of darkness (experiments 7, 8). In these cases the short-day effect was observed regardless of whether the cooling period preceded or followed the dark period. The similarity in the effects of low temperature and of darkness is also seen in experiments 9 and 10. In both cases no effect is shown if the 3-hour action of cold or darkness occurs in the middle of the light period.

The question of the effect of severe overheating on photoperiodic reaction was studied on a pattern close to that used in the cooling experiments. But as the experiments were made on the Sukhumi population of *Acronycta rumicis*, which has a lower critical day-length, for control purposes a daily system of 16 hours of light and 8 hours of darkness was used as a long day (experiment 1) and one of 13 hours of light and 11 hours of darkness as a short day (experiment 2). Heating was applied for the last 3 hours of the dark period. The regular temperature in which development of the larvae took place was 23° in the first series of

TABLE 23

The effect of brief periods of heating on the photoperiodic reaction in *Acronycta rumicis* (Sukhumi form)

Constant temp.	No. of experiment	Hours of the day (2 4 6 8 10 12 14 16 18 20 22 24)	No. of pupae	% of diapausing pupae
23°	1		48	0
	2		41	100
	3	32° △△△	44	100
	4	34° △△△	51	98·1
	5	36° △△△	45	97·8
	6	38° △△△	35	94·3
	7	40° △△△	35	2·8
25°	8		61	87·0
	9	32° △△△	33	27·3
	10	34° △△△	60	33·3
	11	36° △△△	42	28·6
	12	38-39° △△△	28	7·1

Note. Solid lines denote the dark period of the day, dotted lines the light period. Rows of triangles denote the periods of heating.

experiments and somewhat higher (25°) in the second series. The pattern and results of the experiments are shown in Table 23.

In contrast to the action of brief cooling, daily 3-hour overheating during the dark period markedly altered the photoperiodic effect. Heating can overcome the influence of darkness, and even in short-day conditions can induce non-diapause development, i.e. it acts in the same way as light (experiments 7, 12). Such an effect, however, appears only with the action of very high sub-lethal temperatures, above 38°. The general temperature background during the developmental period of the larvae is also important. Therefore in the first series of experiments with a constant temperature of 23° the effect of overheating was not so marked as in the second series with a temperature of about 25°.

Therefore severe temporary cooling and overheating may seriously disturb the normal course of a photoperiodic reaction.

The effects of limiting temperatures can scarcely be looked upon as a special ecological adaptation. This is particularly true of the effect of overheating, which does not occur at night and occurs by day only with direct solar radiation. But the action of low temperatures must be taken into account, since they often occur in autumn in the morning and evening hours, and by thus decreasing the biologically-effective length of the day they may lead to earlier onset of diapause.

6. The physiological significance of light and darkness in the photoperiodic reaction of insects

The above data show that diapause in the seasonal cycle of insects depends on a very complex combination of external factors, often acting on the organism in different directions.

It is evident that the conclusions of authors who saw the cause of initiation of diapause only in the action of temperature expressed the actual situation from a limited and often incorrect point of view. The onset of diapause must also not be attributed exclusively to the action of the light conditions, as the photoperiodic effect is greatly dependent on the temperature level and its periodic fluctuations. For ecological analysis of the seasonal cycle of insects it is essential to consider the joint action of these two factors.

The results obtained by investigations of the effects of temperature and light rhythms are interesting also from the physiological point of view. They compel us to re-examine the views found in the literature about the physiological mechanism of photoperiodic reaction in insects. All authors who have dealt with this question ascribe great or decisive importance in photoperiodic reaction to the dark part of the day. Thus on the basis of experiments with *Acronycta rumicis* (DANILEVSKII and GLINYANAYA, 1949) a deduction was made that a definite duration of the period of darkness is necessary for photoperiodic reaction to appear, the effect of darkness being reversible in its initial phase. DICKSON (1949) came to similar conclusions on the basis of experiments with *Laspeyresia molesta*, as did TANAKA (1950c, 1951a) with *Antheraea pernyi*. BELOV (1951), also working with the Chinese Oak Silkworm, suggests that reaction to day-length is based on changes in sensitivity of the photocentres in their adaptation to light and darkness. According to LEES (1953b), photoperiodic reaction in the mite *Metatetranychus ulmi* depends not on the absolute duration of the dark period of the day but on the relation between two antagonistic stimuli: light, which inhibits diapause, and darkness, which induces it. On the basis of experiments with varying temperature he concludes that the light and dark phases of photoperiodic reaction are concerned with entirely different processes, as the former does not react to temperature and the latter is very sensitive to it (LEES, 1955).

Thus, regardless of differing explanations of the physiological nature of photoperiodic reaction in insects, all investigators are unanimous in stating that under the influence of darkness specific processes take place in the organism substantially affecting the course of development. This conclusion accords with the changes that occur in the photoperiodic reaction of *Acronycta rumicis* and *Leucoma salicis* in consequence of the daily rhythm of temperature (see Figs. 27 and 28).

This conclusion, which would appear to be fully proved, about the physiological action of darkness is contradicted by the results of experiments which show a remarkable similarity between the action of darkness and that of severe cooling down to 0°-5°, which practically causes complete cessation of all developmental processes. Since severe cooling during darkness does not alter photoperiodic reaction, but in light has a very strong effect (see Table 22), we must conclude that during the dark part of the day no specific processes of preparation for diapause take place, and consequently photoperiodic reaction is determined only by the duration of the light period.

The above-noted contradictions in conclusions about the role of darkness may be avoided by assuming that temperature and photoperiod act independently on the general neurohumoral mechanism which regulates the developmental cycle of insects. Prolonged light and high temperature stimulate that system and cause non-diapause development; short photoperiods, like low temperature, induce a specific inhibition leading to diapause. It is evident that, with a temperature below the level required by the photocentres or other links in the regulating system, light stimuli will be ineffective. On the other hand high temperature, as is seen in Table 23, can activate the neurohumoral system even in the absence of light.

This simple theory explains, without allotting an active role to darkness, both the peculiar effects of sharp falls in temperature and the disturbance of photoperiodic reaction as a result of high night temperatures. It explains also why critical day-length depends on temperature. Evidently the more strongly the regulating system is depressed by a fall in temperature, the more prolonged must be the light stimulus which induces non-diapause development. Levels of temperature at which the depressed state of the system cannot be compensated for by any photoperiod determine the temperature limits for the appearance of a photoperiodic reaction.

It is quite possible that other factors—e.g. chemical—that change the degree of activity of the regulating system may affect photoperiodic reaction in the same way as temperature. Probably this is the reason for the changes in the threshold of photoperiodic reaction resulting from qualitative changes in diet.

Of course the above view does not define the physiological nature of photoperiodic reaction in insects, but it does unite within a single system a fairly wide collection of facts and enables us to mark out definite paths for further experimental investigation of the problem.

A close relation between the reactions to periodic changes in temperature and to the light conditions has recently been observed also in plants. It is of particular interest that in plants, as in insects, there is a close similarity between the effects of darkness and of cold. Thus abnormal growth and chlorosis of leaves, observed in tomatoes grown in conditions of continuous light and constant temperature (23°), do not occur if the plants are given a 6-hour period of low temperature (10°) or of darkness (WENT, 1959). *Xanthium pensylvanicum* also reacts similarly to darkness and to cold. This short-day species does not flower with a 16-hour day and a temperature of 23°, but regular cooling to 4° during the first 8 hours of the long day stimulates flowering in just the same way as does the addition of an 8-hour period of darkness (ZEEUW, 1957; NITSCH and WENT, 1959).

Apparently the faculty of reacting similarly to the action of thermo- and photoperiods is one of the general principles of physiological adaptations of organisms to the daily periodicity of external conditions.

Chapter V

GEOGRAPHICAL VARIATIONS IN PHOTOPERIODIC AND TEMPERATURE REACTIONS

The features of photoperiodic regulation of the seasonal development of insects surveyed in the preceding chapters show that this reaction evolved on the basis of parallelism in the seasonal fluctuations in day-length and in temperature. The regularities discovered in experimental investigations enable us to understand phenology in the conditions pertaining to one locality, but they are insufficient to explain the adaptations of insects to a variety of geographical conditions within the range of a species. This applies particularly to widely-distributed species of the polycyclic type inhabiting varied climatic zones.

The difficulty in explaining the universal agreement of phenology with the seasonal dynamics of external conditions is due to the fact that light and temperature regimes vary in opposite directions with season and with latitude. In its seasonal course the shortening of the day is accompanied by a fall in temperature, and this determines the formation of photoperiodic adaptations in insects. With changes in latitude an inverse relationship is found between the two factors. Towards the north, or more precisely with increase in latitude, the temperature and duration of the active period decrease, restricting the number of possible generations; at the northern limits of distribution the majority even of polycyclic species have only a single annual generation. The length of the summer day, on the other hand, increases with increase in latitude, which should cause non-diapause development and thus induce a life cycle out of harmony with the annual temperature rhythm.

Evidently insects possess special adaptations which allow for this contradiction and enable the developmental cycle of a species to fit closely to the seasonal alternations of climatic conditions throughout the whole range of a species. In spite of the importance of this ecological problem, it has as yet been little studied.

Until recently geographical variations in phenology and in the number of generations were looked upon as results of the direct action of the temperature conditions. The principle of the summation of temperatures, it seemed, gave a simple and fairly complete explanation of these phenomena. On the basis of experimental data relating to temperature thresholds of development and to the value of the sum of effective temperatures required for the life cycle, many attempts were made to calculate theoretically the number of generations of various species in different climatic zones (BODENHEIMER, 1926; KOZHANCHIKOV, 1936, 1937b, 1938b; LARCHENKO, 1949; VASIL'EV, 1951). Although such calculations do not always correspond with actual phenology, the basic regularity of the increase in the number of generations towards the south gives them the appearance of an adequate explanation.

Temperature summation, however, although a principal factor in determining the periods of development of active stages and the number of possible generations, is in no way a direct cause of the initiation of diapause. Changes in temperature level with latitude are also insufficient to explain the well-timed commencement of resting stages in different zones. The reason for the chronological correspondence of active and resting stages in the life cycle with the seasonal rhythm of climate must be sought in geographical variation of the photoperiodic reaction.

An adaptation to seasonal changes in day-length at different latitudes may arise by two different methods. There is no doubt that the adaptability of the photoperiodic reaction and its changes under the direct influence of environment can to a definite extent regulate the seasonal cycle of an insect in different climatic conditions. There is also another method, namely, inherited changes in the norm of reaction to light conditions in different geographical populations of a species.

The dependence of geographical variations in phenology on the direct effect of temperature on photoperiodic reaction was analysed in *Acronycta rumicis* by GORYSHIN (1955). He came to the conclusion that in different geographical conditions an increase in critical day-length with a fall in temperature could considerably alter the dates of commencement of diapause. Further investigations on the same species, however (DANILEVSKII, 1956, 1957a,

1957b), showed that adaptations to zonal-geographical conditions were based primarily on inherited differences in the photoperiodic reactions of different geographical populations. As that conclusion involved a number of important ecological consequences, it became necessary to make more extensive comparative studies of intraspecific geographical variability in the physiological adaptations of insects.

The question of intraspecific physiological differentiation is interesting also on a wider scale because of the problem of speciation. Geographical variations in insects have been studied mainly from the morphological point of view. Much information has been accumulated in that field, but it has not yet been adequately analysed. Data on the variation of physiological features, on the other hand, are very limited not only for insects but also for other groups of animals, as is seen from reviews of the problem of intraspecific variation (PROSSER, 1955, 1957; MAYR, 1947). At the same time, in definitions of the concept of species it is always stressed that a species is a system circumscribed not only morphologically but also physiologically. Although the morphological criteria of a species have by now been adequately defined, the question of physiological characteristics of a species is still not clear and calls for specialized experimental investigations.

1. Intraspecific geographical variation in photoperiodic reactions

Fig. 30 shows the results of parallel investigations, at a constant temperature of 23°, of photoperiodic reactions in four geographical populations of *Acronycta rumicis*, taken at different points of its range at approximately every 5° of latitude from the Black Sea coast of the Caucasus to Leningrad province. The day-length which induces diapause in the populations studied varies regularly and very markedly with the geographical location, forming a consecutive series. Its lowest value—14 hours 30 minutes—is found in the most southerly Abkhazian population (43°N.). For the Belgorod population (50°N.) the critical threshold is about 16 hours 30 minutes, and for the Vitebsk population (55°N.) about 18 hours of light per day. The Leningrad population (60°N.) occupies the outermost position in the series. It is characterized not only by a very high value for critical day-length—more than 19 hours—but also by a clearly-manifested tendency to hereditary monocyclism, as a result of which a considerable proportion of the pupae enter diapause even in light lasting from 20 to 24 hours a day.

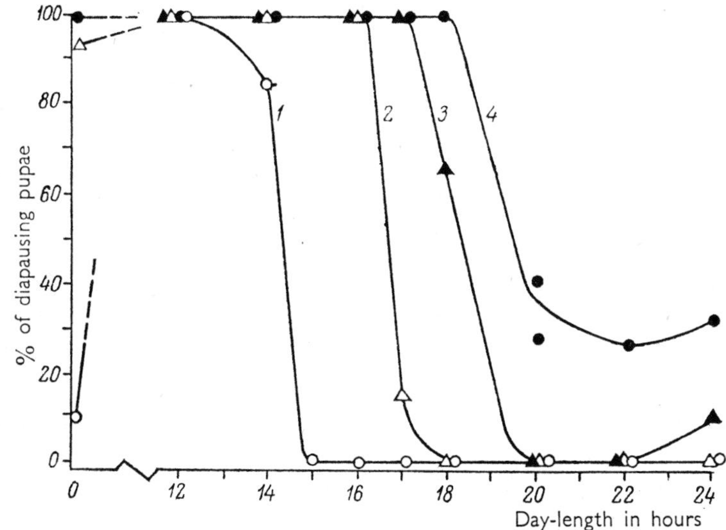

FIG. 30. The geographical variation in the photoperiodic reaction in *Acronycta rumicis*. Temperature 23°.

Populations: 1, Abkhazian (43°N.); 2, Belgorod (50°N.); 3, Vitebsk (55°N.); 4, Leningrad (60°N.).

Thus for every 5° of latitude the critical threshold changes by approximately 1½ hours. We have noted above the significance of this change. As the conditions of all experiments were uniform, it is evident that the observed differences in photoperiodic reaction are due to inherited physiological characteristics of the populations. Each population may in that case be looked upon as a separate and individual ecotype or a local race.

A very similar situation was observed in geographical populations of *Barathra brassicae*. Of the forms studied, the extreme examples came from Adzharia and Leningrad province; two intermediate forms came from adjacent districts of the forest-steppe zone—Sumy and Belgorod—in the same latitude (50°N.). All larvae were reared simultaneously at a temperature of 25°.

The critical day-length in these populations (Fig. 31) varies from 14 hours 30 minutes in the Adzharian to 18 hours 30 minutes in the Leningrad race, i.e. within approximately the same limits as with *Acronycta rumicis*. In the Leningrad form incomplete photoperiodic reaction and partial (about 30%) diapause were also observed, even in continuous light. In other words, in this

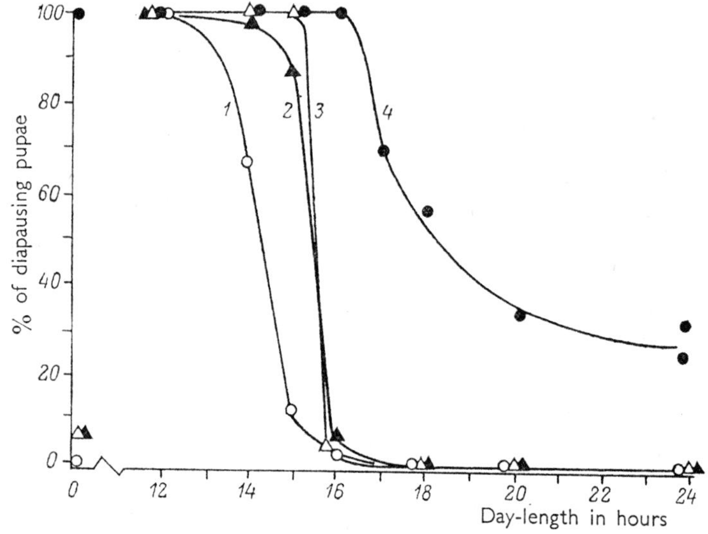

FIG. 31. The geographical variation in the photoperiodic reaction in *Barathra brassicae*. Temperature 25°.

Populations: 1, Adzharian (41°-42°N.); 2, Sumy (50°N.); 3, Belgorod (50°N.); 4, Leningrad (60°N.).

race a hereditary monocyclic type of development has already been established to a considerable extent. It is significant that both forms of the forest-steppe race not only are characterized by an intermediate value of threshold day-length, about 15 hours 30 minutes, but prove to be practically identical in their reaction. This again demonstrates that the investigated changes in photoperiodic reaction depend mainly on latitude and not on other features of the habitat.

Another example of variation in photoperiodic reaction depending on the latitude in which species live is provided by the spider mites Tetranychidae, investigated by BONDARENKO and KUAN KHAI-YUAN' (1958) and also by GEISPITS (1960). These data are particularly interesting because they relate to members of an entirely distinct systematic group of arthropods, and therefore give evidence of the general application of the rule.

According to the investigations of Bondarenko and Kuan Khai-yuan' (1958), the critical day-length for the Leningrad population of *Tetranychus urticae* at a temperature of 20° is slightly over 17 hours (Table 24). With a longer day all females develop continuously. In the southern form the critical threshold is much lower, as a result of which diapause occurs only when the day-length is less than 13 hours, and thus in this species one may see how the threshold depends on latitude. These data are confirmed by GEISPITS (1960) in studies of various natural populations of *Tetranychus urticae*.

TABLE 24

The photoperiodic reaction (percentage of diapausing females) of geographical populations of the mite *Tetranychus urticae*. Temperature 20°

(after Bondarenko and Kuan Khai-yuan', 1958)

Population	Day-length in hours										
	0	9	10	11	12	13	14	15	16	17	24
Leningrad (60° N.)	40·2	—	—	—	—	—	100	100	100	95·3	0
Krasnodar (45° N.)	2·8	—	—	100	84·7	2·2	0	—	—	—	0
Tiflis (42° N.)	1·0	—	90·1	85·4	21·5	0	0	0	—	—	0
Tashkent (41° N.)	1·9	91·3	85·1	82·6	44·6	0	—	—	—	—	0

Equally clearly shown are geographical variations in photoperiodic reaction in the mite *Metatetranychus ulmi*. Comparison of the results obtained by Geispits for the Leningrad (60°N.) and Northern China (40°N.) races of this species with data from the experiments of Lees (1953a) for the south of England (52°N.) show a consistent and well-marked decrease in the critical threshold for southern races as compared with northern (Table 25).

Thus in different polycyclic species with facultative diapause one observes a uniform type of adaptations to zonal-geographical

TABLE 25

The photoperiodic reaction (percentage of winter females) of geographical populations of the mite *Metatetranychus ulmi* (after Geispits, 1960)

Population	Day-length in hours					
	13	14	15	16	17	24
Leningrad (60° N.)	100	100	100	100	94·1	0
Southern England (50° N.)	94·0	54·0	4·0	0	—	0
North China (40° N.)	16·6	6·2	0	0	0	0

variations in climate. These are expressed in the formation of local races possessing different norms of reaction to photoperiodic conditions. As one moves to the north—i.e. with increase in latitude—one observes a regular increase in the threshold of day-length. In the above cases both the general direction of variation and even the amounts of variation of critical day-length are similar.

The connection between the physiological characteristics of local races and their phenology and life cycles in different zones will be discussed below, but the general ecological significance of these adaptations is already fully evident. A higher light threshold for photoperiodic reaction leads to earlier calendar dates for onset of diapause in northern zones, in spite of the longer days there.

Our attention is drawn to the remarkable analogy between inherited variations in photoperiodic reaction with adaptation to geographical conditions, and variations in this reaction caused by the temperature conditions during the developmental period. As has been shown, a fall in temperature during the developmental period produces a marked and regular increase in critical day-length, and may even completely suppress the photoperiodic effect, causing monocyclism to appear. Geographically speaking, temperature usually falls with increase in latitude. Consequently, inherited or phenotypical adaptations will in natural conditions operate in the same direction. This creates an ecologically-unified mechanism, synchronizing the life cycle with the changes of climatic conditions.

In the examples of *Acronycta rumicis* and *Barathra brassicae* it can be seen that the geographical populations studied, with their evident differences in average critical thresholds, actually form a continuous series, and that the extreme individual divergences of adjacent forms are close or even overlap. In other words, here we have a typical case of clinal variation in the reaction that regulates diapause, corresponding to a gradual latitudinal change in day-length. Therefore there are no grounds for seeking clearly-defined geographical ranges for the separate local races of these species. Such clinal variation, however, is not

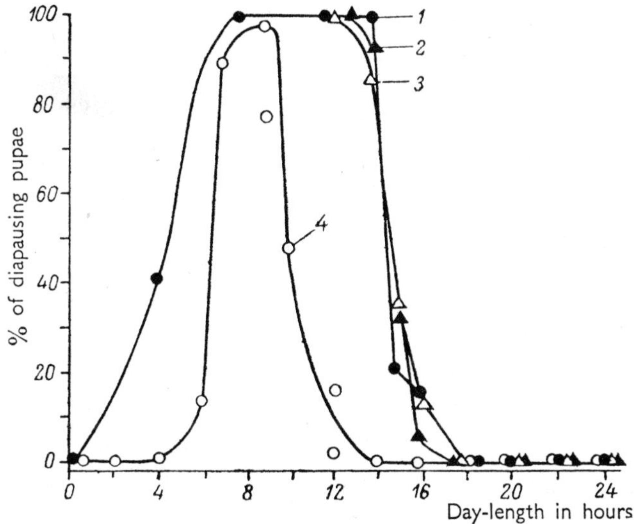

FIG. 32. The geographical variation in the photoperiodic reaction in *Pieris brassicae*. Temperature 23°.

Populations: 1, Leningrad (60°N.); 2, Brest (52°N.); 3, Belgorod (50°N.); 4, Abkhazian (43°N.).

found in all species. Even among those studied by us we have observed cases where a large part of the range was occupied by a monotypic race. A typical example is the Cabbage White Butterfly *Pieris brassicae*, whose photoperiodic reaction is illustrated in Fig. 32. In experimental investigations of stocks obtained from Leningrad, Brest, and Belgorod provinces, a completely identical type of photoperiodic reaction was observed in all populations, with a critical day-length of 15 hours. (The same critical day-length has also been discovered in a Northern Caucasus (Essentuki) population of *Pieris brassicae*.)

Phenological data show that the greater part of the European territory of the USSR is occupied by precisely this form of the Cabbage White Butterfly. Analysis of the phenology of this species in Central Asia and Transcaucasia, however, gives grounds for believing that in the extreme south of its range there exists another form, which requires a considerably shorter day for induction of diapause. This is confirmed by study of the Abkhazian population, which, as is seen from Fig. 32, is markedly

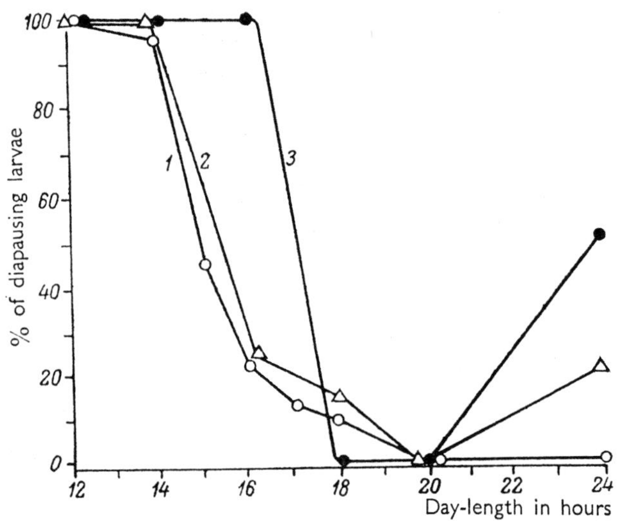

FIG. 33. The geographical variation in the photoperiodic reaction in *Pyrausta nubilalis*. Temperature 25° (from data of Du Chzhen'-ven').

Populations: 1, Abkhazian (43°N.); 2, Dnepropetrovsk (48°N.); 3, Sumy (52°N.).

different from the more northern forms. At a temperature of 23° the northern form reacts definitely to change in day-length, and with photoperiods from 14 to 8 hours of light all pupae enter diapause. In the Abkhazian form the photoperiodic effect appears within very narrow limits at these temperatures. Complete diapause is observed only with day-length of about 9 hours, and the critical threshold appears with a 10-hour day.

Another example of gradual variation in photoperiodic reaction is provided by the European Corn Borer *Pyrausta nubilalis*, investigated by Du Chzhen'-ven' (Fig. 33). In experiments at a temperature of 25°, southern populations from Abkhazia and the steppe zone of the Ukraine (Dnepropetrovsk) showed similar values for critical day-length of approximately 15 hours of light per day, in spite of the considerable distance between them (6° of latitude). A population from northern Ukraine (Sumy province), although geographically closer to that from Dnepropetrovsk, differed greatly from it in having a higher threshold value (17 hours) and a much higher percentage of diapausing pupae when developing in continuous 24-hour light.

Thus we may say that in *Pyrausta nubilalis* there are two geographical races, differing in photoperiodic reaction, with the boundary between them lying along the south of the forest-steppe zone. Apparently these races correspond to the forms mentioned in the literature—the 'hemp' form, which in nature is univoltine, and the 'maize' form, which produces (partly or wholly) two generations.

Similar relationships appear in the butterfly *Hylophila prasinana* L. This species is of interest because in it geographical variation in reaction to day-length is combined with marked dimorphism of the adults. In Chapter I it was shown that the Sukhumi race of this species, in short-day conditions, produces diapausing pupae, from which the 'typical' *Hylophila prasinana* emerge in spring. With long days its development does not include diapause and a differently-coloured summer form emeges, which was formerly thought to be the independent species *H. hongarica* Warr. Extension of the southern dimorphic race to the north has gone as far as the Ukraine forest-steppe zone (Poltava). But from Belgorod province northwards to Leningrad one finds only the monocyclic race of the *Hylophila prasinana* L. type. Even in long-day conditions it is not possible to obtain non-diapause development and the summer form in this race.

Differences in the nature of intraspecific physiological differentiation, observed in various species, lead to the conclusion that the gradient in geographical variation in photoperiodic reaction is determined not only by external conditions (gradual variation in day-length with latitude) but also by the biological peculiarities of a species.

In order to evaluate the significance of photoperiodic conditions as a factor inducing formation of intraspecific local races, we quote also the results of observations on other species of polycyclic Lepidoptera, as yet less fully studied.

Wide variations in critical thresholds of photoperiodic reaction have been observed in the pierids *Pieris rapae* and *P. napi* (Fig. 34) and the arctiid *Spilosoma menthastri* (see Fig. 48). Comparison of the development of Leningrad and Belgorod populations of several species of polycyclic Lepidoptera in short-day and long-day conditions shows that there are always distinct inherited

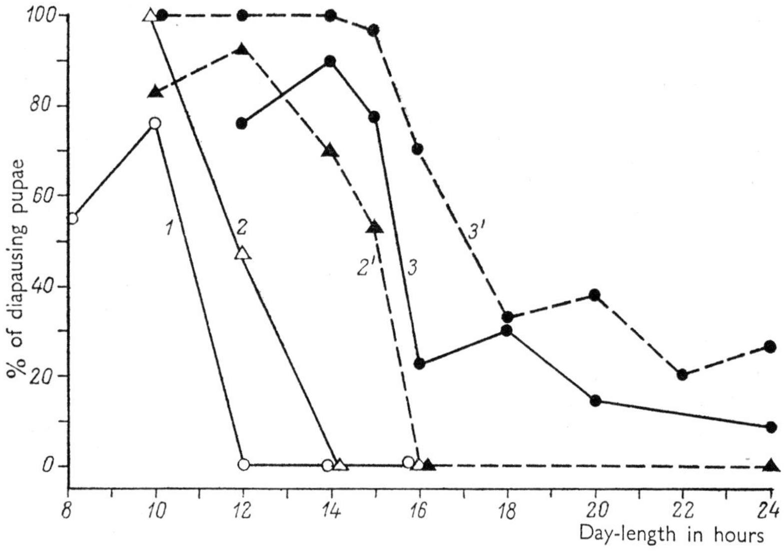

FIG. 34. The geographical variation in the photoperiodic reaction in *Pieris rapae* and *Pieris napi*. Temperature 23°.

Populations: 1, Sukhumi; 2 and 2′, Belgorod; 3 and 3′, Leningrad.
—— *Pieris rapae*; – – – *Pieris napi*.

differences between them. The Belgorod populations of *Smerinthus populi*, *Acronycta leporina*, *A. megacephala*, *Demas coryli*, *Pandemis ribeana*, and *Capua reticulana*, at a temperature of 21°-23° and in long-day conditions (18 hours), develop without diapause, whereas in similar conditions the majority of individuals in the northern populations enter diapause (DANILEVSKII, 1957a). Short days induce diapause in both southern and northern forms.

The formation of local races as a result of geographical

variation in day-length is observed not only in free-living phytophagous species but also in blood-sucking mosquitoes.

The decisive role of day-length in regulation of the gonotrophic cycle and diapause in the malaria mosquito *Anopheles maculipennis messeae* and the common mosquito *Culex pipiens pipiens* has been demonstrated experimentally by DANILEVSKII and GLINYANAYA (1958) and VINOGRADOVA (1958). SHIPITSYNA (1959), on the basis of personal field observations and analysis of extensive phenological data for the whole of the USSR, confirmed that imaginal diapause in the malaria mosquito depends on light conditions during the period of development of the aquatic stages. In this connection she drew attention to the fact that in different climatic zones diapause commences when day-length has different values. The critical day-length always, however, differs from the maximum for the locality by a more or less constant amount—1½ to 2 hours. Shipitsyna expressed the opinion that the onset of diapause in the malaria mosquito is affected not by the absolute duration of daylight but by its decrease by a definite number of hours. From this suggestion it follows that the norm of reaction to the light conditions has a constant value for a species.

New experimental investigations by Vinogradova (1960), however, did not confirm Shipitsyna's hypothesis. Comparison of populations of *Anopheles maculipennis messeae* from Leningrad and Astrakhan showed that adaptation to light and temperature conditions in different latitudes leads to the formation of intraspecific local races differing in their particular requirements. As with other species, the southern forms of mosquitoes are characterized by considerably lower threshold values than those of the northern forms. Thus in the malaria mosquito we must differentiate not only the long-known subspecies but also local races within these subspecies, with inherited differences in features of their life cycles.

In the field of geographical variation the seasonal cycles of parasitic insects are of great interest. The conformity of the life cycles of parasitic insects and of their hosts has been explained by the direct dependence of the parasite's development on changes in the physiological condition of the host (SALT, 1941). From this point of view it seemed unreasonable to expect special adaptations to geographical conditions in parasites. But GEISPITS and KYAO (1953) showed by experiment that in the endoparasitic ichneumon fly *Apanteles* there is an independent photoperiodic reaction, regulating the onset of diapause during hibernation in the pre-pupal stage. Further detailed investigations by MASLENNIKOVA (1958, 1959a) proved full reciprocal independence of photo-periodic reaction in *Apanteles glomeratus* and in its host the Cabbage White Butterfly *Pieris brassicae*, as a result of which parallel adaptations to light and temperature conditions have developed in geographical populations of both partners.

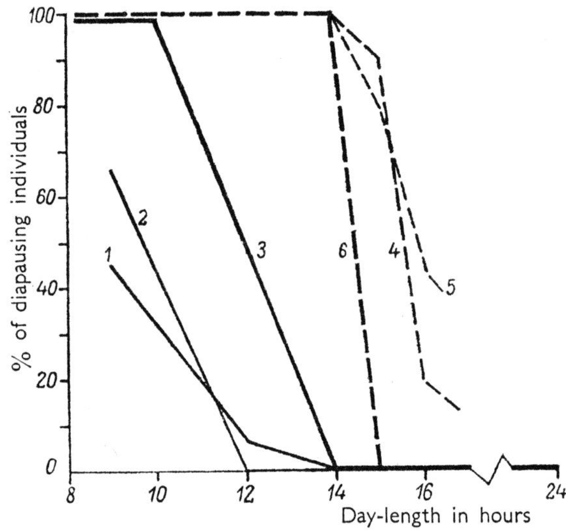

FIG. 35. The photoperiodic reaction of geographic populations of *Apanteles glomeratus* and its host *Pieris brassicae*. Temperature 18° (from Maslennikova, 1959).

——: the reaction of Sukhumi populations: 1, Sukhumi *Apanteles* developing in Sukhumi *Pieris brassicae*; 2, ditto in Leningrad *P. brassicae*; 3, uninfested Sukhumi *P. brassicae*.
– – –: the reaction of Leningrad populations: 4, Leningrad *Apanteles* in Leningrad *P. brassicae*; 5, ditto in Sukhumi *P. brassicae*; 6, uninfested Leningrad *P. brassicae*.

Fig. 35 shows the effect of day-length on the initiation of diapause in the Sukhumi and Leningrad races of *Apanteles* and *Pieris brassicae* at a constant temperature of 18°. As is seen, the critical day-length for the Sukhumi *Apanteles* is 9 hours, independently of the local race of butterflies in whose larvae it develops. The critical day-length for the Leningrad *Apanteles* is

16 hours, also independently of the race of its host. The difference in photoperiodic thresholds between races of the parasite is even greater than that between the Leningrad and Sukhumi races of the butterfly, for which critical day-lengths at the given temperature are 12 and 15 hours respectively. It is to be expected that independent local races will also be found in other parasitic insects.

From the investigations on polycyclic species with facultative diapause it may be concluded that clearly-shown inherited variations in photoperiodic reaction, as an adaptation to latitudinal variations in seasonal conditions, are the general rule for species of this ecological type. Not a single exception was discovered among a score of species investigated. Such variations occur on a large scale.

In far northern forms the raising of the critical threshold is accompanied by the appearance of individuals with hereditary monocyclism which do not react to day-length. The importance of photoperiodic reaction is thereby lessened and in some cases —e.g. in *Hylophila prasinana*—entirely disappears. On the other hand, in southern intraspecific races the reaction to day-length also gradually weakens and appears only within a very narrow range of photoperiods, being generally stronger with lowering of temperature (*Pieris brassicae*). Apparently even complete loss of reaction to day-length is possible. For instance, according to Geispits' observations, some forms of the mite *Tetranychus urticae* are practically homodynamic. In experiments by Vinogradova it was noted that in southern districts of Azerbaijan *Culex pipiens pipiens* also, apparently, does not react to day-length and approaches the continuously-developing *Culex pipiens molestus* in its seasonal cycle.

Thus not only the critical day-length but also the intensity of photoperiodic reaction are not characteristics of a species. These features are primarily characteristic of zonal-geographic adaptation in intraspecific populations. Characteristics peculiar to species appear only in the degree to which the general tendency to diapause appears. It is therefore not surprising that among species that have been considered to be monocyclic a geographical variation in adaptation to day-length has been observed. At a temperature of 23° diapause occurs in larvae of *Dendrolimus pini* from Leningrad province at a day-length of about 17 hours, whereas in forms from the forest-steppe zone (Voronezh province) the critical threshold is an hour less (Table 26).

TABLE 26

The photoperiodic reaction (percentage of diapausing larvae) of different populations of *Dendrolimus pini*. Temperature 23°

(after Geispits, 1958)

Population	Day-length in hours					
	14	15	16	17	18	20
Leningrad (60° N.)	100	100	100	91·7	0	0
Voronezh (52° N.)	100	100	90·0	0	0	0

Still more interesting in this respect is the Satin Moth *Leucoma salicis*, which is considered to be a strictly monocyclic species. Only recently has it been discovered (AVAKYAN, 1953; SERAFIMOVSKY, 1954) that in the extreme south of its general range, which covers a large part of the Palaearctic, a polycyclic form exists. Two or three generations of *Leucoma salicis* develop in some localities in southern Armenia (AVAKYAN, 1953), in Daghestan, in the northern Caucasus, and in southern Kirghizia. Apparently this form does not occupy a continuous range and occurs in more or less isolated patches.

The predominant, monocyclic form of *Leucoma salicis*, according to the experimental data of KOZHANCHIKOV (1948), possesses a very stable form of diapause, which cannot be averted by the effect of temperature. GEISPITS (1953), however, showed that even in this form diapause is to a great extent regulated by day-length, but continuous development takes place within a very limited range of photoperiods (20 hours) and only in some individuals. Experimental comparison of Satin Moths from Leningrad, Belgorod, and Alma-Ata provinces has confirmed these data. All these populations are characterized by stable monocyclism, and at a temperature of 25° long days stimulate their development very weakly (Fig. 49, *a*). The polycyclic Armenian race is sharply distinguished by its type of photoperiodic reaction, and in these temperature conditions even short days (9 to 12 hours) do not induce complete diapause in it; but with greater day-length development proceeds in all individuals without interruption. We may suppose that such cases are not exceptional among other monocyclic species.

So far we have examined the reaction of geographical populations to photoperiods corresponding to fluctuations in day-length during the active period. But the reactions of geographical forms in photoperiods less than 6 hours and in total darkness are different. From Fig. 32, which shows complete photoperiodic curves for geographical populations of *Pieris brassicae*, it is seen that in the southern form lowering of the critical threshold of reaction is accompanied by a simultaneous sharp decline in the percentage of diapausing individuals within the zone of short photoperiods. A regular increase in the number of diapausing individuals in conditions of total darkness, corresponding to increase in critical day-length, is seen in geographical populations of *Acronycta rumicis* (see Fig. 30), *Barathra brassicae* (see Fig. 31), and *Spilosoma menthastri* (see Fig. 48). The ability to develop without diapause in darkness is lost when the threshold exceeds 16-17 hours. It is of interest that a fully analogous phenomenon can be observed even in a single population when critical day-length changes under the influence of temperature. In general, irrespective of the factor inducing the increase in critical day-length, the latter is always followed by an increase in the tendency to diapause in conditions of total darkness. This indicates that the reaction to darkness is a function of the general physiological mechanism causing photoperiodic reaction. It is quite evident that the features of the reaction to total darkness have no ecological significance, as free-living species do not encounter that situation in nature. The above-mentioned phenomenon clearly demonstrates that not every feature that exhibits regular geographical variation is an adaptation, a fact that is not yet always remembered in investigations into geographical variation, in which consideration is often given to features that are merely fortuitous and that have not been given proper biological evaluation.

2. The relation of the photoperiodic reaction in geographical races to temperature

The variation in day-length with latitude is accompanied by considerable variation in the temperature conditions. Thus in order to understand the regulating mechanism of seasonal cycles in different climatic conditions one must determine the extent to which the photoperiodic reaction in geographical races depends on the direct influence of the ambient temperature.

Experimental data indicate that the temperature limits and optima for photoperiodic reaction in northern races always incline strongly towards high temperatures as compared with these features in southern races (DANILEVSKII, 1957a, 1957b). This may be illustrated by the results of a series of experiments made

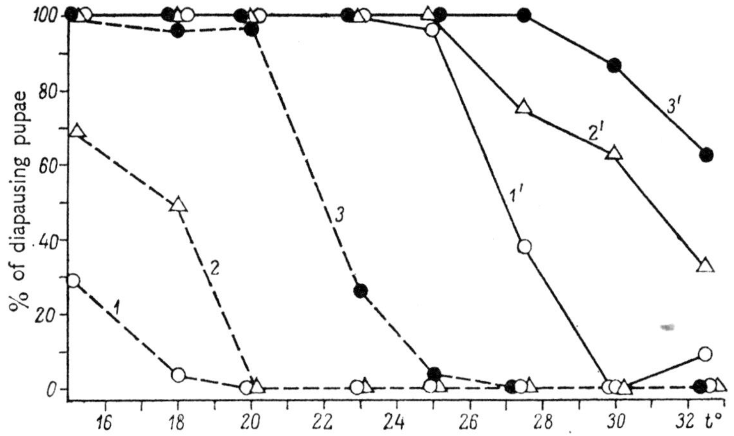

FIG. 36. Changes in the numbers of diapausing pupae in geographical populations of *Acronycta rumicis* depending on the temperature, at different light conditions during the development of the larvae.

Populations: 1 and 1′, Sukhumi; 2 and 2′, Belgorod; 3 and 3′, Leningrad.
– – –: continuous light; ——: with 12-hour day.

with three populations of *Acronycta rumicis*, in which the effects of long and short days in different temperature conditions were investigated (Fig. 36).

In the Sukhumi population, in short-day conditions, active pupae begin to appear under the influence of comparatively moderate temperatures of about 25°, and at 30° diapause is completely absent. It is much more difficult to induce non-diapause development in short-day conditions in the Leningrad population. For the latter, a temperature at least 5° higher than that for the Sukhumi population is required. Even at the upper developmental limit (33°) more than half the pupae enter diapause. The Belgorod race occupies an intermediate position. On the other hand, with development in long-day conditions low temperatures stimulate the initiation of diapause more strongly in northern than in southern populations. Thus the Leningrad *Acronycta rumicis*, when developing at a temperature of 20° or

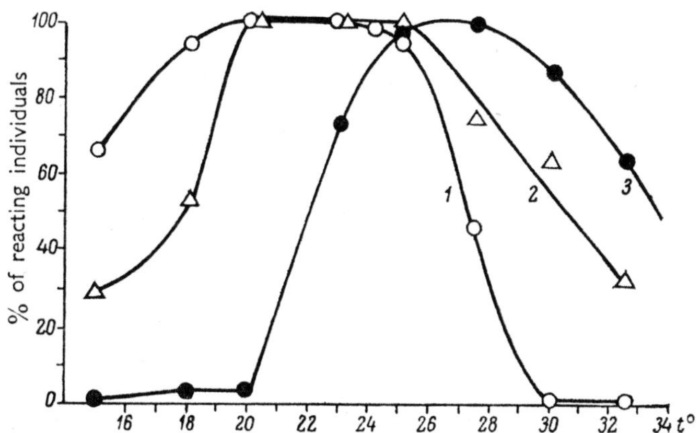

FIG. 37. The temperature optima of the photoperiodic reaction in different geographical populations of *Acronycta rumicis*. The percentage reacting to day-length when developing at different temperatures.

1, Sukhumi population; 2, Belgorod; 3, Leningrad.

less, produces only diapausing pupae, whereas in the Sukhumi race the percentage of diapausing pupae even at 15° is very small. In this respect also the Belgorod population is intermediate between the Leningrad and the Sukhumi.

In all the geographical populations of *Acronycta rumicis* that were studied, the temperature range in which photoperiodic reaction normally takes place is similar, covering approximately 12°-14°. Only its position on the temperature scale varies (Fig. 37). The region of optimum temperature for photoperiodic reaction, in which it is fully displayed, lies between 20° and 25° for the Sukhumi population, somewhat higher for the Belgorod population, and considerably higher (25° to 28°) for the Leningrad population. Thus the temperature limits for manifesting the photoperiodic reaction and its optimum may vary not only with the species (see Fig. 23) but also no less markedly within the limits of a single species as a result of adaptation to zonal-geographical conditions.

Similar data were obtained in experiments with populations of *Barathra brassicae*. In this species the appearance of diapause in short-day conditions is suppressed by high temperatures, also especially in the southern forms. Thus with a temperature of 28° and a 12-hour day the Batum population develops without diapause, whereas in the Sumy population 26% and in the Leningrad 100% of the pupae enter diapause. In long-day conditions the Batum population does not enter diapause even at 14°, whereas in the Sumy population about 50% of the pupae enter diapause at 16°, and in the Leningrad population even at 18° the long-day effect is totally suppressed and only diapausing pupae are produced.

Similar changes in the temperature limits of the photoperiodic reaction were observed in the experiments of MASLENNIKOVA (1959a) with geographical populations of *Pieris brassicae* and its parasite *Apanteles glomeratus*. In short-day (9-hour) conditions, diapause in the southern forms of both species is inhibited by temperatures considerably lower than in the northern species. Thus in the Sukhumi Cabbage White Butterfly non-diapause development is observed at 25°-26°, and in the Leningrad form at 29°-30°. For *Apanteles* these limits are about 20° and 25° respectively.

A more complex and peculiar relation between the photoperiodic reaction and temperature is observed in geographical races of *Spilosoma menthastri* (Fig. 38). When the larvae develop in short-day conditions the Leningrad race produces only diapausing pupae, and this reaction is not disturbed even at the upper limit of permissive temperature (30°). In the Sukhumi race the short-day effect disappears at high temperatures, and non-diapause development ensues. In continuous light diapause is induced not only by lowered temperature but also by high sublethal temperature. This unusual phenomenon is particularly evident in the Leningrad race.

This type of 'thermal' diapause in *Spilosoma* pupae differs from normal diapause, induced by short-day and moderate-temperature conditions, in its short duration and the possibility of resuming development without chilling. In this respect it recalls the short summer diapause which occurs in long-day conditions in the subtropical Japanese form of *Barathra brassicae* (MASAKI, 1956a). But in *Spilosoma menthastri* it is more difficult to explain the ecological significance of the phenomenon, especially as it is more pronounced in the northern forms.

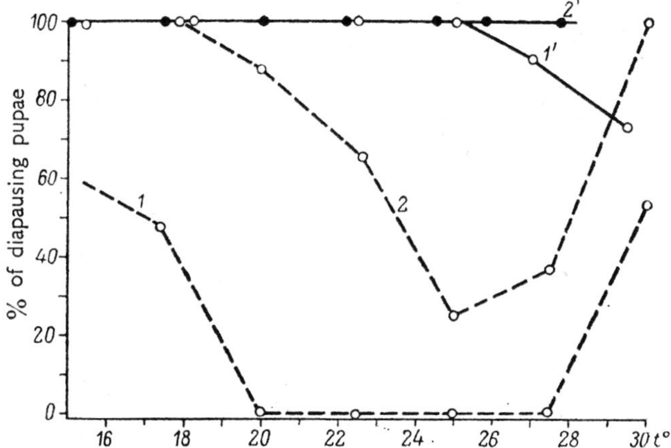

FIG. 38. Changes in the numbers of diapausing pupae in geographical populations of *Spilosoma menthastri* depending on the temperature and light conditions during the development of the larvae.

Populations: 1 and 1′, Sukhumi; 2 and 2′, Leningrad. – – –: in continuous light; ——: with 12-hour day.

In several species substantial differences between geographical races also appear in the degree of variation of the critical day-length under the influence of temperature. In northern races of *Pieris brassicae*, for instance, the critical day-length of 15 hours remains almost constant with development of larvae in different temperatures (see Fig. 26). In the southern race, as may be seen by comparing the graphs in Figs. 32 and 35, the critical day-lengths in individuals developing at 18° and at 23° differ by 2 hours (10 and 12 hours).

In the experiments of Du Chzhen'-ven' the critical day-length for the southern (Sukhumi) form of *Pyrausta nubilalis*, when developing at temperatures of 18° and 23°, remained the same (15 hours), whereas in the northern form it had a much higher value at 18° than at 25°. These peculiarities of the reactions of geographical races have a strong effect on their phenology.

3. The degree of variation of temperature reactions in active stages

The wide range of geographical variation in the reactions regulating the seasonal cycles of insects makes it necessary for us to determine the extent to which other eco-physiological character-

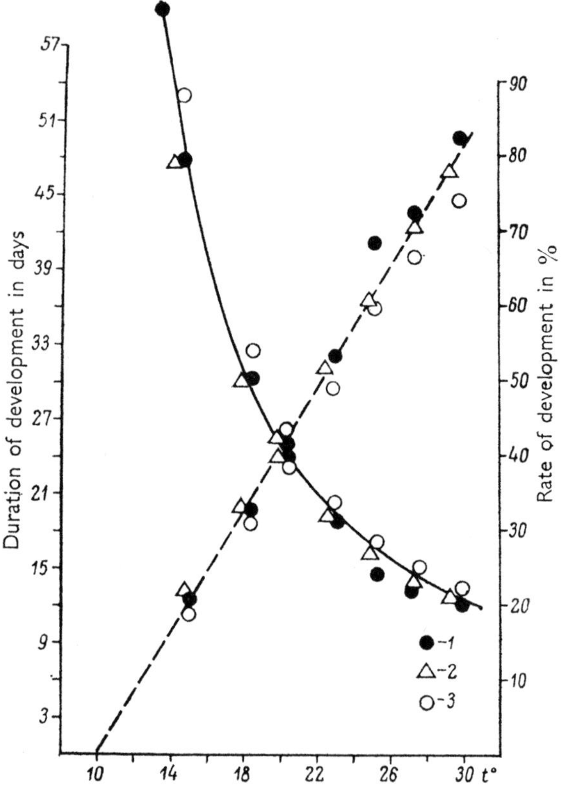

FIG. 39. The effect of temperature on the development of larvae of different geographical populations of *Acronycta rumicis*.

Populations: 1, Leningrad; 2, Belgorod; 3, Sukhumi. ——: the duration of development in days; - - -: the rate in % per day.

istics of species are subject to variation. This is particularly important for such indicators as the sum-total and the threshold of temperatures effective for growth and development, and the optimum temperature for development, which are widely used in analysis of the geographical distribution, phenology, and population changes of insects. The degree to which these quantities are constant for a species has until recently been unknown.

The reaction of the active stages to temperature conditions during development has been investigated for geographical populations of *Acronycta rumicis* and *Spilosoma menthastri* (DANILEVSKII, 1957a). Fig. 39 shows the results of the experiments with *Acronycta*. In all the three populations investigated, no substantial differences were observed in the changes of rate and duration of development due to temperature. The threshold of effective temperature, determined by the rate of development, was uniform at 10° for all forms. The somewhat delayed development of the Sukhumi larvae, as a result of which the sum of effective temperatures for them is almost 10° higher than that for the Belgorod and Leningrad larvae, may be noted. But such divergences lie within the limits of permissible experimental error.

The duration of development of *Acronycta rumicis* pupae and changes in it due to temperature also proved to be quite similar in different geographical populations. As with the larvae, the threshold of effective temperatures for all three populations must be taken as being 10°. In Table 27 we present data on the totals of effective temperatures required for development of separate stages and for the whole life cycle of this species. The differences in the values for different geographical populations are so small that we may confidently speak of this feature as being constant for the species.

TABLE 27

The sum-total of effective temperatures (Σ) above 10° during the development of different populations of *Acronycta rumicis*

Population	Σ (in day-degrees) during development			Σ (in day-degrees) during the entire cycle
	eggs	larvae	pupae	
Leningrad	76 (67-78)	245 (223-265)	197 (189-204)	518
Belgorod	72 (69-74)	243 (232-249)	199 (187-205)	514
Sukhumi	69 (66-79)	267 (262-275)	208 (188-220)	544

In *Spilosoma menthastri* also great similarity may be seen in the temperature indicators characterizing rates of growth and development of larvae of different geographical populations (Fig. 40). The upper limits of development are also the same.

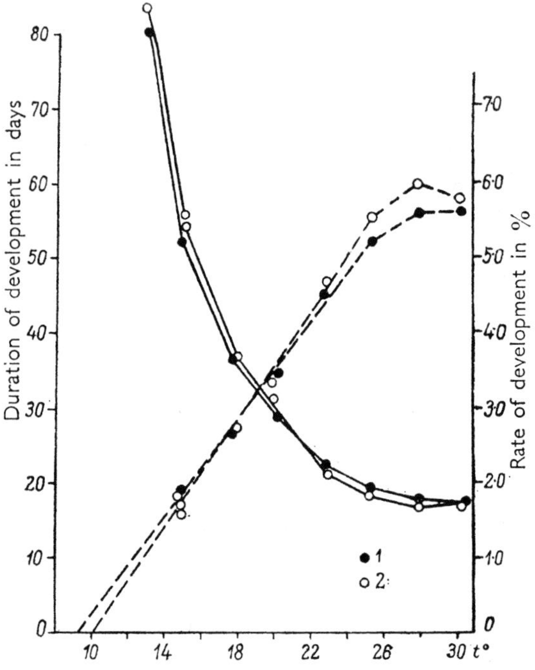

FIG. 40. The effect of temperature on the development of larvae of different geographical populations of *Spilosoma menthastri*.

Populations: 1, Leningrad; 2, Sukhumi.
——: the duration of development in days; - - -: the rate in % per day.

Comparison of the reactions to temperature by pupae of this species is impossible, as almost all the Leningrad individuals undergo diapause. For pupae of the Sukhumi form the threshold of the effective temperature is 10°, and the sum-total of effective temperatures is 200-210 day-degrees.

The great constancy of the periods of development of species and their dependence on temperature are also shown by comparing data in the literature obtained by various authors from material of different geographical origins. As an example, Fig. 41 compares the relation to temperature of the duration of development in the Leningrad and Sukhumi populations of *Pieris brassicae*, as determined in laboratory experiments by V. A. Maslennikova, with the experimental data of MAERCKS (1934) for the Central European (Berlin) form and the field observations of KLEIN (1932) in Palestine. All points proved to be exceedingly close and

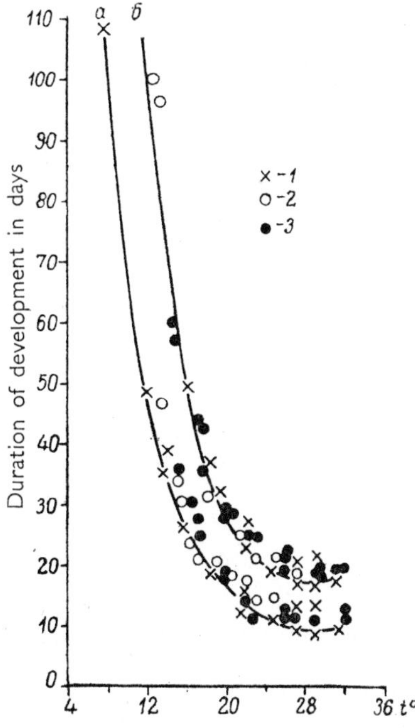

FIG. 41

The effect of temperature on the duration of development in *Pieris brassicae* (from data of several authors).

a. The development of larvae;
b. The development of larvae and pupae.

Observation points: 1, Berlin (from Maercks, 1934).
2, Palestine (from Klein, 1932).
3, Leningrad (from data of V. A. Maslennikova).

showed no regular differences. According to the data of PANTYUKHOV (1959), the lower thresholds, the rates of development, and the sum-totals of temperatures for different geographical populations of *Euproctis chrysorrhoea* and also for the Gypsy Moth *Lymantria dispar* are practically identical.

The optimal temperature for development of the active stages is an important eco-physiological characteristic of a species. There are as yet few experimental data of adequate precision for assessing geographical variation in it. Available records, however, provide grounds for believing that this characteristic also is not subject to substantial adaptational variation within a geographical range.

To determine optimum temperature, data on size and weight and also on survival in different temperature conditions are the most often used; but one must bear in mind that weight and linear

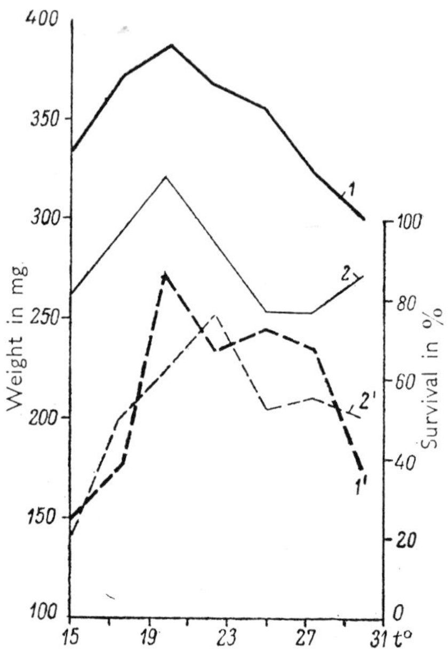

Fig. 42. The effect of temperature on the survival of larvae and the weight of pupae of different populations of *Spilosoma menthastri*.

Populations: 1 and 1′, Leningrad; 2 and 2′, Sukhumi. ——: weight; – – –: survival.

dimensions are often inherited features of a geographical population. For instance, the weight of *Spilosoma menthastri* pupae from Leningrad exceeds the weight of those from Sukhumi by 20%-25% in all conditions. Similar variations are found in *Pieris rapae* and several other species. In *Acronycta rumicis* geographical differences in size and weight are considerably less pronounced, and in different developmental conditions the reverse tendency appears: the southern forms from Sukhumi are usually larger than the northern ones from Leningrad and Vitebsk.

Data on optimum temperatures for *Spilosoma menthastri* are

given in Fig. 42. In both geographical forms (Sukhumi and Leningrad), unaffected by the constant difference in weight, maximal weight occurs at a temperature of 20°; as the temperature deviates from that point the weight progressively declines. The survival of larvae also varies correspondingly. In the optimal range for growth (20°-22°) one observes not only the lowest mortality of larvae but also the greatest fertility of adults. All of these data, which fairly clearly characterize the temperature adaptation of *Spilosoma menthastri* as a species, also show the absence of adaptational variations in the optimal temperature for the zonal-geographical forms within the species.

A difference between the geographical populations of *Spilosoma menthastri* is found only in the sublethal temperature zone (27°-30°), which induced abnormal pupation of Leningrad individuals in long-day conditions; in darkness both populations developed at the same rate. Geographical populations of some other species (*Acronycta rumicis*, *Barathra brassicae*, *Pieris brassicae*), which have clear specific differences in temperature limits and optima for development, also showed no regular differences.

The relative constancy of temperature requirements for the active stages of intraspecific geographical populations makes it probable that other forms of adaptation to climatic conditions exist; in particular, one may expect differences in the behaviour determining selection of microhabitats. Further investigations are needed in this field.

4. Variation in temperature adaptations in wintering stages

The literature throws very little light on intraspecific variation in the ecological characteristics of wintering stages. SIEGLER (1946) found no differences in frost-resistance in hibernating larvae of the Codling Moth *Enarmonia* (*Carpocapsa*) *pomonella* taken from different geographical regions of North America. KOT (1958) came to the same conclusion after studying the frost-resistance of that species at three points in its European range. On the other hand, according to PANTYUKHOV (1956) the frost-resistance of populations of *Hyponomeuta malinellus*, *Malacosoma neustria*, and *Exaereta ulmi* from the lower Volga basin proved to be higher than that of those from the northern Caucasus. He regards this as an adaptation to the more severe winter of the lower Volga. With regard to reactivation, observations have been made on the locust *Austroicetes cruciata*, populations of which have been found to differ in their temperature requirements during egg-diapause (ANDREWARTHA, 1944, 1952). Cases are also known of differences in the duration of diapause in geographical populations of the Gypsy Moth (GOLDSCHMIDT, 1934).

Most of these data have been obtained from specimens taken in the field and therefore subject to the influence of different conditions before the experiments. It is therefore difficult to decide to what extent hereditary physiological features of local races are reflected in them. Solution of this problem, within the scope of the present work, is of considerable interest.

Table 28 shows comparative data regarding frost-resistance in intraspecific local races of several species of Lepidoptera. The experiments were made on homogeneous material reared in short-day conditions and in uniform temperature. Before freezing, the diapausing pupae were kept for one or two months at a temperature of 5°-6°. The temperature of supercooling was determined by means of a thermocouple, at a cooling rate of 2°-3° per minute.

TABLE 28

The frost-resistance of diapausing pupae of different geographical populations of Lepidoptera

Name of species	Population	No. of pupae in experiment	Average temperature of cooling (°)	Limits of individual variation (°)	
Acronycta rumicis	Sukhumi	28	-23·2	-18·7	-25·6
	Belgorod	7	-22·6	-18·5	-23·2
	Leningrad	24	-22·0	-20·0	-25·0
Spilosoma menthastri	Sukhumi	40	-22·3	-17·6	-24·4
	Leningrad	40	-22·7	-17·8	-26·6
Barathra brassicae	Batum	10	-19·1	-12·0	-28·0
	Belgorod	5	-18·7	-16·8	-21·0
	Sumy	10	-18·2	-14·4	-20·1
	Leningrad	8	-19·6	-17·2	-26·0
Pieris brassicae	Sukhumi	15	-21·2	-16·4	-24·0
	Leningrad	15	-22·5	-19·6	-24·1

The ability to survive freezing was found to be quite uniform in geographical populations of a single species. These results were particularly unexpected in view of the wide differences in winter temperature recorded in the territories from the Black Sea coast of the Caucasus to Leningrad. In the subtropical climate of the Black Sea coast, the average temperature of even the coldest month is positive (+6·5°), and the absolute minimum does not fall below −10°; at Leningrad the average temperature in February is −7·7°, and the absolute minimum reaches −35°.

The recorded figures, however, do not give a complete picture of the relative degree of frost-resistance of different populations. This is clearly seen in Table 29, which shows periodic variations in frost-resistance in pupae of *Acronycta rumicis* hibernating in natural conditions in Leningrad province in the open, above the snow cover (DANILEVSKII, 1957a).

TABLE 29

The variation in frost-resistance of *Acronycta rumicis* pupae hibernating in a natural environment

Date of test	Minimum temp. (°) during preceding period	Population	No. of pupae in test	% that died	Temperature of cooling (°)	
					Average	Limit
		Above the snow				
1 XI	−3	Sukhumi	30	0	−23·7	−25·6
		Belgorod	25	0	−23·2	−25·1
		Leningrad	30	0	−23·1	−25·0
8 XII	−26	Sukhumi	25	88	−23·5	−27·0
		Belgorod	25	64	−27·5	−29·2
		Leningrad	25	28	−29·2	−32·0
21 XII	−34·0	Sukhumi	50	100	—	—
		Belgorod	25	100	—	—
		Leningrad	50	92	−26·0	−27·0
		Under the snow				
9 II	−2·7	Sukhumi	50	0	−25·5	−29·6
		Belgorod	25	0	−26·3	−30·6
		Leningrad	50	0	−29·7	−34·8
22 III	−2·2	Sukhumi	50	0	−26·4	−29·4
		Belgorod	25	0	−24·3	−31·9
		Leningrad	50	0	−29·6	−34·6

While the average temperature was above 0° and the minimum did not fall below −3°, resistance of the pupae to freezing was the same in all forms. But when the air temperature fell to −26°, i.e. to the critical level for *Acronycta rumicis*, different populations suffered from the frost to different degrees. The majority (88%) of the Sukhumi population froze to death, whereas comparatively small mortality was observed in the Leningrad pupae. Resistance to further freezing among the surviving pupae of different populations varied remarkably in comparison with that of the original groups. Those of the Belgorod form survived a temperature 4° lower than that endured by the original group, and those of the Leningrad a temperature 6° lower (−29·2° on an average). The maximum limit of frost-resistance also varied correspondingly in geographical populations. Among those from Leningrad, some pupae survived freezing down to −32°. The frost-resistance attained in these cases is apparently the extreme limit for *Acronycta rumicis*. After a period with continual frosts of the order of −15° and −20°, with a minimum of −34°, all pupae of the southern forms perished; only a few of the Leningrad pupae survived, but they also perished later.

An increase in frost-resistance under the influence of negative temperatures was equally clearly shown in a parallel experiment with *Acronycta rumicis* hibernating in natural conditions, on the surface of the soil under deep snow cover (Table 29). During the winter the minimum temperature under the snow was very constant and remained at an average level of −2·2° to −2·7° (absolute minimum −9°), far from reaching the critical temperature. In such conditions, by February frost-resistance in different geographical forms had changed from its original conditions, as in the pupae that had hibernated in the open. It remained until spring at the level then attained. No mortality of pupae was observed in this experiment. Pupae of all three populations overwintered well and produced normal adults in spring.

From the above experiments it is seen that frost-resistance results from two processes which are largely independent of each other. The first is connected with the onset of diapause, and characterizes a level of frost-resistance common to the species. The second develops during the process of hibernation as a direct result of the toughening action of negative temperatures. Only in the capacity for toughening do we observe the adaptational characteristics of geographical populations. The ability of northern populations to increase their frost-resistance as a result of the direct action of negative temperatures may play a substantial role in the preservation of hibernating stocks through winters of little snow and severe falls in temperature in autumn and in spring.

In order to discover the duration of diapause and the conditions for reaction of hibernating pupae of geographical populations of *Acronycta rumicis*, insects obtained in the laboratory in early October, within two weeks of pupation, were placed in thermostatic containers with constant temperatures of 30°, 25°, 20°, and 14°, with atmospheric humidity about 70%. The effects of lower and negative temperatures were observed in pupae hibernating in natural conditions under the snow.

From the data in Table 30 we may conclude that the Leningrad population of *Acronycta rumicis* undergoes a stable diapause as compared with that of the southern forms and requires lower winter temperatures for reactivation. We have not yet succeeded in determining the biological significance of these features. Hibernation under the snow in natural conditions in Leningrad province resulted in normal reactivation in all the populations studied. Control tests showed that until the end of December all pupae were in stable diapause. By the beginning of February diapause came to an end in all populations, and on incubation all adults emerged together. Therefore the process of reactivation was completed in January and lasted about four months. It is probable that in the conditions of southern latitudes with a short mild winter the importance of temperature thresholds of reactivation would be displayed more clearly.

Apparently geographical variation in the temperature requirements of diapausing stages is shown more strongly in *Pieris brassicae* and *Pieris rapae* than in *Acronycta rumicis*. Prolonged cooling is essential for normal development of diapausing pupae of the Leningrad form of *Pieris brassicae*. With a constant temperature above 20° diapause is not broken, or else after 4 to 6 months only isolated adults emerge, always very weak and unable to survive (DANILEVSKII, 1950). In the Sukhumi form diapause proved to be of much shorter duration. When pupae of this form were kept at a constant temperature of 23°, within 2½ to 3 months

TABLE 30

The effects of positive temperatures for six months on diapausing pupae of *Acronycta rumicis*

Temp. (°)	Population	No. of pupae in experiment	Result (%)		
			dead	diapausing	developing
30	Leningrad	25	100	—	—
	Belgorod	25	100	—	—
	Sukhumi	25	100	—	—
25	Leningrad	25	100	—	—
	Belgorod	25	92·0	8·0	—
	Sukhumi	25	88·0	12·0	—
20	Leningrad	25	56·0	44·0	—
	Belgorod	15	20·0	13·4	66·6
	Sukhumi	25	36·0	12·0	52·0
14	Leningrad	32	16·1	22·5	61·3
	Belgorod	35	11·5	0·0	83·5
	Sukhumi	50	12·0	0·0	88·0

fairly uniform development and the emergence of apparently-normal adults were observed. Similar differences were noted in geographical populations of *Pieris rapae*. In *Pyrausta nubilalis*, according to the experiments of Du Chzhen'-ven', reactivation under the influence of low temperatures is completed more rapidly in southern forms than in northern.

Thus distinct inherited differences in temperature norms for reactivation were found among geographical populations in all the cases studied. Hence we may conclude that intraspecific differentiation of this feature is a general rule in widely-distributed insect species.

5. Peculiarities of intraspecific geographical variation in physiological characteristics of insects

The above data show that the physiological reactions on which climatic adaptations of insects are based fall into two sharply-defined groups: (1) reactions that are subject to marked intra-specific geographical variation as a result of adaptation to zonal-geographical conditions, and (2) reactions that are relatively constant for a species.

The first group includes photoperiodic and temperature reactions determining the onset of diapause, and also those temperature adaptations of the diapausing stages on which depend the duration of the resting stage and the rate of reactivation. In other words, all physiological mechanisms that regulate the synchronization of the life cycle with the seasonal rhythm of climate are subject to variation. The biological significance of these adaptations is obvious. It stands out particularly clearly in experiments in the transfer of intraspecific local races to regions within the range of the species that are not occupied by them (DANILEVSKII, 1957a).

In this chapter we have cited experimental data concerning only physiological divergence of populations resulting from the change in climate with geographical latitude, but there is no doubt that similar phenomena occur in other cases. Even within a single latitude the temperature conditions vary with longitude and depend on the degree to which the climate is continental in nature; and these often cause great changes in the calendar dates of insect development, as a result of which the stages sensitive to photoperiod occur in different localities at periods with different day-lengths. This must inevitably result in the formation of local races with differentiated photoperiodic reaction. This possibility is confirmed by the investigations of GEISPITS (1960), which showed significant differences in critical day-length in populations of the mite *Tetranychus urticae* from Alma-Ata province and from the Black Sea coast of the Caucasus, i.e. from districts on the same parallel of latitude (see Table 31). In connection with the duration and the temperature of the winter period, doubtless, temperature norms of reactivation of such races may be differentiated, as was noted by PANTYUKHOV (1959) for the Far Eastern and European races of *Lymantria dispar*.

A similar process of ecological differentiation, to all intents and purposes, takes place also in populations inhabiting altitudinal zones in mountainous districts. In this case, because of the decrease in length of the vegetative period and the fall in temperature with altitude, critical day-length must increase in populations in the highest zones, as it does in northern forms, and in extreme cases hereditary monocyclism may arise. This was confirmed by the observations of MÜLLER and KAUTZ (1940), who demonstrated hereditary variations in seasonal cycles and in the onset of diapause in populations of *Pieris bryoniae* from different altitudinal zones of the Austrian Alps. For instance, the high-altitude form remained univoltine even when it was reared at a higher temperature and at a lower altitude, where the local population had two generations.

The reason for the great intraspecific variability in this group of reactions is that they are all indirect adaptations to the seasonal changes of a complex of external factors. Since separate components of this complex vary seasonally and geographically to different degrees, and even in opposite directions, it is impossible to have a universal physiological mechanism capable of producing precise synchronization of the cycles everywhere. On the other hand, a hormonal mechanism regulating the seasonal cycle facilitates the development of intraspecific differentiation as it involves not the development of new types of processes but only quantitative changes in the action of separate components of the endocrine system.

The second group of reactions, which is characterized by great specific constancy, differs radically from the seasonal-cyclic group in its ecological significance and its physiological basis. This group includes, as we have seen, dependence of rates of growth and development on temperature, optima and limits for development of active stages, and also original frost-resistance of the diapausing stages, i.e. direct adaptations to the temperature conditions in which the organisms live.

From the ecological point of view the lack of clearly-shown intraspecific differentiation of temperature adaptations of the active stages can be explained by the relative uniformity of the temperature conditions in summer in different geographical zones and by the possibility of adaptation to it by selecting the most favourable microclimatic conditions. As for adaptations of the diapausing stages to negative temperatures, they call for practically no obligatory geographical differentiation, as a sufficiently high original frost-resistance enables these stages to hibernate in any climatic zones within the range of the species.

Specific constancy of temperature adaptations, perhaps, also has a profound physiological basis. USHAKOV (1956, 1958, 1959a, 1959b, 1959c), who investigated the heat-resistance of the tissues of a large number of representatives of various groups of animals, came to the conclusion that that is an important characteristic of a species. In intraspecific geographical populations and even subspecific forms, taken from regions differing widely in climate, there are no adaptational differences in the resistance of muscle protein to limiting high temperatures. At the same time such differences between different species, even those closely related, are fairly clearly shown, and are directly linked with living conditions. Ushakov explained this fact as being due to specific differences in the structure of cellular proteins.

The similarity of these data to ours is probably not accidental. Since growth and development are primarily a process of protein formation, the adaptation of an organism to temperature must be linked to a considerable extent with its specific characteristics. It is fully admitted that the specificity of basic frost-resistance in hibernating stages of insects (due, as is known, to the colloidal nature of plasma) is also to some extent connected with the characteristics of protein formation. Adaptational variations in frost-resistance as a result of low temperature (toughening) are simpler in their nature and, according to PANTYUKHOV (1959), are determined by changes in protective reducing substances.

One must, of course, keep in mind the fact that the reactions of the whole organism may be complicated by additional adaptations of a different physiological nature and therefore may be more variable than the reactions of the tissues alone. This probably explains the differences in temperature optima of intraspecific races of *Drosophila funebris*, noted by TIMOFEEV-RESSOVSKII (1935). But the scale and the adaptational significance of such changes are incommensurably smaller than the geographical variation in seasonal-cyclic adaptations.

The morphological characteristics of a species also are distinguished by great stability. All of the intraspecific populations of Lepidoptera investigated by us, even those of widely-differing geographical origins, were very similar morphologically, displaying no features sufficient to separate them systematically into subspecies or clearly-isolated races. We observed only small, and usually not very constant, differences in average measurements and sometimes in minor details of colouring. Thus even in cases of wide eco-physiological divergence a species does not lose its morphological integrity.

Chapter VI

THE INHERITANCE OF PHOTOPERIODIC REACTION

As long as photoperiodic reaction was looked upon as a characteristic of species, the question of its inheritance in the event of hybridization did not arise; but as a result of observations of clearly manifested adaptational changes in photoperiodic reaction in geographical populations of a single species, the problem of its inheritance has acquired an independent ecological significance. Investigations in this direction are of interest to the ecologist in many respects. They are important both for understanding the paths leading to the formation of physiologically-distinct local races and for discovering the causes and conditions leading to the biological integrity of a species and the continuity of its geographical range.

There are no data in the literature about the inheritance of photoperiodic reaction, but studies of inheritance of diapause have a close relation to this subject. A large proportion of such works deal with the question of voltinism in races of silkworms, which is of practical importance. The deductions put forward in them are extremely contradictory. It is known only that in the first generation the maternal type of cycle usually predominates, which is naturally explained by the characteristics of endocrinal regulation of diapause in early embryonic stages.

A cause of contradictions exists in the fact that in genetical studies diapause is looked upon as an independent inherited feature, without sufficient regard being paid to its dependence on external conditions. Only in recent studies by Japanese investigators (Tanaka, 1953), apparently, has proper attention been given to the latter. Data on the genetic nature of local races of the European Corn Borer *Pyrausta nubilalis* in America (Arbuthnot, 1944) and the sawfly *Gilpinia polytoma* (Prebble, 1941; Smith, 1941), like all other facts on the inheritance of diapause in other insects, were obtained without taking account of photoperiodic conditions, and it is therefore difficult to use them in the present work.

The complex physiological mechanism of diapause and the great dependence of its manifestation on external conditions clearly show that it is necessary to throw light, not only on the inheritance of diapause as such, but also on the inheritance of the photoperiodic reactions that determine it. In this chapter we set forth data obtained in the entomological laboratory of the University of Leningrad on the study of photoperiodic reaction in hybrids between different intraspecific races.

1. Variation and inheritance of photoperiodic reaction in geographical races

Before passing on to discuss experiments on intraspecific hybridization, we must determine the degree of variation in photoperiodic reaction within the confines of a single population and its stability as an inherited character. Observations show that variation in photoperiodic reaction is a characteristic and ecologically-conditioned feature of every geographical population. A difficulty in determining variation consists in the fact that it is not displayed uniformly in response to different photoperiods, and depends to a great extent on temperature and other external factors. Therefore we shall restrict ourselves to only the most common characteristic of variation in photoperiodic reaction, observed in experiments at optimum temperature.

The greatest individual variation is observed in all species and geographical forms in response to very short photoperiods of less than 6-8 hours, i.e. in conditions of no ecological significance, since insects do not occur in them in nature. It is obvious that no definite adaptational norm of reaction to such photoperiods can be determined.

The reaction to the short day, typical for a given form, which induces diapause in all individuals without exception, is remarkable for its extreme constancy. Such monotypy is doubtless a result of very intensive natural selection, which during the winter eliminates all non-diapausing individuals. Only in extreme southern populations, e.g. in the Transcaucasian *Chloridea obsoleta*, do some individuals continue to develop in both natural and experimental conditions, even with a short day and moderate temperature.

The reaction to a long day of forms that in natural conditions have more than one generation is also usually very uniform. In *Pieris brassicae*, southern forms of *Acronycta rumicis*, *Pieris rapae*, and others, diapause is never induced when they are reared in long-day conditions. But in several (even relatively southern) species such as *Loxostege sticticalis*, *Loxostege verticalis*, and *Plodia interpunctella* diapause is frequently observed in such conditions, especially in continuous light. Considerable individual variation in reaction is characteristic of the Colorado Beetle, of which from 5% to 30% of individuals enter diapause in such conditions, even at high temperatures (25°-27°).

For northern populations, which in natural conditions are univoltine, great individual variation in reaction to long days is actually the rule. It is characteristic that the percentage diapausing in such conditions varies greatly among the progeny of different females. For instance, with a temperature of 23°-24° and continuous light, diapause occurred in from 0% to 42% in different families of the Leningrad form of *Acronycta rumicis*; the corresponding figures for *Spilosoma menthastri* were from 35% to 60%, and for *Pieris napi* from 0% to 60%. For a monocyclic race of *Leucoma salicis*, with 20 hours of light the number of diapausing larvae in different broods was recorded as varying from 10% to 60%. This variation in reaction of northern forms has not, however, any substantial ecological significance. In natural conditions it is usually completely masked by the effects of low temperature, which induces diapause in all individuals whatever the day-length may be.

As was shown in the preceding chapter, differences between geographical forms appear mainly in the length of the critical photoperiod. Individual variation in this characteristic has great ecological importance, as it determines the precision of response by a population to natural fluctuations in day-length. From comparison of numerous graphs of photoperiodic reaction it is seen that the steepness of the threshold section of the curves, which denotes individual variation in the critical photoperiod, is not the same in different species and forms. Very small individual variation is seen, for instance, in the Sukhumi form of *Spilosoma menthastri*, which with a 15-hour day produces only diapausing pupae, and with a 16-hour day only developing pupae. Consequently individual deviations from the average critical photoperiod do not exceed ±30 minutes. Variation of the same order is characteristic of *Dendrolimus pini*, the northern Caucasus form of *Chloridea obsoleta*, and several others. It would be unreasonable to expect a more uniform reaction, as the actual day-length in nature, because of cloudiness and shade, fluctuates at least as much in their habitats. In the majority of species—e.g. in *Pieris brassicae* and southern forms of *Acronycta rumicis*—extreme deviations from the average critical photoperiod are usually larger and reach ±1 hour, although the main body of individuals—60% to 80%—gives deviations which do not exceed 30 minutes. An example of very large individual variation in the critical photoperiod is provided by some blood-sucking mosquitoes. For instance, in *Anopheles maculipennis messeae* the number of diapausing females falls gradually as the day lengthens, with a photoperiod range from 15 to 20 hours (VINOGRADOVA, 1958, 1960), and individual deviations may thus reach ±2 hours.

The biological significance of different variations in the critical photoperiod is not very clear, but they doubtless are norms for given populations. According to phenological observations, in a species with little variation in the critical region diapause usually begins in all individuals at the same time in natural conditions, whereas with great variation there is a gradual increase in the number of diapausing individuals towards autumn. The latter fact has long been known for the malaria mosquito.

It is important to note that in the progeny of different females taken in the same locality the average value of critical photoperiod does not fluctuate widely. Thus for *Pieris brassicae* and *Acronycta rumicis* the threshold did not fluctuate more than an hour. The average critical threshold must therefore be considered to be a fairly stable characteristic of a population. In series of investigated geographical forms it may be seen that extreme individual deviations in the critical photoperiod overlap in forms from neighbouring territories, and such forms may provide only an average value for the threshold. In forms from localities in widely-differing latitudes a wide gap appears between even the extreme individual deviations.

The question of the degree of inheritance of photoperiodic reaction in geographical races is of independent importance. The constancy of its features has been traced through a number of successive generations of three geographical populations of *Acronycta rumicis.* Each of the traced lines was derived from a single female, taken from nature and kept in uniform conditions. To obtain offspring of the summer generations, adults were taken from long-day series (20 to 24 hours of light), and a hibernating stock was obtained from those reared in 12-hour days. In the southern forms, in which all individuals react similarly to such

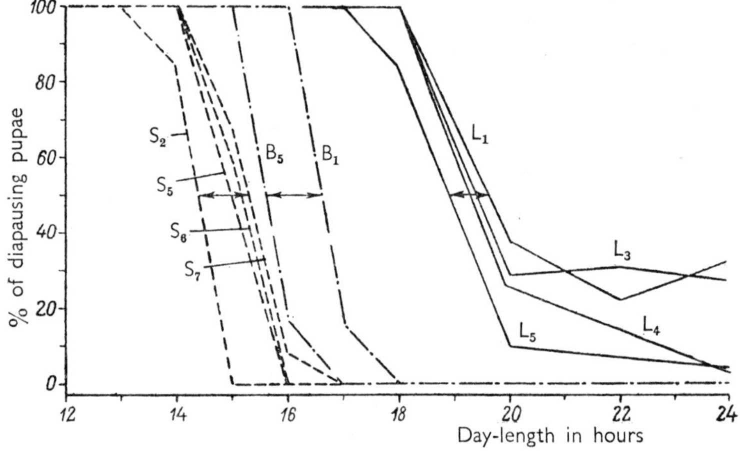

FIG. 43. The threshold of the photoperiodic reaction of geographical populations of *Acronycta rumicis* reared through several generations in constant temperature (23°-25°)

Populations: S, Sukhumi; B, Belgorod; L, Leningrad. Figures denote the numbers of the successive generations.

conditions—developing in long days and diapausing in short days—this method eliminated any special selection of material. But for the Leningrad race, which has partial diapause even in long days, it was necessary to use only the offspring of non-diapausing individuals for the second and later summer generations. The photoperiodic reaction of the Sukhumi form was recorded for the second, fifth, sixth, and seventh laboratory generations; of the Belgorod form, for the first and fifth; and of the Leningrad form, for the first, third, fourth, and fifth. The results of all the experiments are shown in Fig. 43.

In a series of successive generations of the Sukhumi form a tendency for the threshold to rise gradually can be observed. In contrast, the threshold of the Belgorod form was somewhat lower in the fifth generation. In the Leningrad form the threshold remained almost constant, but the percentage of diapausing individuals fell remarkably with 24-hour illumination—from 42% in the first to 3%-5% in later generations. It is possible that this was a result of using the progeny of non-diapausing individuals to obtain summer generations. In spite of the observed variations, the specific features of each of the geographical forms studied remained fairly constant. In all the forms the amplitude of fluctuations in the critical day-length that induced diapause in 50% of the pupae did not exceed 1 hour, i.e. it lay within the limits of normal variation in natural populations.

For other species only the first two generations were studied. Such data were obtained for the Sukhumi form of *Spilosoma menthastri*, the Sukhumi and Leningrad forms of *Pieris brassicae* and *Barathra brassicae*, the Voronezh form of *Dendrolimus pini*, and a number of others. In no case were any notable variations in photoperiodic reaction observed.

MASAKI (1956a), who studied the reaction of several geographical races of *Barathra brassicae* from different climatic regions of Japan in two or three laboratory generations, also came to the conclusion that the characteristics of each of them were retained in full. Therefore one may consider that high hereditary stability of the photoperiodic adaptations of local races is typical in Lepidoptera.

The data of LEES (1953a) point to great stability in photoperiodic reaction in races of the mite *Metatetranychus ulmi* in the south of England. Mites that had developed without diapause at a temperature of 25° and with a 16-hour day laid diapausing eggs when exposed to a short day (8 to 12 hours), just like individuals of an overwintering generation.

Different results were obtained by GEISPITS (1960) in investigations of the critical day-length in geographical races of the spider mite *Tetranychus urticae*. In the first generation from naturally-reared females from different geographical areas, clear differences were found in photoperiodic reaction at a temperature of 18°, taking the form of a critical day-length which was lower in southern than in northern races (Table 31). But these features proved to be unstable and dependent on the conditions in which the preceding generations were reared.

TABLE 31

The photoperiodic reaction (percentage of diapausing females) of geographical populations of *Tetranychus urticae*. Temperature 18°
(after Geispits, 1960)

Population	Day-length in hours						
	24	18	17	16	15	14	13
Leningrad (60° N.)	0	0	1·8	23·1	50·0	100	100
Tashkent (41° N.)	0	0	0	0	33·8	59·5	69·3
Alma-Ata (43° N.)	0	0	0	0	18·7	24·1	—
Black Sea (43° N.)	0	0	0	0	0	12·7	38·5

Mites of two geographical races were kept for several months in continuous light and at different temperatures: the Leningrad race at 25°, and the Tashkent at 15°-16°. Periodical checks made in standard conditions (18°) showed regular changes in critical day-length, which decreased in the Leningrad race and increased in the Tashkent race (Figs. 44 and 45). After seven months the critical day-length of the southern form had increased by more than 2 hours and practically coincided with the original threshold of the northern form (16 hours 30 minutes); the threshold of the northern form had decreased to an equal extent, and even more rapidly (Fig. 45). On the whole the critical day-length of the Tashkent mites was higher than that of the Leningrad mites, i.e. the relation was the reverse of that observed in the first experiments with natural populations. It is characteristic that the rate of variation of the reaction decreased as time passed and, as is seen from Fig. 44, after seven months further maintenance of the southern race at low temperature ceased to have any substantial effect on the value of the threshold.

These interesting features in the reaction of mites are still unexplained, both as to their biological significance and as to the mechanism that determines them. They apparently cannot be explained by the selective effect of living conditions. But in any case the facts of the great adaptability of the photoperiodic reaction in *Tetranychus urticae* and its dependence on the conditions in which preceding generations have developed are beyond doubt. In this connection the data of SHULL (1943) are of interest. He observed an unexpected inversion of the photoperiodic reaction

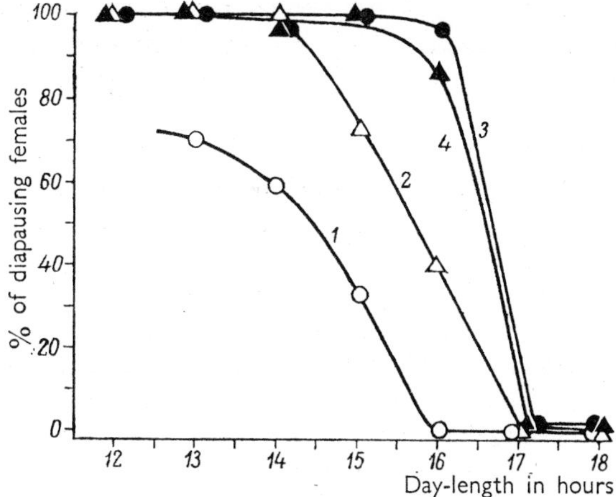

FIG. 44. Changes in the reaction to day-length of the Tashkent race of the mite *Tetranychus urticae* at a temperature of 18° as a result of previous keeping at low temperature.

1, the reaction of a natural population; 2, the reaction after 5 months at a temperature of 15°; 3, ditto after 7 months; 4, ditto after 8 months.

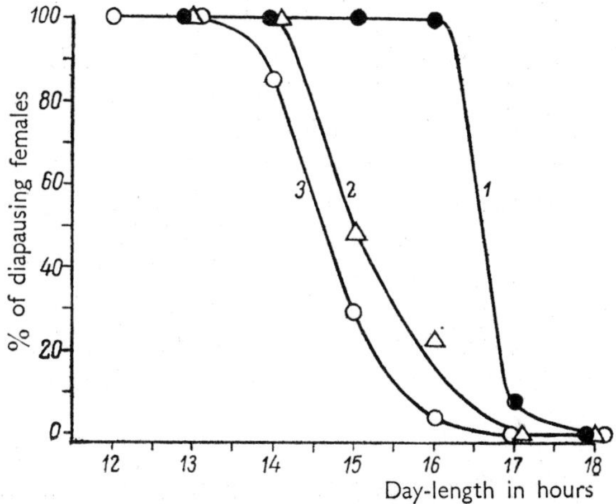

FIG. 45. Changes in the reaction to day-length of the Leningrad race of the mite *Tetranychus urticae* at a temperature of 18° as a result of previous keeping at high temperature.

1, the reaction of a natural population; 2, the reaction after 1 month at a temperature of 25°; 3, ditto after 5 months.

from long-day to short-day in the course of laboratory breeding of types of *Macrosiphum solanifolii* over a period of several years. Clones with different cycles were also found by him in natural populations.

The genotypic nature of several of the individual deviations from the normal type of seasonal development is evident from the high effectiveness of artificial selection for diapause. Although all such work has been done without regard to photoperiodic conditions, some of it is quite convincing. For instance, LE BERRE (1953) succeeded within a short period (six generations) in separating two clearly distinct lines from a natural population of the migratory locust *Locusta migratoria gallica*: one was strictly monocyclic, producing only diapausing eggs in any temperature conditions, and the other was non-diapausing and polycyclic.

ARBUTHNOT (1944) selected from a natural population of Corn Borers, which in the state of Ohio produced a partial second generation, a line which was strictly monocyclic in the conditions of his experiment; but he could not isolate a stable bivoltine form. PREBBLE (1941) readily selected from a bivoltine population of the sawfly *Gilpinia polytoma* from New Brunswick, Canada, non-diapausing lines, one of which developed continuously through 22 generations; but he was unable to obtain a polycyclic form by selection from a more northerly population from the Gaspé Peninsula, which in nature produced only occasional non-diapausing individuals.

Nowadays, when the importance of the light conditions in regulating diapause has been demonstrated, we may be certain that such changes in the seasonal cycle of development as the result of artificial selection were due to the selection of individuals that diverged from the norm in their photoperiodic reaction, although the authors themselves did not take this into account. The reasons for the observed cases of ineffective selection have become clear.

The very interesting results obtained by S. S. Chetverikov with the Chinese Oak Silkworm *Antheraea pernyi* show how unexpected changes in photoperiodic reaction may take place as a result of selection. He set himself the task of obtaining a race that would be univoltine in northern zone conditions, i.e. that would produce diapausing pupae in the first generation. In the first year of selection he obtained a considerable increase in the number of univoltine individuals (CHETVERIKOV, 1940), and later produced an almost completely monocyclic form. Analysis of one of such lines (DANILEVSKII and GEISPITS, 1948) revealed that diapause was not induced in it by an internally-operating factor but was regulated by the light conditions. In contrast, however, to the common races of Oak Silkworms, the 'univoltine' type had a short-day, not a long-day reaction (see Table 4). In this case, therefore, as a result of selection of diapausing pupae, a complete inversion of photoperiodic reaction was obtained in the conditions of the long northern day.

There is no doubt that knowledge of the photoperiodic laws of development can greatly facilitate and accelerate selection. The practical importance of selection of insects for seasonal cycle and diapause characteristics is not restricted to-day to the field of silkworm-breeding. The development of a biological method of controlling harmful creatures by the use of predatory insects has already faced us with the task of breeding highly-effective forms that will be suitable for acclimatization in different zones. In this field we may look for results of interest and practical importance.

2. Inheritance of photoperiodic reaction in hybridization

It is convenient to discuss the changes in photoperiodic reaction that occur in intraspecific hybridization for the following investigated species separately:

1. *Acronycta rumicis.* Photoperiodic reaction was studied in hybrids obtained by reciprocal crossings of the Sukhumi and Leningrad races of this species. In each experiment more than 100 larvae obtained from various broods were used. Both the original forms were reared as controls, simultaneously with the hybrids. Larvae of the first hybrid generation (F_1) were raised in photothermostats at a temperature of 23° and with electric lighting by 40-watt filament lamps; in experiments with the second generation of hybrids (F_2) the temperature was slightly higher (24·5°) and the light sources were 15-watt fluorescent lamps. All crosses between local races were made without difficulty, and the eggs developed normally.

Heterosis was observed in the first-generation hybrids. The

average duration of development of larvae of both the original forms was 20-21 days in the photoperiods which induced diapause, or about 19 days in long-day conditions. The developmental period of both hybrids averaged 2 to 2·5 days less than that of the parent forms, and was 18 days in short photoperiods and about 16 days in continuous lighting. The positive effect of hybridization also appeared in the intensity of growth of the larvae. Table 32 shows the average weight of diapausing pupae from the short-day series of hybrids as compared with the parent stocks.

TABLE 32

The average weight of diapausing pupae of first-generation hybrids between races of *Acronycta rumicis*

Form	Males		Females	
	No. of pupae	Weight (mg)	No. of pupae	Weight (mg)
Leningrad	69	239 (231-253)	68	274 (263-296)
Sukhumi	46	276 (263-288)	61	310 (301-329)
♀ Sukhumi × ♂ Leningrad	116	300 (292-305)	136	320 (306-331)
♀ Leningrad × ♂ Sukhumi	113	260 (253-267)	97	297 (280-313)

A constant characteristic of the Sukhumi form is its great size and weight as compared with the Leningrad form. Hybrids of the Sukhumi female × Leningrad male cross surpassed the Sukhumi pupae in weight. Those of the reciprocal cross (Leningrad female × Sukhumi male) were smaller, but still were nearer in weight to the Sukhumi than to the Leningrad form. The relatively larger number of pupae obtained from the hybrid series suggests that viability is higher in the hybrids than in the parent forms.

Data comparing the photoperiodic reactions of the hybrids and the parent forms are presented in Fig. 46. Each point represents about 70 pupae (minimum 53, maximum 83). The critical thresholds of the Leningrad and Sukhumi races differed by 4 hours—19 and 15 hours respectively. The photoperiodic reaction of the hybrids was intermediate. From the total percentage of diapausing pupae we may note that the Leningrad female × Sukhumi male (Fig. 46, curve L × S) have somewhat higher thresholds than the reciprocal cross (S × L). The differences between the hybrids are much more pronounced when one takes the photoperiodic reactions of males and females separately. The reactions of females in both crosses were quite similar, and

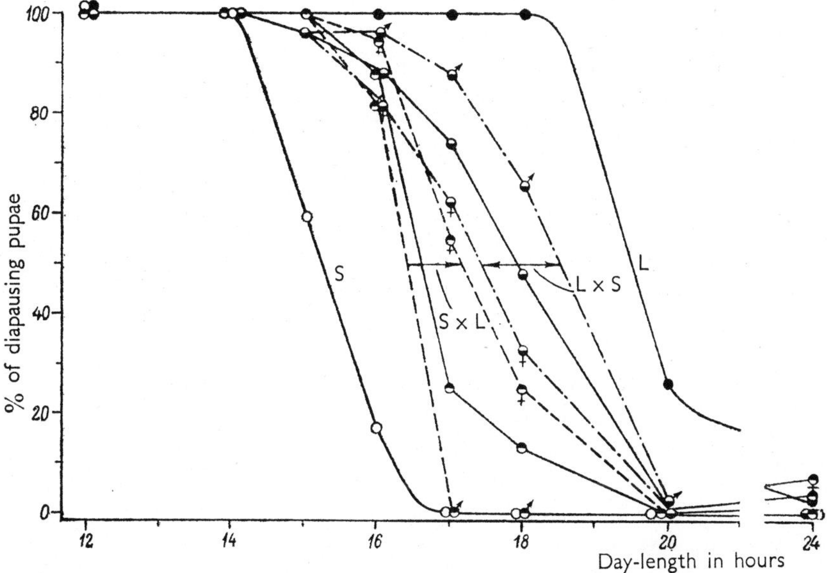

FIG. 46. The photoperiodic reaction of first-generation hybrids (F_1) between Leningrad and Sukhumi populations of *Acronycta rumicis*.

Populations (control): L, Leningrad, S, Sukhumi; (hybrids) L × S and S × L, the first letter denoting the maternal form.

their critical day-length was 17 hours, i.e. it was exactly intermediate between those of the parent forms. The reaction of hybrid males clearly inclines towards the maternal characteristics, as a result of which the difference between their thresholds reaches almost 2 hours. In the parent forms no constant differences between the sexes were observed.

It is of interest that the observed features of photoperiodic reaction in hybrids occur in a definite correlation with the diapausing stages' requirements of temperature conditions for reactivation. Hibernating diapausing pupae from the above experiments, after surviving to the end of December at a temperature of 5°-6°, were transferred to a temperature of 18°-20°, after which adults began to emerge. It was then seen that the Sukhumi pupae, having a less stable diapause, were completely reactivated by that time, whereas the majority of the Leningrad pupae remained in diapause. Males of the Sukhumi female × Leningrad male cross behaved like the Sukhumi race; those of the reciprocal Leningrad female × Sukhumi male cross were nearer the Leningrad race in their requirements. Therefore, in spite of the general intermediate nature of the physiological features of the hybrids, in *Acronycta rumicis* the first generation still shows some effects of its maternal inheritance.

Comparing the curves in Fig. 46, we may note increased individual variation in photoperiodic reaction in the hybrids as compared with the pure parent forms. Great variation was also seen in the colour of hybrid adults. Occasional melanistic, almost black, individuals, not found in the parent lines, appeared among them.

Data on the reaction of second-generation hybrids (F_2) and on the back-cross between first-generation hybrids (F_1) and the parent forms are important in the study of inheritance of photoperiodic reaction. As the conditions of these experiments with *Acronycta rumicis* differed somewhat from those of experiments with the first generation, parallel control experiments were carried out not only on pure populations of the Leningrad and Sukhumi forms but also partly on first-generation hybrids.

First-generation hybrid adults possessed entirely normal fertility, and all crosses took place without difficulty; but no effect of heterosis appeared in the second hybrid generation, in contrast to the first. Moreover, the hybrid larvae lagged behind the Leningrad and Sukhumi controls in development and, in spite of the higher temperature of the experiment, developed more slowly than the first generation. The weights of the pupae were not recorded. It must be noted that the higher temperature caused some change in the reaction of the controls as compared with preceding generations. In particular, non-diapause development of some individuals was observed in 12-hour-day conditions among the pure Sukhumi population and also in the control groups of first-generation hybrids.

The results of the experiments are shown in Fig. 47. No

substantial differences between the sexes were observed in the reactions of the second generation. Therefore in the diagram all curves show the total percentage of diapausing pupae without regard to sex. Comparing Figs. 46 and 47 we may see that a photoperiodic reaction intermediate between those of the parent forms is shown much more clearly in the second hybrid genera-

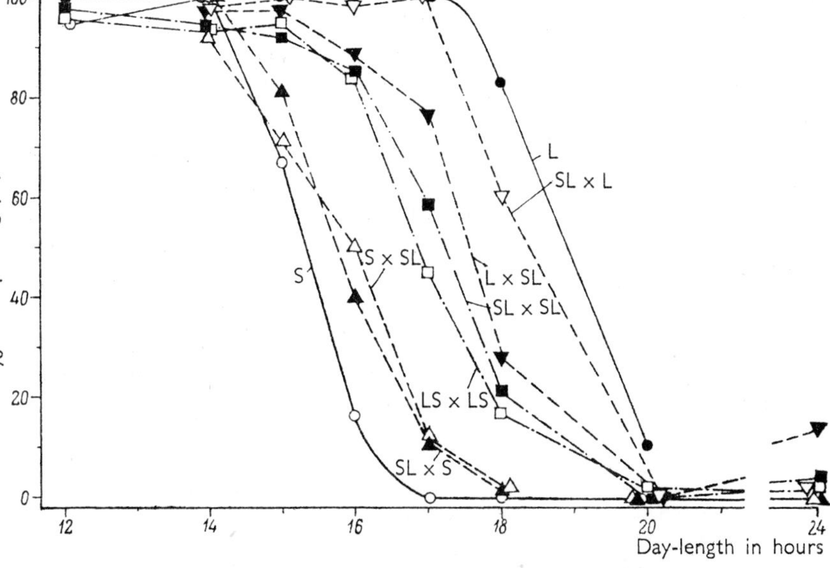

FIG. 47. The photoperiodic reaction of hybrids between Sukhumi and Leningrad populations of *Acronycta rumicis*.

Populations (controls): L, Leningrad; S, Sukhumi. *Hybrids*: □, ■, F_2; △, ▲, the progeny of back-crosses of F_1 with parent forms, the first letter denoting the maternal form.

tion. Both the hybrids investigated showed an identical reaction in the second hybrid generation; the critical day-length for them (17 hours) corresponded exactly with the average for the control Sukhumi (15 hours) and Leningrad (19 hours) populations.

From these data an important deduction follows: in the second hybrid generation of *Acronycta rumicis* no noticeable filial segregation is observed in the characteristics of the photoperiodic reaction, and the amplitude of variation in that reaction is approximately the same as in the first generation. The appearance of a small number of active individuals in the short-day groups

(11-12 hours) cannot serve as an indication of higher variability in the second hybrid generation, as cases of non-diapause development were also observed among the controls, and consequently were due basically to the action of environmental factors.

Experiments with offspring of the back-cross between first-generation hybrids and the parent forms were carried out simultaneously with, and in the same conditions as, the experiments with the second hybrid generation. Complete photoperiodic characteristics of the back-cross of S × L hybrids (Sukhumi female × Leningrad male) are shown in Fig. 47. For the reciprocal cross only the reaction at the critical day-length of 17 hours has been recorded (Table 33). From Fig. 47 it is seen that, with a back-cross between hybrids and parents, there arises a photoperiodic reaction transitional between those found in the first hybrid generation and in the original form with which it was crossed. The sex-combinations in such crosses are apparently not significant: in the crosses with the Sukhumi form there is no difference in the reaction, and too much weight should not be given to the small differences (less than one hour) obtained in the crosses between the hybrids and the Leningrad form.

TABLE 33

The appearance of diapause in *Acronycta rumicis* in the offspring of back-crosses between ♀ Leningrad form × ♂ Sukhumi form (L × S) hybrids and the parent forms, developing at threshold day-length (17 hours of light)

No. of experiment	Hybrids	Males		Females		Total	
		No. of pupae	% diapausing	No. of pupae	% diapausing	No. of pupae	% diapausing
1	♀ LS × ♂ LS	35	37·2	25	56·0	60	45·0
2	♀ L × ♂ LS	15	100	6	100	21	100
3	♀ LS × ♂ L	55	98·2	46	100	101	99·0
4	♀ S × ♂ LS	38	18·4	21	57·1	59	32·2
5	♀ LS × ♂ S	50	0	56	3·5	106	1·9

Note. The first letter in the conventional designation of a hybrid designates the maternal form.

As with other hybrids, individual variation in the reaction is large in the offspring of the back-crosses; for instance, in the group L female × SL male the characteristics of both the original forms persist in a peculiar way: in short-day conditions some individuals developed without diapause, i.e. like the Sukhumi form, but with continuous light about 15% of the pupae entered diapause, which is characteristic of the Leningrad race.

Data for the reciprocal cross L female × S male, as may be seen from Table 33, support the above conclusions. At the threshold day-length the second generation of these hybrids (experiment 1) produced 45% of diapausing pupae. With a back-cross of the first generation with the Leningrad form (experiments 2 and 3) the number of diapausing pupae rose sharply, approaching 100%, whereas with a back-cross with the Sukhumi form (experiments 4 and 5) it fell heavily.

From the entire series of experiments with intraspecific hybrids of *Acronycta rumicis* the following deductions may be drawn. With any cross, either of natural populations or of hybrids with them, the photoperiodic reaction of the offspring is intermediate between those of the parents. Some effect due to sex on the appearance of diapause, observed in the first generation, does not substantially affect this statement. It remains absolutely true for the reaction of offspring from a back-cross of first-generation hybrids with the original forms. In this way we may obtain by hybridization any number of types of photoperiodic reaction transitional between given forms.

Individual variations in photoperiodic reaction show no noticeable increase in the second hybrid generation as compared with the first. Consequently no noticeable genotypic splitting can be discovered in the second hybrid generation.

2. *Spilosoma menthastri.* The photoperiodic reaction of hybrids between the Sukhumi and Leningrad races of this species was investigated simultaneously with the reaction of the parent forms at a temperature of 23°. As with *Acronycta rumicis*, the crossing of the adults and the development of the larvae proceeded normally. The photoperiodic reaction of the hybrids is shown in Fig. 48. It is interesting to note that dominance of the characteristics of either of the original forms is absent in the data obtained. The reaction of the hybrids is strictly intermediate between those of the parents, as is shown not only in the location of the critical threshold but also in the nature of the response to continuous light. In such conditions no fewer than 50% of the pupae of the Leningrad race entered diapause, whereas diapause was entirely

absent in the Sukhumi race; in L female × S male hybrids a small percentage of the pupae entered diapause.

Other features that must be stressed are the practically complete identity of reaction in the offspring of reciprocal crosses, and the absence of differences in the reactions of the two sexes. Thus the relation is simpler in this case than in *Acronycta rumicis*. The hybrid adults obtained by crossing both among themselves

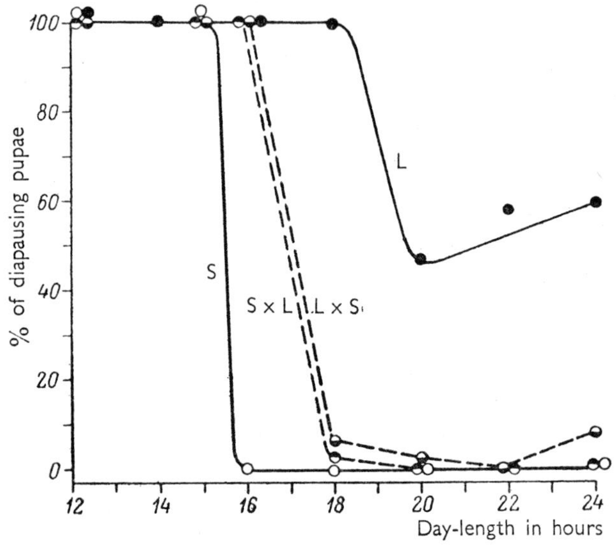

FIG. 48. The photoperiodic reaction of geographic populations of *Spilosoma menthastri* and their hybrids.

Populations: L, Leningrad; S, Sukhumi; L × S and S × L, F_1 hybrids, the first letter denoting the maternal form.

and with the parent forms produced offspring which developed normally, but the photoperiodic reaction of the second generation was not investigated.

3. *Pieris brassicae*. The critical day-length in first-generation hybrids between the Leningrad and Sukhumi races of the Cabbage White Butterfly was investigated by V. A. Maslennikova. Both the original forms and the hybrids were reared at a temperature of 18°. From 24 to 77 pupae were obtained in each light condition. It is seen from Table 34 that in this case also the hybrids are characterized by a critical day-length intermediate between those of the parent forms.

TABLE 34

The photoperiodic reaction (percentage of diapausing pupae) of geographical populations of *Pieris brassicae* and their hybrids. Temperature 18°

Form	Day-length in hours					
	9	12	14	15	16	18
Leningrad	100	100	100	70	8	0
Sukhumi	100	32	0	0	0	0
♀ Leningrad ×♂ Sukhumi hybrid	100	95	2	0	0	0
♀ Sukhumi ×♂ Leningrad hybrid	100	92	56	0	0	0

4. *Pyrausta nubilalis.* Du Chzhen'-ven' investigated the photoperiodic reaction in first-generation hybrids between the Dnepropetrovsk (maize) and Gomel'sk (hemp) populations of this species. As already stated, the differences in the photoperiodic reaction of these two forms are considerable. The critical threshold for the southern form is about 15 hours, whereas for the northern form it is 2 hours higher at 17 hours. For Gomel'sk female × Dnepropetrovsk male hybrids a normal photoperiodic curve was obtained with a threshold of 16 hours. Thus the results in this case are the same as for the preceding species.

For this reason the error in the findings of ARBUTHNOT (1944) on the genetic structure of different populations of *Pyrausta nubilalis* in the U.S.A. and on the nature of the inheritance of life-cycle features in their hybrids becomes evident. His results, no doubt, were due to the existence of different thresholds of photoperiodic reaction in the forms investigated, which he did not take into account. There are indications of difficulty in crossing different geographical races of *Pyrausta nubilalis.* This was noted by ARBUTHNOT (1944) with regard to the monocyclic and polycyclic forms of this species in North America, and also by KARPOVA (1959) with regard to its southern and northern forms in the European parts of the USSR. Apparently the difficulty in hybridization is due to the mating behaviour of the adults and not to genetic incompatibility. In the experiments of Du Chzhen'-ven', crossing of the Sukhumi and northern forms took place normally, and no lowering of fertility in the females or laying of infertile eggs was observed. In any case, this points to the absence of any physiological divergence between the southern and northern races.

5. *Leucoma salicis*. There are two main races of this species:

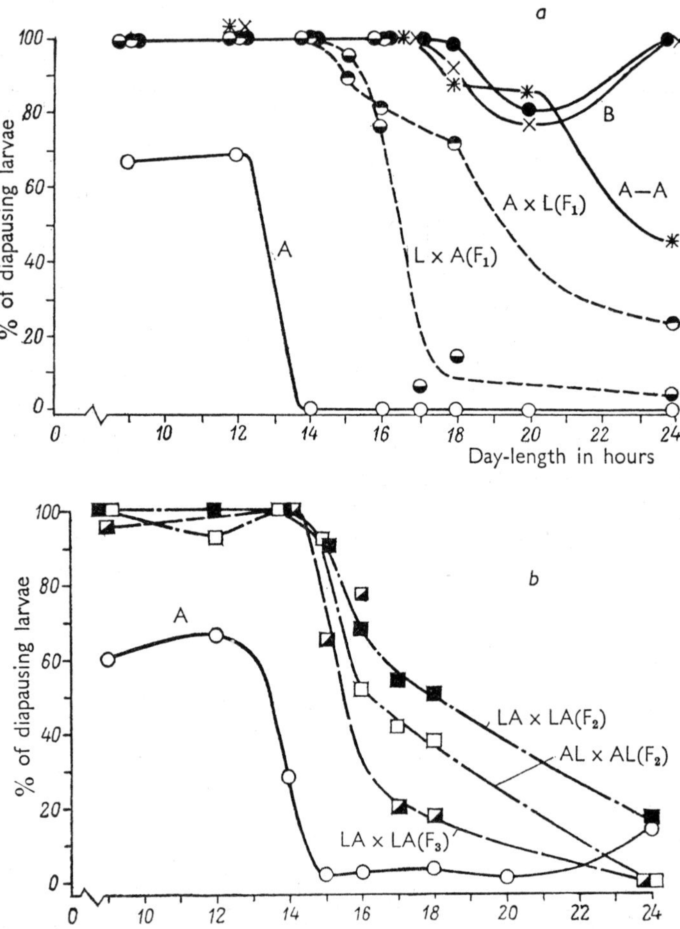

FIG. 49. The photoperiodic reaction of geographic populations of *Leucoma salicis* and their hybrids. Temperature 25°.

a, F_1 hybrids; *b*, F_2 and F_3 hybrids.
Populations: L, Leningrad; B, Belgorod; A-A, Alma-Ata; A, Armenian. In hybrids the first letter denotes the maternal form.

the northern (monocyclic) and the southern (polycyclic), to a considerable degree isolated geographically and differing sharply in type of development and reaction to light conditions. Genetically, however, these races are not segregated, as they interbreed readily and their hybrid offspring develop normally.

The photoperiodic reaction of first-generation hybrids at a temperature of 25° is shown in Fig. 49, *a*. The curves for the hybrids occupy a position intermediate between those for the original forms. In type they are very close to the curves for northern populations of long-day polycyclic species, and are characterized by a high threshold and a certain proportion of individuals diapausing in long-day conditions. In the first hybrid generation there is some differentiation in photoperiodic reaction between the different combinations. In the offspring of a cross between an Armenian female and a Leningrad male the critical threshold of photoperiodic reaction is higher and the characteristics of monocyclism are expressed more strongly than in the reciprocal cross. Consequently, in contrast to the case of first-generation hybrids of *Acronycta rumicis*, we may here speak of a certain dominance in the characteristics of the male.

In the second hybrid generation the difference between reciprocal crosses levels out, and the intermediate character of the reaction with respect to those of the original forms is more clearly shown (Fig. 49, *b*).

The same type of reaction is maintained in hybrids of the third generation.

6. *Apanteles glomeratus*. The Sukhumi and Leningrad races of this ichneumon fly differ in their photoperiodic reaction even more than the populations of their host *Pieris brassicae*. All experiments were carried out at a temperature of 18°; the Leningrad race of *Pieris brassicae* served as host. Hybrids of the first and second generations gave very similar reactions to day-length, intermediate between the reactions of the parent forms (Table 35).

7. *Culex pipiens*. E. B. Vinogradova investigated the gonotrophic cycle and the photoperiodic reaction of hybrids between two subspecies of the common mosquito, *Culex pipiens pipiens* and *Culex pipiens molestus* Forsk. These subspecies not only are clearly differentiated physiologically but possess fairly constant morphological distinctions, mainly in the structure of the larvae and in the form of the ovipositor.

TABLE 35

The photoperiodic reaction (percentage of diapausing individuals) of geographical populations of *Apanteles glomeratus* and their hybrids. Temperature 18°

Form	Day-length in hours					
	9	12	14	15	16	18
Leningrad	—	100	—	0	4	0
Sukhumi	0	0	0	0	—	—
F_1 hybrid: ♀ Leningrad × ♂ Sukhumi	—	60	0	8	0	0
F_2 hybrid: do. do.	53	—	0	—	—	—

The typical form of *C. p. pipiens* has well-marked imaginal diapause, induced by short days (DANILEVSKII and GLINYANAYA, 1958; VINOGRADOVA, 1958). Diapausing females suck blood very reluctantly and therefore do not mature. In active individuals maturation of oocytes occurs only after sucking blood. *C. p. molestus* differs from the above subspecies in that it does not undergo diapause and develops continuously with any day-length, i.e. it has no photoperiodic reaction. It is characteristic of this subspecies that the first batch of its eggs can mature spontaneously, i.e. without ingestion of blood. The range of *C. p. pipiens* extends over the temperate zone of the Palaearctic wherever there is a definite winter season. The original range of *C. p. molestus* is believed to have been the southern Mediterranean, where this form occurs in natural biotopes. At the present time *C. p. molestus* is widely distributed and has penetrated far northwards into the range of *C. p. pipiens*, but it occurs there only in towns, developing in winter in warm buildings.

Physiological divergence between the subspecies has gone so far that partial infertility is observed when they are crossed. In Vinogradova's experiments the only viable hybrids were those obtained by crossing a female *C. p. molestus* with a male *C. p. pipiens*. With the reciprocal cross infertile eggs were laid.

First-generation hybrids displayed mingling of the characteristics of both subspecies, both in reaction to day-length and in other features of the gonotrophic cycle. A marked lowering of blood-sucking activity in hybrid females developing in short days

(12-14 hours), as compared with those developing in long days (20 hours), indicates a rudimentary photoperiodic reaction and brings the hybrids close to *C. p. pipiens*. But all the females that sucked blood, including the short-day ones, matured, i.e. they did not undergo diapause, like *C. p. molestus*. The hybrid females proved to be incapable of spontaneous maturation and in this respect resembled *C. p. pipiens*.

In the second hybrid generation the picture was much changed. Females capable of maturing without sucking blood appeared. On the basis of analysis of gonads of 134 females, the proportion maturing spontaneously was 25·3%. At the same time the reaction to day-length was more clearly displayed. All females that developed in long-day conditions (20 hours) matured on sucking blood. With a shorter day individuals occurred that did not mature after sucking blood, i.e. they underwent diapause. With a 16-hour day the latter amounted to 8% of the total, and with a 12-hour day 28·2%.

These observations show that the inheritance of physiological features of different subspecies of the common mosquito, when hybridized, is more complex than in the preceding cases, and the second hybrid generation, because of filial segregation, differs considerably from the first.

8. Intraspecific hybrids of *Dendrolimus*. In conclusion, we quote the results of V. I. Kuznetsov's experiments on intraspecific hybrids between the Pine Moth *Dendrolimus pini* and the Siberian species *Dendrolimus sibiricus*, compared with the parallel data of K. F. Geispits for these species.

There is no doubt that *Dendrolimus pini* and *Dendrolimus sibiricus* are independent species. The differences in structure of the genital apparatus, and also in the colours of the adults and of the larvae, although not great, are absolutely constant. The ranges of these species are for the most part separate. *D. pini* occupies the whole of Europe, and beyond the Urals is found only in the south of western Siberia. The main range of *D. sibiricus* lies in north-eastern Asia, extending to the Urals. Thus these species come into contact only in a very narrow zone.

The independence of the species is also demonstrated by their genetic separation. Crossing was possible only between a female *D. pini* and a male *D. sibiricus*. In this case mating took place readily and the eggs developed normally. With the reciprocal cross of a female *sibiricus* and a male *pini* mating was rarely observed, and the eggs laid did not develop. In first-generation hybrids the characteristics of *pini* (i.e. of the mother) clearly predominated in the colours of the larvae and of the adults and in the genital structure, but isolated specimens were found with *sibiricus*-type colouring; in genital structure these individuals also leaned towards *sibiricus*.

TABLE 36

The photoperiodic reaction (percentage of diapausing larvae) of *Dendrolimus pini*, *D. sibiricus*, and their hybrids. Temperature 20°
(from data of V. I. Kuznetsov and K. F. Geispits)

Form	Darkness	Day-length in hours							
		12	14	15	16	17	18	20	24
Dendrolimus pini	—	100	100	100	100	0	0	0	0
Dendrolimus sibiricus	10	100	100	100	100	0	0	0	0
F_1 hybrid: ♀ *pini* × ♂ *sibiricus*	56·5	100	100	100	100	0	0	0	0

The photoperiodic reactions in the two species were very similar. First-generation hybrids, as is seen from Table 36, had the same type of reaction as the parent forms. The critical photoperiod is well marked in them, and at a temperature of 20° lies between 16 and 17 hours. With a shorter day all larvae entered diapause at the normal period (30 to 35 days); with long days development proceeded without interruption. A great similarity between *D. sibiricus* and *D. pini* appeared also in the temperature reactions regulating diapause (the age-shift of diapause in accordance with temperature, the duration of diapause, and the effect of temperature on the dates when the larvae entered hibernation).

All of these reactions appeared also in the hybrids and, as a rule, were intermediate in nature or approached those of the maternal form. Thus in the first hybrid generation no breakdown of the seasonal-cyclic reactions was observed, and the latter remained fully adaptational. Unfortunately the experiments did not succeed in determining the degree of fertility and the possibility of obtaining a second hybrid generation.

3. The adaptive significance of characteristics of inheritance of photoperiodic reaction

The following deductions may be drawn from the experiments described above. In the first place, first-generation hybrids between local populations always have a photoperiodic reaction intermediate between those of the parent forms, and dominance is either absent or very weakly expressed. In the second place, the intermediate nature of the reaction is maintained even in the second generation, with individual variation being approximately the same as in the first generation, and consequently filial segregation does not appear to any considerable extent. This rule remains valid even with respect to back-crosses of first-generation hybrids with the parent forms.

The discovery of the genetic mechanism of these phenomena does not enter into our present task. In a general way the observed facts can be interpreted by multiple definition of the characteristics of photoperiodic reaction and diapause (CHETVERIKOV, 1940; TANAKA, 1953). Within the scope of this work it is of more interest to regard the results obtained from the point of view of their ecological significance.

We must first stress that the reaction of hybrids always preserves the normal adaptive type. The general character of graphs relating to hybrids remains the same as that of the parents, differing only in the critical thresholds. There is a widespread view that hybrids between two ecologically-divergent forms must be less well adapted than either of them, and therefore will be more forcefully eliminated by natural selection. This view, founded more on logic than on concrete facts, is far from being universally true, particularly with regard to adaptational divergences occurring as a result of geographical variations in climatic conditions. The results of our experiments even lead to the opposite conclusion. Hybrids appearing in a zone where two different populations meet, because of the intermediate nature of their reaction to day-length, should be better adapted to the local conditions than their parents.

Confirmation of the above statement is found in the data obtained from experiments with *Acronycta rumicis*. Hybrids between the Sukhumi and Leningrad populations of this species are very close to the natural Belgorod population in their reaction to day-length. Their critical threshold (17 hours) corresponds to conditions in the forest-steppe zone between 50° and 55°N.

As is seen from Fig. 47, by crossing two extreme geographical forms we may obtain any number of transitional hybrid forms, constant in their photoperiodic reaction. These forms are analogous to the series of natural populations from localities differing in geographical latitude (see Fig. 30). The difference between them consists only in somewhat less abrupt thresholds in the hybrid forms, due to increased individual variability in their reaction. In a natural environment a norm completely adapted to local conditions must be established quickly, as non-adaptational individual deviations are inevitably eliminated in the first generations.

It does not follow from the above, of course, that all differences in geographical populations within the range of a species have arisen as a result of hybridization between two extreme forms. In most cases differentiation took place during the progressive extension of the species' range of distribution. But hybridization maintains the biological and geographical integrity of a species, without disturbing the high adaptability of local populations to local conditions. The gradual variation in photoperiodic reaction with change in latitude, observed in many insects, may be looked upon as a result of continuous hybridization controlled by natural selection.

Less clear are the causes and conditions leading to gradual variation in photoperiodic reaction within the range, i.e. to formation of geographical races occupying large areas with clearly-defined transitional zones, as in *Pieris brassicae*, *Leucoma salicis*, and *Pyrausta nubilalis*. Such a type of variation points to different relations between selection and hereditary interchange in different regions within the range, and in general to a relative or absolute weakening of selection within the confines of a single race.

Concrete reasons for variations in this balance may be quite different in different species. There are not enough data available to draw final conclusions. Still the suggestion obtrudes itself that in the case of *Pieris brassicae* the uniformity of the populations inhabiting the European plain is due to the exceptionally high migrational capacity of the adults. PETERSEN (1947, 1949) also attributes to intensive migration the absence of geographical variation in morphological features in this species in contrast to the non-migratory *Pieris napi*, which has a large number of local morphological races. Probably there are other causes that weaken selection for photoperiodic reaction in *Pieris brassicae*. In particular, the duration of imaginal life and the observed delay in the maturation of adults in unfavourable conditions, which strongly affect the course of seasonal development at least in the northern zone, may have significant effects.

For *Leucoma salicis*—a species of very little mobility—the uniformity of photoperiodic reaction within most of the range is due to other causes. Analysis of the seasonal cycles shows that wherever this species develops in one generation the light conditions play no substantial part in initiating diapause. It is therefore natural that the differentiating action of selection does not affect the photoperiodic reaction in *Leucoma salicis*.

We must dwell particularly on the importance of seasonal-cyclic adaptations in the process of further divergence.

The results of crossing even geographically-remote forms, strongly differentiated in seasonal cycles and in photoperiodic reaction (e.g. the Leningrad and Armenian *Leucoma salicis*, and the Leningrad and Sukhumi *Acronycta rumicis*, *Pieris brassicae*, and other forms) have shown that hybrids have normal fertility and viability. Consequently the territorial and ecological separation of intraspecific populations are in most cases not accompanied by reproductive isolation.

Reproductive isolation, however, arising as a result of seasonal cyclic adaptations, may in some cases lead to the accumulation of more profound genotypic differences and to an inability to interbreed, i.e. to the formation of local races on the verge of specific identity.

We have such a picture in the case of the subspecies of the common mosquito *Culex pipiens pipiens* and *Culex pipiens molestus*. The latter, apparently, is a southern Mediterranean subspecies that arose in subtropical climatic conditions. According to the observations of E. B. Vinogradova, the marked differences in seasonal cycles existing between *C. p. molestus* and northern populations of *C. p. pipiens* diminish towards the south, and the morphological differences between them decrease similarly. Thus in Azerbaijan the mosquito populations have proved to be very diverse. Together with populations of *C. p. pipiens*, fairly typical morphologically but differing from the northern races in having a weak photoperiodic reaction, populations occur there intermediate between *C. p. pipiens* and *C. p. molestus* in the siphonal index of the larvae. At a temperature of 24° they do not react to day-length at all, developing without interruption in all conditions; spontaneous maturation, however, has not been observed in them. In addition, typical populations of *C. p. molestus*, with spontaneous maturation and without diapause, occur.

It is very probable that such diversity is due to hybridization between the above subspecies. Such a possibility is also indicated by observations in Italy (ROSSI-ESPAGNET, 1957). In the department of Lazio there are found in natural conditions forms intermediate between *C. p. pipiens* and *C. p. molestus*, which the author believes to be hybrids between these subspecies.

Thus the southern European and Transcaucasian populations of the two subspecies of the common mosquito do not show much genetic individualism, whereas their extreme forms are much more strongly isolated. When acclimatized in towns in the northern zone *C. p. molestus* does not interbreed with the local *C. p. pipiens*, and hybrids obtained in artificial conditions are semi-sterile. In other words, these forms behave like independent species and are regarded as such by some systematists. Here we encounter a phenomenon fully analogous with that observed in so-called 'ring species'.

Of no less interest in our present discussion are data found in the literature regarding the Oak Silkworm *Lasiocampa quercus*. This species, distributed from the extreme north of Europe to the Mediterranean, splits up into a number of geographical forms of stable colouration, differing markedly in their seasonal cycles. The northern form (*calunae*) hibernates as young larvae, but sometimes hibernates again as adults and produces diapausing hibernating pupae. Its cycle therefore lasts not less than two years. The central European typical form (*quercus*) has an annual cycle with hibernation only in the larval stage, and winter diapause is never observed in it. The extreme southern form *sicula*, which differs considerably from the others in colour, has pupae that undergo diapause in summer. According to PICTET (1936, 1937), forms with adjacent ranges and similar seasonal cycles (e.g. *quercus* and *spartii*) interbreed readily and produce normal viable offspring. When territorially-remote forms with different cycles are crossed (e.g. *spartii* with *calunae*, or *spartii* with *sicula*) the hybrids are completely sterile. Similar data have been obtained for forms of this species inhabiting different altitudinal zones of the Alps. The typical form *quercus* occupies the plains up to an altitude of 600-800 m. The high-mountain form *alpina* is found in the zone from 1,200 to 1,800 m. These forms, which have different seasonal cycles, do not produce offspring on interbreeding, but each of them produces fully-fertile hybrids with populations from zones intermediate in altitude.

Similar results were obtained by Pictet for the mountain forms of the arctiid *Parasemia* (*Nemeophila*) *plantaginis*. Gradual genetic divergence, extending to sterility or profound disturbance in development of hybrids between distant geographical forms, has been demonstrated in *Lymantria dispar* in the well-known work of GOLDSCHMIDT (1934).

Therefore inability to produce fertile hybrids, which is generally regarded as a basic criterion of a species (MAYR, 1947), is not an adequate indicator of specific independence. In nature we may trace all steps of geographical divergence from the original, in which genetic affinity is retained, to the most remote, reaching the boundary of specific individuality. Up to the present, however, as long as an unbroken continuity of the population is maintained (through intermediate forms) throughout its range, we must regard it as a single species, even though the extreme forms have diverged so far that they have lost the ability to interbreed with each other. The reasons why some seasonal-cyclic adaptations are accompanied by genetic divergence whereas in others the genetic integrity of the species is retained remain undiscovered. There is no doubt, however, that photoperiodic adaptations may serve as one of the important early steps in the process of divergence.

In conclusion, we should estimate the rate at which differentiation of geographical populations takes place and adaptations to new light conditions arise. There is no direct evidence on this point; but we may consider that such a process takes place very quickly, since the selection of photoperiodic adaptations is very intensive and is always strictly direct. This view is supported by interesting observations on the European Corn Borer *Pyrausta nubilalis*, recently transported from Europe to North America. In 1921 a form of this species was first observed in the state of New York, corresponding to the northern European form in its type of life cycle. It quickly spread through the Great Lakes region of the U.S.A. and Canada, but originally remained strictly monocyclic there, and the number pupating in the first generation did not exceed 1%. Climatically these regions newly occupied by the Corn Borer are similar to the range of the southern European race, and their temperature conditions make development of two complete generations possible. By the end of the 1930's a considerable increase in the number of individuals producing two generations was observed in Ontario, Ohio, and Indiana (VANCE, 1939; NEISWANDER, 1947; WISHART, 1947). According to data from systematic counts of adults flying into light-traps at two points in southwestern Ontario (WRESSEL, 1952), the proportion of second-generation specimens rose from 2% in 1932 to 71%-81% in 1951. The rise was particularly noticeable from 1942 onwards.

In this way the conversion of an originally univoltine race into a bivoltine one took place in a short time in the southern areas of acclimatization. That phenomenon was doubtless due to a change in the seasonal-cyclic reactions and not to external conditions. To judge from the data of VANCE (1939) a change in the duration of diapause is taking place and, linked with that, earlier pupation of hibernating larvae. It is also very probable that the critical threshold of the photoperiodic reaction is changing. At present it is 15 hours in the Ontario race (MUTCHMOR, 1959), which corresponds to the threshold of our southern race (see Fig. 33). To settle this question it would be important to discover the threshold of the American univoltine race in districts where it has not yet been changed into a bivoltine race.

The opposite process—raising the critical threshold with spread to the north—must take place still more rapidly, as selection in that respect is more intensive and all individuals not diapausing will perish during the winter. The answer to this question may be given by comparative study of geographical populations in Europe of such species as the Colorado Beetle and *Hyphantria cunea*, whose origins, times of arrival, and means of distribution are well known.

Chapter VII

THE REGULATION OF SEASONAL DEVELOPMENT OF INSECTS IN NATURE

In the discussion of experimental data the importance of photoperiodic adaptations in insect ecology is constantly emphasized. This subject, however, is so important from a practical point of view that we must examine it with special care, basing our discussion on data from field phenological observations.

The original theory of the photoperiodic regulation of the seasonal development of insects was simple: the autumnal shortening of the day to a definite critical value induced the appearance of hibernating stages. Since seasonal changes in day-length are constant in each locality, it appeared that to analyse the cyclic development in nature it would be sufficient to determine only the critical day-length for each species. Further investigations disclosed, however, that reaction to the light conditions is very changeable and depends both on the hereditary characteristics of a population and on the direct influence of environment, particularly temperature. Consequently it is necessary to take into account the whole complex of external factors when analysing phenology.

For an ecological interpretation of the annual cycle, mere knowledge of the characteristics of the photoperiodic reaction is not sufficient. Of no less importance are other eco-physiological features, particularly the dependence of the periods and rates of development of active stages on the direct influence of temperature, and also the requirements of heat and moisture for reactivation of the diapausing stages. With regard to the latter, however, experimental data are still quite inadequate.

In this chapter an attempt is made to estimate the extent to which the relatively-simple eco-physiological laws established by experiments help to explain the extraordinary diversity in the seasonal cycles of species in nature and their variation with the conditions of a given year and locality.

Special attention is also given to the role of the physiological characteristics of intraspecific geographical populations in the phenomena of distribution and acclimatization of insects.

1. The dependence of phenology on specific characteristics of reactions to temperature and to day-length

The seasonal cycles of species with a long-day type of development

As this type of seasonal-cyclic adaptation is the most widely distributed in temperate latitudes, it must be considered first.

A very simple form of dependence on external conditions is seen in *Acronycta rumicis* in the forest-steppe zone, where this species develops in two clearly-defined generations. Fig. 50 shows the changes in the flight of adults, estimated from daily counts in a light-trap during three years at the Poltava experimental station. The dates of larval development and the onset of diapause are given from my own observations.

The phenology of *Acronycta rumicis* in Poltava is very constant. The flight period of the adults of the spring generation occurs regularly from mid-May to mid-June, reaching a maximum in the last days of May. Adults of the second generation, always more numerous, fly from mid-July to the beginning of September. A well-marked maximum of flight occurs in the last five days of July. First-generation pupae develop without diapause, whereas second-generation pupae all undergo diapause. This seasonal cycle is easily explained on the basis of the experimental data quoted above. The sum-total of effective temperatures above 10° for a single generation amounts to about 550 day-degrees (see Table 27). In Poltava during the active period it amounts to 1150 day-degrees, i.e. it is enough for development of two generations. Thus the calculated number of generations agrees with the actual number.

Experimental data on temperature indices for separate stages enable us to determine the calendar dates of their appearance in nature. Only the time of flight of first-generation adults must be taken empirically, because of the difficulty of calculating the course of springtime temperatures in the layer of vegetable débris in which the pupae hibernate. By calculating the 10-day sum-totals of effective temperatures from the date of maximum flight of adults, we find that mass hatching of larvae (70 day-degrees) should be expected on June 10; larval development,

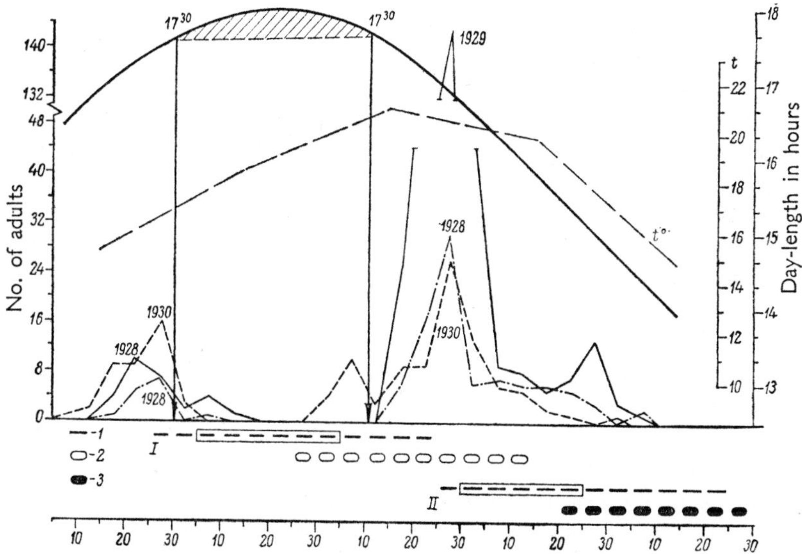

FIG. 50. The phenology of *Acronycta rumicis* in forest-steppe zone conditions.

Shaded area: day-length period inducing non-diapause development. *Curves*: changes in the flight of adults in different years in Poltava, from light-trap counts. I and II, generations. 1, larvae; 2, developing pupae; 3, diapausing pupae.

requiring 245 day-degrees, should last until July 7-8, and mass flight of second-generation adults may be expected from July 25, when the total will amount to the 520 day-degrees required for a full generation. These calculations agree well with the course of development in nature.

The majority of second-generation offspring develop from the first days of August, and according to the sum-total of effective temperatures required for development of eggs and larvae (315 day-degrees) they should pupate in the first ten days of September. Larvae from later adults, which emerged at the end of

August, may be encountered until October. All of these expected dates correspond closely with phenological observations.

The causes of the onset of diapause are also easily explained. Since the average temperature during the development of larvae of both generations (in June for the first and in August for the second) is approximately the same (18° to 20°), it is quite obvious that the onset of diapause in the second generation cannot be attributed to the temperature conditions. First-generation larvae, however, develop with the day-length over 17½ hours, which, according to experiments (see Fig. 24), induces only active development in the forest-steppe form of *Acronycta rumicis*. Second-generation larvae develop from early August through September in conditions of day-length decreasing from 16½ hours to 14-13 hours, which, as experiments prove, inevitably induces diapause. Variation in the period of development of first-generation larvae in accordance with the temperature conditions of the year does not extend beyond the limits of effective day-length, and the hibernating stock is always derived from the second generation.

The pattern of regulation of seasonal development ascribed to *Acronycta rumicis* is also basically typical of other long-day polycyclic species, but it is far from appearing always in such a simple form. Even comparatively small differences in the temperature requirements and critical thresholds of the photoperiodic reaction greatly change the course of development. The characteristics of the mode of life and of the microclimatic conditions of the habitat often have a profound effect on the formation of seasonal cycles. All these circumstances lead to the extreme divergence in the phenological patterns of species, which is observed even in a single locality. Let us examine a few instances.

The dependence of seasonal cycles on specific characteristics of temperature and light requirements is clearly evident in comparative analyses of the phenology of the arctiid *Spilosoma menthastri* and the butterflies *Pieris napi* and *Pieris brassicae* in Leningrad province. These species are suitable for comparison as they have much in common in their basic biological features. They are all potentially polycyclic, and in southern provinces may have several generations a year. Hibernation is possible only in the state of pupal diapause. The photoperiodic reaction in all of them is of the long-day type, although in each one it has its peculiarities. The stage sensitive to photoperiod is the larval stage. All three species live in herbaceous vegetation, with fairly similar microclimatic conditions.

In spite of the observed biological similarities, the seasonal

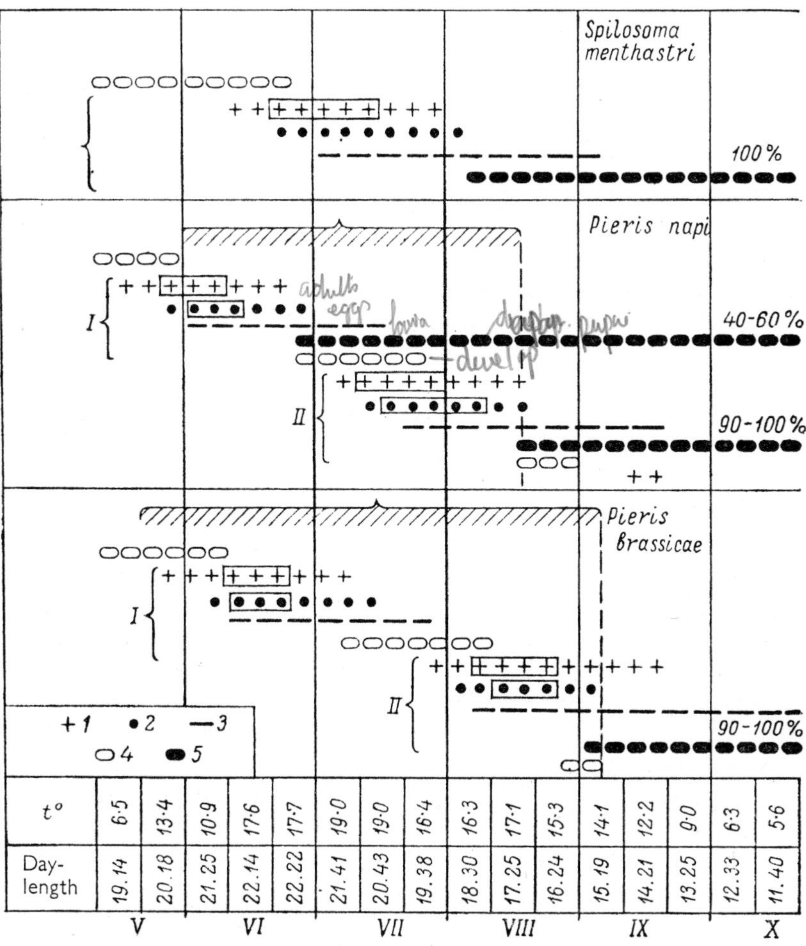

FIG. 51. The phenology of *Spilosoma menthastri*, *Pieris napi*, and *Pieris brassicae* in Leningrad.

I and II, generations; *Shaded area*: the period of non-diapause development. 1, adults; 2, eggs; 3, larvae; 4, developing pupae; 5, diapausing pupae. Peak periods are enclosed in rectangles.

cycles of these species in Leningrad are very different. *Spilosoma menthastri* always develops in one generation there. *Pieris napi* has two generations, although in the first a considerable proportion of the pupae undergo diapause. *Pieris brassicae* also develops in two generations, but only the second-generation pupae hibernate. Fig. 51 shows the phenological patterns according to observations made in 1954 and 1955.

Experimental investigations lead to the conclusion that the phenological characteristics of each of these species may be explained by both temperature and photoperiodic adaptations. The primary cause, however, lies without doubt in specific differences in the requirements of sum-totals of effective heat, since this feature is distinguished by great specific constancy.

From Table 37 it may be seen that *Spilosoma menthastri* requires a greater sum-total of effective heat for its development than do *Pieris brassicae* and *Pieris napi*. Thus although the threshold is identical the sum-total of effective temperatures for its full cycle is almost one-third greater than that for *Pieris brassicae*; *Pieris napi* is less thermophilic. The sum-total of temperatures for the latter, as for *Pieris brassicae*, is 425 day-degrees, but its temperature threshold for development is 2° lower. The significance of these differences becomes clear when they are compared with temperatures during the active period. In Leningrad the sum of effective temperatures over 10°, calculated from 10-day averages, is about 600 day-degrees. Even with correction for the effective temperatures in spring and autumn (to be discussed later), which were not included in the 10-day averages, the sum-total is insufficient for the development of a second generation.

The reactions regulating diapause in the Leningrad *Spilosoma menthastri* also correspond with the temperature conditions. Although the photoperiodic reaction in this form is weak, with higher temperature (23°) it is still fairly clear (see Fig. 48). In such conditions, with a long day of over 18 hours a considerable proportion of individuals develop without diapause. With lower temperature the reaction to long days disappears, and at a temperature of 18° all pupae enter diapause regardless of the light conditions (see Fig. 38). The suppression of photoperiodic reaction by lowered temperature is an important adaptation to survival of *Spilosoma menthastri* in northern latitudes. From the

TABLE 37

Specific differences in the sum-totals of effective temperatures required for development

Species	Threshold of effective temp. (°)	Sum-total of effective temperatures (in day-degrees)				
		Eggs	Larvae	Pupae	Maturation of adults	Entire cycle
Spilosoma menthastri	10	85	285	200	—	570
Pieris brassicae	10	50	200	125	50	425
Pieris napi	8	60	200	115	50	425

phenological diagram it may be seen that the day in Leningrad is very long during the larval development of this species, and with twilight included considerably exceeds 18 hours. During this period, however, the average temperature is always below that at which the stimulating effect of the long day is shown. This explains the obligatory onset of pupal diapause in Leningrad conditions.

The experimental data thus enable us to understand why *Spilosoma menthastri*, while retaining its polycyclic potentiality, behaves in natural conditions as a strictly monocyclic species. The photoperiodic reaction observed in it arose as a protection against the prolongation of development in conditions when the sum-total of effective temperatures is insufficient for completion of the following cycle. On the whole the seasonal-cyclic reaction of this species proves to be well adapted to the climatic conditions of a given locality. Probably this is one of the chief reasons why *Spilosoma menthastri* is always very common in Leningrad.

Different conditions obtain in Leningrad province for *Pieris napi*, whose development is possible at a lower temperature level. In nature the sum-total of temperatures above the threshold for this species (8°), according to data collected over many years, is 865 day-degrees, and in fact approaches 1000 in its habitats. This makes possible the development of two full generations of *Pieris napi*. In such conditions the regulation of diapause in it might be of the type usual for polycyclic species; but observations on its development in natural environments and in market gardens

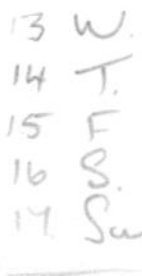

have revealed that in the first generation only about half of the pupae develop and produce adults in the same year. The remainder (40% to 60%) enter diapause and, as observations show, hibernate normally. It is characteristic that the percentage of diapausing pupae does not depend on the time of year of development of the larvae. It is high even among the earliest pupae. The cause of the first-generation diapause becomes clear from experimental analysis of photoperiodic reaction in the Leningrad race of *Pieris napi*.

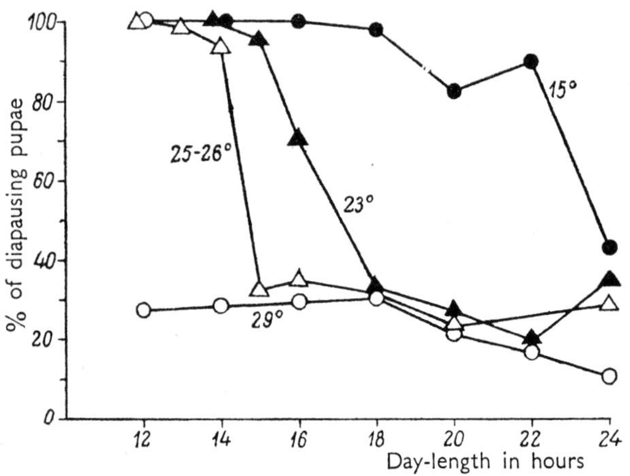

FIG. 52. Changes in the photoperiodic reaction of Leningrad population of *Pieris napi* under the influence of temperature during larval development.

Fig. 52 shows the dependence of diapause in the Leningrad form of *Pieris napi* on day-length at different temperatures during the period of larval development. In its photoperiodic reaction there is a peculiar combination of a low critical threshold, permitting non-diapause development, with hereditary monocyclism, as a result of which about 30% of diapausing pupae are always observed in the long-day conditions. The number of diapausing pupae during long days does not fall even when the larvae are reared at a temperature of 29°, which suppresses the effect of a short day. Lowering the temperature has less effect on *Pieris napi* than on *Spilosoma menthastri*, and even at 15° the photoperiodic reaction is still fairly well displayed.

In connection with these data, let us examine the developmental conditions of *Pieris napi* larvae in nature. The period of development of first-generation larvae lasts from the end of May to the middle of July; most of them develop from June 15 to July 10, i.e. during the period of 'white nights', when light is practically continuous. Temperatures at that time remain at the 15°-18° level. In such conditions, according to experimental data, we should expect to find about 50% of the pupae in diapause, i.e. precisely the proportion observed in nature.

Second-generation larvae develop from the end of July until late autumn, but mainly in autumn, when the day-length is less than 19 hours and the temperature below 18°. Judging from the photoperiodic reaction, this should induce diapause in an overwhelming majority of pupae. Earlier second-generation larvae, which develop in late July and the first half of August with day-length of 17-20 hours, may produce (especially in warm summers) non-diapausing pupae and adults of a third generation. In Leningrad one not infrequently observes freshly-emerged adults, apparently of the third generation, in mid-September. In warm years third-generation adults are seen even in Finland (KAISILA, 1954).

Although experimental data throw light on the phenology of *Pieris napi*, the biological significance of the formation of wintering stocks beginning with the first generation has not been adequately clarified. Apparently this adaptation provides for the survival of the population in years of exceptionally low temperatures, when effective heat may prove insufficient for full development of the second generation. In Leningrad such cases have not been observed, although the sum-total of temperatures in the cold year of 1958 was close to the limit for two generations. In the adjoining districts of Karelia, however, a shortage of heat appears regularly, and there the early diapause of *Pieris napi* is biologically justified. In the Arctic form of this species hereditary monocyclism is still more strongly manifested (PETERSEN, 1947, 1949). The characteristics of the photoperiodic reaction in the Leningrad *Pieris napi* give firm grounds for believing that this form has a northern origin.

Analysis of the phenology of the Cabbage White Butterfly *Pieris brassicae* is more complex than that of the preceding species. Its development in Leningrad proceeds in conditions of constant shortage of effective temperatures. According to data from laboratory experiments, 850 day-degrees are required for development of the two generations observed there. Nevertheless the sum-total in Leningrad, according to 10-day averages during the growth period, is only 600, which is far from being sufficient for two generations.

The experiments of V. A. Maslennikova, intended to check the validity of experimental data for determining the dates of development of the Cabbage White Butterfly in nature, have shown that during the period of development of the first generation the sum-total of effective temperatures from egg to emergence of adults varies from 353 to 390 day-degrees. In laboratory experiments it averaged 375 day-degrees. Thus the experimental data fairly accurately express the temperature requirements of *Pieris brassicae*. The discrepancy between the actual number of generations and the sum-total of effective temperatures during the active period is evidently explained by the fact that standard daily-average and 10-day-average data do not fully take into account the actual effective temperatures in nature. The micro-climatic observations and field experiments of V. A. Maslennikova have revealed the following sources of error.

(1) For the spring period, when night temperatures fall below the threshold for development, the daily-average and 10-day-average standard data lead to an underestimate of the effective temperatures, as they do not take into account the midday warming-up and the brief hot periods which stimulate development in hibernating pupae. How great this error is may be seen from the fact that butterflies often emerge in May when the 10-day-average temperature is near the threshold (10°), although more than 100 effective day-degrees are still required for their development.

(2) In summer the average daily temperature at a level of 25 cm above the ground, where Cabbage White Butterflies develop, is 0·5° to 1° higher than at the standard meteorological recording points. This provides about 70 or 80 additional day-degrees.

(3) The daily-average temperatures in autumn, as in spring, mask the effective midday temperatures, which may induce larval development.

With these corrections the sum-total of effective heat proves to be sufficient for development of two generations. Usually, however, it is near the minimum limit, and—as field observations show—only those second-generation larvae derived from early eggs laid not later than mid-August succeed in pupating; later ones perish without having completed their development. In cold years (e.g. 1958) the majority of second-generation larvae perish.

The life cycle of the Cabbage White Butterfly also does not fully correspond with local conditions in its photoperiodic reaction. In the first generation, because of the great day-length, diapause is never observed. Pupation of the second-generation larvae begins in most cases in the first 10 days of September, and in warmer years at the end of August. In field experiments larvae developing before August 20 (i.e. with day-length over 17 hours) produced only active pupae. Later the percentage of diapausing pupae rose rapidly, and all individuals that pupated after September 1 entered diapause, although development of larvae continued while day-length exceeded the critical value, i.e. 15 hours. Therefore in nature diapause may appear earlier than might be expected from experimental data. It has not yet been possible to explain this feature of the reaction in *Pieris brassicae*, which is worthy of special investigation. Doubtless with early dates of development of the second generation the number of pupae capable of hibernation decreases.

The inadequate adaptation of the Leningrad form of *Pieris brassicae* to local conditions is shown also in the comparatively low frost-resistance of the hibernating pupae. KOZHANCHIKOV (1936) noted that the north-eastern limit of distribution of this species coincides with the January isotherms of $-16°$ and $-20°$. In our experiments (see Table 28) pupae survived cooling, on an average, to $-22{\cdot}5°$, but at $-24°$ all perished. In Leningrad there are more severe frosts almost every year, and consequently pupae that hibernate above the snow cover may freeze to death.

The wide fluctuations in the numbers of *Pieris brassicae* from year to year are the result of its seasonal-cyclic reactions being ill-adapted to Leningrad climatic conditions. In this respect *Pieris brassicae* clearly differs from *Pieris napi*, whose numbers are very stable.

The above facts lead to the conclusion that the form of *Pieris brassicae* found in Leningrad province has arrived there recently from more southerly regions. Its distribution is apparently connected with the extension of cultivation of cruciferous plants.

This is indicated by a number of facts and considerations. Unlike *Pieris napi*, in Leningrad province *Pieris brassicae* is confined to cultivated areas and is entirely absent from wild crucifers in natural habitats, whereas in the forest-steppe zone its larvae are frequently found in natural habitats on *Aliaria* and other crucifers.

In Western Europe—where the Cabbage White Butterfly, judging from its reaction to temperature (MAERCKS, 1934) and light conditions (BÜNNING and JOERRENS, 1959) is a representative of the same race—its seasonal cycle agrees exactly with the local climatic conditions. There, especially in the Baltic basin, it constantly maintains very high numbers, and that region is the source of mass migrations of butterflies to distant areas (NORDMAN, 1954).

North of Leningrad the Cabbage White Butterfly is known as far as Kola Peninsula, but there it is scarce and sporadic. It is not certain that it is a permanent resident in these districts and that its occasional appearances are not the result of migration. Its cycle, apparently, is adapted even less to conditions in northern regions than to the Leningrad climate. Pupating larvae collected on August 15-20, 1957, in northern Karelia (66·5°N.) by L. A. Stepanova produced only non-diapausing pupae, unfit for hibernation. Apparently the long day of northern latitudes prevents the formation of a wintering stock, and by the time the day has shortened to the critical level the temperature is too low for development.

It is not possible to continue here with detailed examination of other long-day-type species, especially since the literature contains data on the Pine Moth *Dendrolimus pini* (GEISPITS, 1958), the malaria mosquito *Anopheles maculipennis* (DANILEVSKII and GLINYANAYA, 1958; SHIPITSYNA, 1959), *Orgyia antiqua* (DOSKOČIL, 1957a), and on several other species. The phenology of the spider mite *Metatetranychus ulmi* has been studied by LEES (1953a).

Let us pause to consider only the results obtained by GORYSHIN (1953, 1958a) in experimental analysis of the complex phenology of the Cotton-boll Worm *Chloridea obsoleta* in the northern Caucasus. These data are of interest because they show the leading role in phenology of the special post-diapause adaptations which determine the commencement of spring development. The threshold of effective temperatures for the active stages of *Chloridea* is 11°, and the sum-total for the entire cycle is 600 day-degrees (KOZHANCHIKOV, 1938a; RUBTSOV, 1941; GORYSHIN, 1958b). According to these data, in the Stavropol' district, where the phenological observations were made, one might expect development of two or three generations; but, as Goryshin has shown, most individuals there are univoltine. The phenological characteristics of this species are to a large extent determined by the fact that the threshold of effective temperatures for the initial phase of development of hibernating and already-reactivated pupae is much higher than that for active pupae, being 18·5°. As a result the emergence of adults from hibernating pupae occurs late—only in late July or early August, and larval development occurs mainly in a period when the day-length is below the critical level for this species (see Fig. 29). Consequently most of the pupae undergo diapause and remain in hibernation. Some individuals, having pupated before the day-length reached the critical level, produce second-generation adults, whose offspring perish without completing development.

This basic pattern is complicated by the fact that in spring adults emerge early (at the beginning of June) from certain pupae which had, possibly, hibernated in an active state or in weak diapause, and they succeed in producing two generations or even a partial third generation. The first generation, however, is always small in numbers.

The special temperature threshold for post-diapause development of *Chloridea obsoleta* has, no doubt, an adaptational significance. The larvae eat mainly the growing parts of plants and are very thermophilic. It is known that, in spite of the low threshold of effective temperature (11°) calculated for their rate of development, they cannot in fact develop at a temperature below 18°, while the optimum lies between 25° and 30°. A high temperature threshold at the beginning of spring development, by delaying the emergence of adults, synchronizes the appearance of larvae with a period suitable for their feeding and development.

The post-diapause reactions which regulate the dates of resurgence of activity in spring have not yet been investigated, but they are probably also widely distributed among other species.

The seasonal cycles of short-day species

The biology and seasonal cycles of short-day species are known much less completely than those of species of the long-day type, but the cases investigated prove to have their own peculiar features.

The adaptational significance of the short-day reaction is quite clear in the so-called bivoltine race of the silkworm, which has two generations a year, with winter diapause in the early embryonic stage. As already stated, diapause in this species is determined by conditions operative in the period of embryonic development after blastokinesis (KOGURE, 1933). Short days and low temperature at that time make possible the continuous development of eggs of the next generation, and long days and higher temperature induce diapause (see Fig. 21).

Since in southern districts, where the bivoltine race mainly occurs, development of overwintering eggs begins early in spring at a low temperature and with days still short, first-generation adults lay non-diapausing eggs in summer. Embryonic development of the next generation proceeds in the long-day conditions of summer and at high temperature, as a result of which second-generation adults lay diapausing wintering eggs. The short-day type of development has arisen in this case because the stage sensitive to light follows immediately after the wintering stage.

It is of interest that precisely the same kind of seasonal cycle may arise also with a long-day type of development in cases where sensitivity to light appears in phenologically-later stages of development. For instance, *Orgyia antiqua*, which resembles the silkworm, has a facultative diapause in the early embryonic stage, but it is its larva that is sensitive to light (DOSKOČIL, 1956, 1957a, 1957b). In Czechoslovakia first-generation larvae develop in early summer and the adults lay non-diapausing eggs. The second generation develops during shorter days, in July and early August, as a result of which eggs of this generation undergo diapause.

The short-day type of photoperiodic reaction leads to some unusual seasonal cycles, the physiological mechanism of which is still not at all understood. An interesting example is the Tussock Moth *Dasychira pudibunda*, investigated by K. F. Geispits. This species is univoltine everywhere, even in the most southerly parts of its range, and winters in the form of diapausing pupae. The adults appear in May and June, and throughout the whole summer the larvae feed and develop slowly; only in autumn does their development speed up and pupation begin. As the length of the active period increases, so does the duration of larval development. On the Black Sea coast of the Caucasus (Sukhumi) larval development extends from the beginning of June to October, i.e. for more than four months, but in Leningrad it is shortened to 2-2½ months.

The periods of larval development therefore vary with geographical latitude, in a direction opposite to that observed in other insects. Experimental analysis has shown that in this case the seasonal cycle is regulated by the light and temperature conditions. Unlike the majority of other species, *Dasychira pudibunda* larvae develop much more rapidly in short-day than in long-day conditions (GEISPITS, 1953). The reaction to temperature is also very unusual. With a rise in temperature the total duration of larval development, in both long-day and short-day conditions, is greatly increased (Table 38). These facts are very difficult to interpret from the point of view of the usual concepts of the dependence of insect development on temperature.

TABLE 38

The duration of development (in days) of larvae of the Sukhumi form of *Dasychira pudibunda* depending on the temperature and day-length (from data of K. F. Geispits)

Temp. (°)	Long day (24 hours)	Short day (10 hours)
15	91·0 (85-107)	63·3 (50- 78)
20	113·1 (97-133)	73·4 (57- 86)
25	121·3 (101-148)	117·0 (115-120)

When we consider the reaction of different instars, however, we can see (Fig. 53) that up to instar VI the larvae react normally to temperature, development accelerating as it rises. In conditions of falling temperature (15°) pupation takes place in instars VI and VII without delay; but higher temperatures inhibit the onset of metamorphosis and induce an additional moult, so that at a temperature of 25° the larvae pupate only after reaching instars X to XII. The histological structure of fatty tissue in larvae in the additional instars, and the characteristics of their behaviour and feeding, lead to the conclusion that the check to development observed at high temperatures is due to the onset of a peculiar form of diapause.

The data provided by the experiments explain the seasonal cycle of *Dasychira pudibunda*. The summer check in development (diapause) induced by high temperature and long days is apparently caused by the weak heat-resistance of the larvae, which cannot survive constant temperatures above 25°. The great dependence of the periods of development on day-length gives grounds for believing that in *Dasychira pudibunda*, in spite of its universal monocyclism, there ought to exist geographical forms differing in their norms of photoperiodic reaction. This supposition is

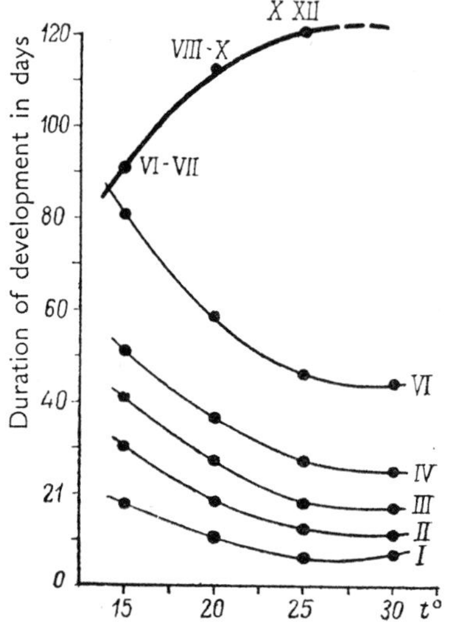

FIG. 53

The effect of temperature on the duration of development of larvae of *Dasychira pudibunda* (Sukhumi) in continuous light (from data of K. F. Geispits).

Upper curve: duration of larval development until pupation.

Lower curves: duration of development by instars.

Roman numerals: instars of larvae.

supported by experiments in the simultaneous rearing of the northern and southern forms in natural conditions in Leningrad province.

In recent studies MASAKI (1957a, 1958) analyses the complex seasonal cycle of *Abraxas miranda* in the subtropical climate of the Pacific coast of Honshu (34° 42′ N.). This geometrid develops on the evergreen Japanese spindle-tree (*Euonymus japonicus*) and has two generations a year; in the hot season (June-August) with a temperature of 25°-26° it is found in a resting pupal state, and its active development is mainly confined to the cool season. The adults emerge in April-May and September-October. In winter it occurs both as active larvae and as active and diapausing pupae. This peculiar seasonal cycle is controlled by the mechanism of pupal diapause.

The onset of diapause and its duration are linked mainly with the effect of long days during development and partly with the simultaneous action of temperature. By the nature of its photoperiodic reaction *Abraxas miranda* belongs to the short-day type. With a day-length of 14 hours and upwards it produces only pupae with a long diapause (averaging $2\frac{1}{2}$ to $3\frac{1}{2}$ months); as the day shortens the percentage of diapausing pupae falls and the

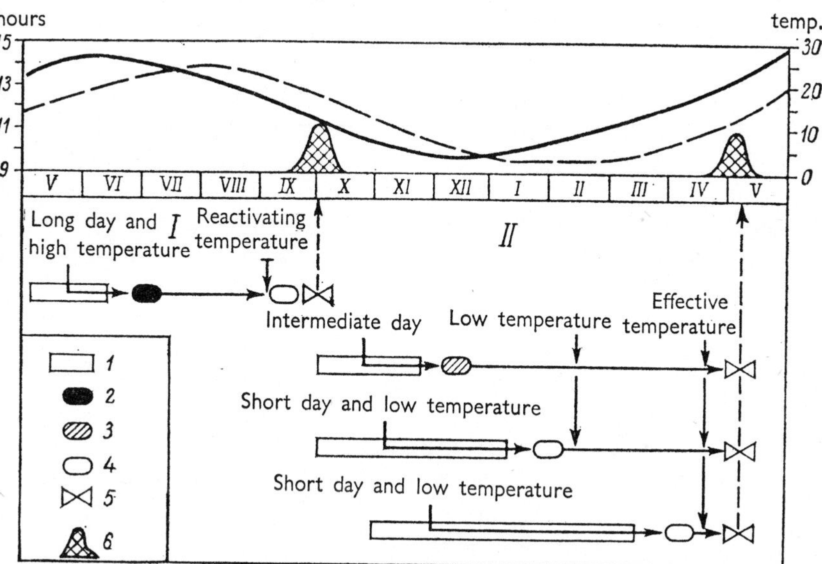

FIG. 54. The pattern of the seasonal development of the geometrid *Abraxas miranda* in Japan (from Masaki, 1958).

Solid curve: day-length in hours;
Broken curve: temperature. I and II, generations.
1, larvae; 2, pupae with a long diapause; 3, pupae with a short diapause; 4, non-diapausing pupae; 5, adults; 6, flight of adults.

duration of diapause decreases, reaching a minimum with a day of 7-10 hours. High temperature acts in the same direction as long days, increasing the percentage of diapausing pupae and also the duration of diapause; low temperature enhances the effect of short days, stimulating development.

The characteristics of its reaction to temperature and photoperiod enable us to interpret the course of seasonal development of *Abraxas miranda* in nature (Fig. 54). First-generation larvae develop in May and early June with day-length from $13\frac{1}{2}$ to

$14\frac{1}{2}$ hours and temperature of 16°-20°. According to experimental data, such conditions induce long pupal diapause, lasting the whole summer. The general emergence of adults in autumn takes place in response to a fall in temperature. The offspring of autumn adults, because of rapidly-falling temperature, encounter different conditions. The earliest larvae succeed in developing in the fairly high temperature of October and November and with days shortening from 11 hours 50 minutes to 10 hours 30 minutes. They produce pupae with a short diapause, sufficient, however, to delay further metamorphosis until the beginning of winter.

The development of later-hatching larvae is checked by the onset of the cold season. They grow slowly during the winter months in short-day conditions (in December, 9 hours 50 minutes), and gradually pupate. According to experimental data, such pupae are mainly non-diapausing; but because of the comparatively high temperature-threshold required for their active development, they remain in a retarded state until spring. The general development of all hibernating pupae begins only in March and April, when temperatures exceed the threshold.

Seasonal cyclic reactions of the *Abraxas miranda* type can arise only in subtropical climatic conditions with a diet of evergreen vegetation. It is probable, however, that summer and winter diapauses of different duration form one of the basic elements in the seasonal cycles in southern latitudes.

The regulation of seasonal development in parasitic insects

The problem of seasonal adaptation in parasitic insects is complicated by the fact that their cycles must be adapted not only to the rhythm of external conditions but also to the rhythm of their host's development.

Many instances have long been known where the development of parasitic insects and that of their hosts have synchronized precisely. SALT (1941), reviewing these data, supposed (like other authors) that the rates of growth and development of parasites were directly determined by those of their hosts. In many cases this is actually so. For instance, BRADLEY and ARBUTHNOT (1938) stated that the life cycle of *Chelonus annulipes* (Braconidae), which parasitizes the eggs of the Corn Borer and completes its development in the pupae, always corresponds strictly with the development of its host. In the polycyclic form of the Corn Borer the development of the parasite, like that of the host, lasts about two months, and in the monocyclic form almost ten months, as the parasite hibernates in the body of the diapausing larva and concludes its development only in spring after the latter has pupated. Thus the duration of development and diapause in the parasite is entirely determined by the host. This ensures that the imaginal stage of the parasite coincides with the stage at which the host is attacked. MARCHAL (1936) established a close connection for *Trichogramma cacoeciae*, which parasitizes the eggs of the leafroller *Cacoecia rosana.*

A case of most exact parallelism of development and diapause in parasite and host was investigated by SCHNEIDER (1950, 1951) in the ichneumon fly *Diplazon fissorius*, which is parasitic on various species of syrphid-flies. It attacks young larvae of the host, but its development is checked in its first larval instar, and recommences only when the host pupates. In the polycyclic *Epistrophe balteata* the delay in development of the parasite is correspondingly brief and it, like the host, has several generations in a year. When infesting the monocyclic *Epistrophe bifasciata*, which hibernates as a larva in diapause, the parasite hibernates inside it and is monocyclic also. By transplanting parasitic larvae of the first instar into hosts with a different cycle or in a different physiological state, Schneider demonstrated that humoral influences of the host were the direct stimuli to moulting and further development. Their action on the parasite was made possible by the great permeability of the cuticle of first-instar larvae. Probably these stimuli are the hormones that regulate metamorphosis.

LEES (1955) observed that diapause in parasitic insects is determined by the physiological state of the host only when it occurs in the first larval instar of the parasite, and was inclined to regard such delays in development as induced states of a type similar to quiescence. They may, however, be considered to be true diapause, analogous in their physiological mechanism to diapause in early embryonic stages, which also is regulated by a hormonal system other than that of the diapausing organism itself. It is evident that when such a dependent type of development of parasites is observed in nature adaptation of their seasonal cycles to the rhythm of external conditions is produced by the seasonal-cyclic adaptations of the host.

In cases, however, where diapause in the parasite begins in the later stages of development, one observes a different form of regulation. GEISPITS and KYAO (1953) showed that in *Apanteles glomeratus*, a parasite of *Pieris brassicae*, and also in *Apanteles spurius*, which parasitizes larvae of Sphingidae and Notodontidae, prepupal diapause is induced directly in the parasite by photoperiodic conditions during its larval development in the body of the host. Thus when *Apanteles spurius* develops in the monocyclic forms of *Smerinthus ocellatus* and *Dicranura vinula*, in long-day conditions the emerging larvae pupate, and in short-day conditions they enter diapause.

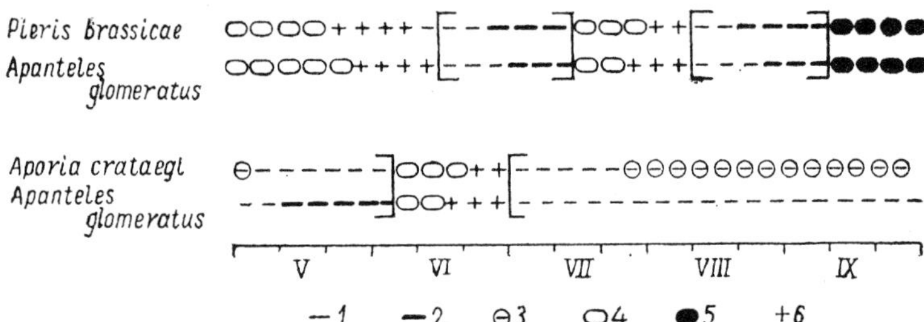

FIG. 55. The pattern of the phenology of *Apanteles glomeratus* in Leningrad with development in different hosts (from data of V. A. Maslennikova).

1, larvae in first instars; 2, larvae in older instars; 3, diapausing larvae in winter cocoons; 4, prepupae and pupae, developing; 5, ditto, diapausing; 6, imago. In square brackets: the period when the parasites occur in the host's body.

The independence of the temperature and photoperiodic reactions regulating prepupal diapause in *Apanteles glomeratus* when it develops in the larvae of *Pieris brassicae* is confirmed by the detailed investigations of MASLENNIKOVA (1958, 1959), the results of which have been shown in Fig. 35. Together with independent regulation in this species, however, a dependent form is also observed in the first larval instar.

Fig. 55 shows the phenological pattern of *Apanteles glomeratus* when it develops in different hosts: monocyclic (*Aporia crataegi*) with diapause in the young larval stage, and polycyclic (*Pieris brassicae*) with development in the pupal stage. In correspondence with the host's cycle the parasite may behave either as a monocyclic or as a polycyclic form. In both cases the development of the parasite is well adapted to the seasonal rhythm of external conditions, and its imaginal stage coincides in time with the stage in which the host becomes parasitized (larvae of the first instar). This result, however, is attained through different mechanisms.

When developing in *Aporia crataegi* the parasite hibernates in the body of the diapausing larva in the first larval instar. Its own cycle in this case is determined entirely by the physiological influence of its host. Special experiments have shown that high temperature and long days are incapable of stimulating development of the young larva of the parasite in autumn (MASLENNIKOVA, 1958), and it is activated only in spring on termination of the host's diapause. But even while developing in *Aporia crataegi, Apanteles* retains the capacity for independent regulation of prepupal diapause. Thus if overwintering parasitized host larvae are kept in spring in short-day and low-temperature conditions, the prepupae of the parasite enter diapause after spinning up, although these conditions have no effect on the development of the host larvae.

When *Apanteles* develops in *Pieris brassicae*, the correspondence in the number of generations and the onset of diapause is due to similarity in the independent reactions of the partners to temperature and light conditions; but the duration of the endoparasitic stages of *Apanteles* in this case also depends on the humoral stimuli from the host.

Normally *Apanteles glomeratus* infests larvae of the first and second instars and completes its development before they pupate. In artificial conditions, however, it may attack older larvae and the period of its development is shortened correspondingly. This shows that the development of the parasitic larva is checked at the beginning, and its main growth takes place only during the later instars of the host. Thus the emergence of the adult parasite is synchronized with the appearance of young larvae of the next generation of *Pieris brassicae.*

Apparently the adaptation of the cycle to both external conditions and the host's development, observed in most parasitic insects, is based on the two types of regulation of development described above. The relative roles of independent and dependent reactions, judging by data for *Pteromalus puparum* and *Trichogramma* spp. (MASLENNIKOVA, 1958, 1959b), may be different.

The possibility of dual regulation of periods of development and diapause increases the ecological adaptability of parasites and facilitates parasitization by them of a wider variety of hosts. Independent reactions to external conditions certainly induce the appearance of intraspecific geographical differentiation, whereas with dependent development synchronization with the host is achieved in any climatic conditions.

2. The causes of variation in insect phenology from year to year

It is known that insect phenology in a single locality does not remain constant and fluctuates in accordance with weather conditions, especially temperature, during the active period. This is shown not only in variation in the calendar dates of development of active stages but also in the onset of diapause, as a result of which the number of generations in polycyclic species may vary. Such variation, it would seem, contradicts the strict constancy of photoperiodic conditions in nature. It is still beyond doubt that fluctuation in the number of generations is determined mainly by the characteristics of the reaction to day-length, and these phenomena must not be attributed, as has been done up to the present, only to the direct effect of temperature. Since variation in phenology is reflected in the numbers of a population and in the formation of a hibernating stock, it is necessary to discuss the mechanism which determines it.

Fluctuation in the number of generations in accordance with weather conditions may be produced by two different causes: (1) shifting of calendar dates of development under the influence of temperature, as a result of which stages that react to photoperiodic conditions coincide with a period of different day-length; (2) changes in the critical thresholds of photoperiodic reaction under the direct influence of the ambient temperature and other external factors. These two causes may operate simultaneously in natural conditions.

Let us examine some examples of variation in phenology depending on seasonal temperature conditions.

The indirect effect of temperature on the onset of diapause was convincingly demonstrated by KOMAROVA (1949, 1954), who investigated the seasonal development of a serious enemy of viticulture—the Grape Berry Moth *Polychrosis botrana*—in

Azerbaijan, where it develops in three generations. In the first generation diapausing pupae are never observed; third-generation pupae always undergo diapause. In the second generation, development of which takes place in July and August, the percentage of diapausing pupae varies greatly in accordance with the conditions of the year and the locality. On that account the extent of damage done by the Grape Berry Moth also varies. In Kirovabad diapause is almost entirely absent in the second generation, and therefore one observes progressive growth in the numbers of the pest up to the third generation, which causes the greatest damage. In Khanlar, situated only 8 km from Kirovabad but in the foothill zone, most of the second generation usually enter diapause and the numbers of the third generation are not high, thus decreasing the amount of damage done.

Komarova found that the decisive factor in inducing diapause in *Polychrosis botrana* is reduction of day-length, whereas hygrothermal and food conditions have no appreciable effect. Sensitivity to photoperiod appears during embryonic development and partly in the first two larval instars. Thus the number in diapause depends mainly on the calendar dates of egg-laying. The critical day-length occurs on July 20.

Fig. 56 shows the periods of development and the percentage of diapause in the second generation for two years in Kirovabad and Khanlar. In 1947 mass egg-laying took place in Kirovabad before the critical date, and only occasional egg-laying was seen afterwards. Consequently diapausing pupae were very scarce (1·8%). In Khanlar, because of the lower temperature, development was much delayed. Egg-laying took place mostly after July 20, and 76% of pupae entered diapause. In 1948 higher summer temperature accelerated the development of *Polychrosis botrana*, and egg-laying began earlier than usual, which led to the complete absence of diapause in Kirovabad and to a decrease in the number of diapausing pupae in Khanlar to 40%.

This example shows that a change in temperature may strongly affect the number of pupae in diapause without having a direct effect on the physiological process that regulates diapause. In the above case the temperature affected only the rate of development, as a result of which the stages sensitive to photoperiod came under the influence of a different day-length, and this determined the final effect.

Apparently the numbers of diapausing larvae of the apple Codling Moth *Enarmonia* (*Carpocapsa*) *pomonella* in different years also depend on the indirect influence of temperature. This is shown by the great constancy from year to year of the critical calendar dates of the onset of diapause, noted by several authors (KÜTHE, 1937; GARLICK, 1948; SHEL'DESHOVA, 1956) in field

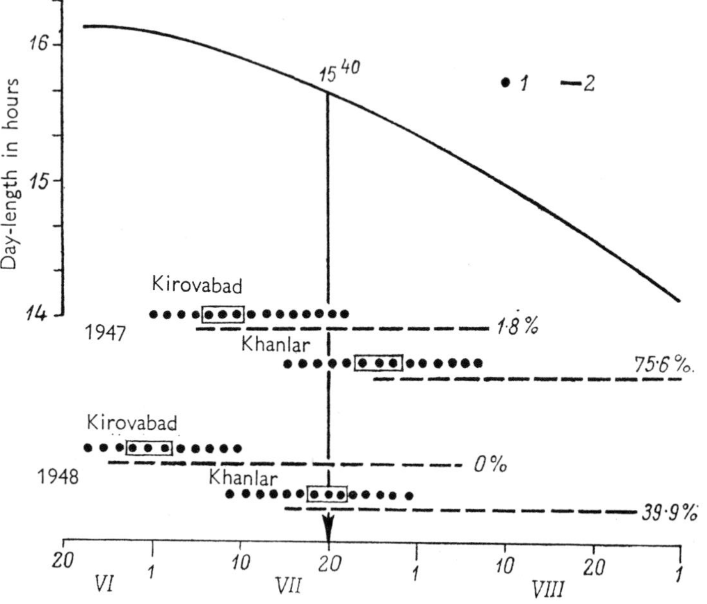

FIG. 56. The variation in the numbers of diapausing pupae of the second generation of *Polychrosis botrana*, depending on the dates of oviposition (from Komarova, 1949).

Upper curve: day-length; *arrow*: critical date. 1, eggs; 2, larvae; mass oviposition in rectangles.

observations in various regions. For instance, according to Garlick the number of diapausing larvae in Ontario in different years fluctuated from 27% to 37%, depending on the number of larvae which had completed development before the arrival of the critical date, which occurs there on August 24.

More often, however, the effect of temperature appears in a more complex form, and simultaneously with variation in the dates of development the temperature exerts a direct influence on the photoperiodic reaction. As an example we may look at the variation in the onset of diapause and in the number of generations in the Colorado Beetle *Leptinotarsa decemlineata* in Poland.

The seasonal cycle of the Colorado Beetle is more complex than that of the other species we have discussed, as its imaginal stages are active for more than a year, which leads to the co-existence of different generations. Both diapausing beetles of the preceding year and beetles of different generations of the current year go into hibernation at the same time. In Poland, however, females that have completed egg-laying mostly die during the winter (KOVAL'SKAYA, 1958; VENGOREK, 1958a; WĘGOREK, 1957b, 1959a). Therefore in order to forecast the numbers of the pest in the following year it is necessary to know the proportions of the different categories of hibernating females.

According to WĘGOREK (1957a, 1959a), only one generation usually develops in Poland. The second is sporadic and small in number, as most of the first-generation beetles that emerge in summer enter diapause without maturing, or they lay very few eggs and their offspring do not manage to complete development before the onset of cold weather, as happened in 1954 (Fig. 57). The number of first-generation beetles in diapause fluctuates in accordance with the temperature of the summer. In a warm summer (e.g. in 1953) a considerable number of them mature and their fecundity is high, and the second generation succeeds in developing and preparing for hibernation. In the coldest years all summer beetles enter diapause and there is no second generation.

Fluctuations in the number of generations cannot be explained as being due merely to fluctuations in the effective temperatures. For instance, in 1953 and 1954, when the phenology was very different in the two years, the sum-totals of temperatures above the threshold for the Colorado Beetle (11·5°) for the whole active period were almost identical, being 786 and 752 day-degrees respectively. Development of two full generations might have been expected in each year, as one generation requires 360 day-degrees (LARCHENKO, 1958b, 1958c, 1958d).

Consequently in studying phenology one must take account of the conditions that regulate the onset of diapause. LARCHENKO (1955, 1958a) attributed the onset of diapause in the Colorado Beetle to the effects of age and seasonal changes in the biochemical composition of its food plants. As has been found, however, the leading role is taken by the photoperiodic conditions (DE WILDE, 1954, 1955; JERMI and SARINGER, 1955; GORYSHIN, 1956, 1958a;

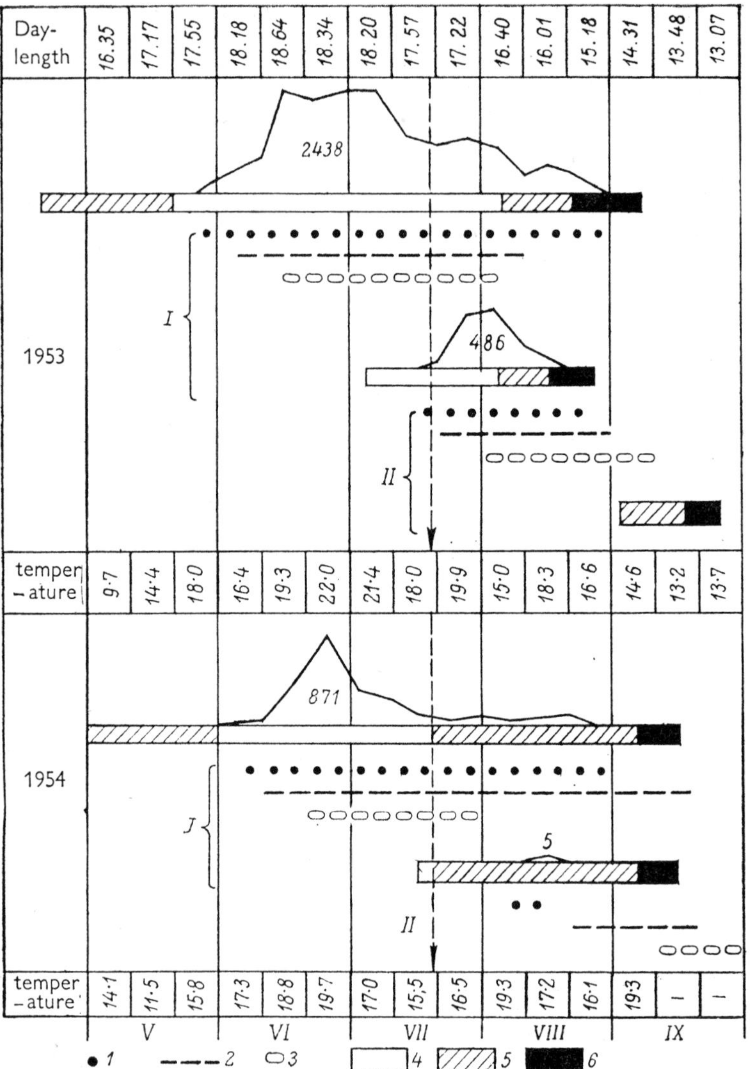

FIG. 57. The variation in the phenology of *Leptinotarsa decemlineata* in Poznan in accordance with the temperature during the summer (from data of Węgorek, 1957, 1959, and Larchenko, 1958).

Arrows: critical day-length. I and II: generations. *Curves*: fecundity; figures inside them—average number of eggs per female. 1, eggs; 2, larvae; 3, pupae; 4, sexually-mature beetles; 5, immature beetles; 6, beetles entering the soil for hibernation.

WĘGOREK, 1958c, 1959b; DE WILDE, DUINTJER and MOOK, 1959). The data of GORYSHIN (1956, 1958a) are of particular interest in analysing the causes of variation in the phenology in nature. He discovered that short days induce diapause in Colorado Beetles by directly affecting not only the imaginal, but also the larval, stage. The critical day-length varies greatly, depending on temperature and also on the food plants. At a temperature of 30° it is 14 hours 30 minutes, and at 18° it exceeds 18 hours (see Fig. 25). At 20° the critical day-length is about 17 hours 30 minutes. As the day lengthens the maturation of the beetles is accelerated and the intensity of egg-laying is increased. These data satisfactorily explain the reasons for the variations in diapause and fecundity of the beetles in different years.

From Fig. 57 it is seen that in 1953 and 1954, with similar totals of effective temperatures during the active period, the courses followed by temperature during the year were different. The year 1953 was distinguished by a very warm June and July, when the temperature remained near 20°. In 1954 July was very cool (16·3°). These differences had both direct and indirect effects on the course of development of the Colorado Beetle.

The direct influence of photoperiodic and temperature conditions is clearly seen in the fecundity of overwintering beetles. Maturation and first ovipositions were observed at a temperature above 15°, but not until the third decade of May, i.e. after the day-length exceeded 17 hours. The period of maximum fecundity coincides with a day-length above 18 hours. In July, immediately after the day-length has decreased to the critical level, the intensity of egg-laying falls abruptly, and in August, when the day-length becomes less than 17 hours, most of the beetles gradually cease to lay and enter the stage of preparation for hibernation. The character of their sexual activity, as pointed out by WĘGOREK (1957a, 1959a), remains similar in the different years, but from the diagram it can be seen that the intensity of egg-laying during the long-day period increases with rising temperature. After the day-length has fallen below the critical value, however, even a considerable rise in temperature is incapable of restoring the beetles' activity.

The indirect influence of temperature is shown more clearly in diapause and fecundity of the beetles of the summer generation. In 1953 high temperature accelerated the development of larvae and pupae, and beetles of the first summer generation were observed at the beginning of July, i.e. when the day-length was over 18 hours. As a result all females of the first emergence were active and soon began to oviposit. Their fecundity was high, averaging 486 eggs with a maximum of 997 for one female. In August egg-laying began to fall rapidly in intensity, and it ended simultaneously with the beginning of diapause in beetles that had hibernated. Second-generation beetles, which hatched in September (i.e. during very short days), all entered diapause.

In 1954, because of the cool July, first-generation beetles began to appear on July 16—i.e. two weeks later than in the preceding year—and so encountered the period of critical day-length. Even among the first-hatched females fewer than 10% matured. They laid a few eggs (5·6 on an average) in August, although the temperature was then high (19·3°).

In general we may conclude that among beetles of the summer generation sexual activity may be observed only in individuals that emerged in the first half of July, i.e. when the day-length exceeded 17 hours 30 minutes. Beetles that emerge in August, when the day-length is below 17 hours, are not capable of maturation and enter diapause. In the intervening period the number of active individuals is not large and depends on temperature and the state of the food plants. These conclusions are supported by phenological observations in different districts of Poland. In northern districts, because of the lower summer temperature, first-generation beetles appear at the end of July and the beginning of August and generally do not lay any eggs.

Immediately after cessation of sexual activity in the beetles a period of definite preparation for diapause begins, during which fat reserves are accumulated and there is loss of water from the tissues. The shorter the day, the more rapid the preparation for diapause. The duration of this process is also affected by diet (Larchenko, 1958a; Węgorek, 1958a) and temperature. According to the experimental results of Goryshin (1958a), a rise in temperature considerably accelerates the preparation for diapause. An abrupt fall in temperature may serve as a direct stimulus for the beetles to burrow into the soil. This complex relationship leads to considerable fluctuations in the dates of burrowing into the soil for hibernation in different years.

The characteristics of the photoperiodic reaction in the

Cotton-boll Worm *Chloridea obsoleta* have a peculiar effect on the formation of wintering stocks of this pest in southern districts of its range. In Azerbaijan wintering pupae of this species are extremely diverse in their physiological states. They include some with prolonged diapause as well as others with short diapause, or even active individuals. The percentage of survival through the winter and the dates of spring development vary in the different categories. Such diversity in the wintering stocks, according to KOMAROVA (1959), is due to variation in the photoperiodic reaction under the influence of temperature.

In laboratory experiments (see Table 17) the photoperiodic reaction in *Chloridea obsoleta* is fully displayed only at a temperature of about 23°. Higher or lower temperatures suppress the action of the short day and decrease the number of diapausing pupae. The duration of diapause also depends on the temperature at which the larvae develop. It is longest at high temperatures, and at temperatures below 20° only short diapause, lasting about 40 days, occurs.

These data explain the diversity of wintering stocks in nature. Fig. 58 shows the light and temperature conditions during the formation of wintering stocks of *Chloridea obsoleta* in Azerbaijan. The first diapausing pupae were observed in mid-September, and while the temperature remained above 20° the number of diapausing pupae rose quickly as the day shortened, reaching a maximum (90%-92%) at the beginning of October. Later, when the temperature fell below 20°, the proportion of active pupae again rose and on October 20 only 45% were in diapause. The duration of diapause in pupae obtained at different times also varied. Deep diapause was observed in the early periods of pupation, while the temperature was fairly high (21°-25°). Later the duration of diapause decreased, and in the last pupae diapause was very short.

As is seen from Fig. 58, in 1954 the majority of larvae pupated during the period when light and temperature conditions were appropriate for the greatest number of them to enter diapause. With different temperature conditions in summer and autumn the maximum of pupation might coincide with less favourable conditions, as a result of which the number of cold-resistant diapausing pupae would decrease. This is confirmed by the observations of MANUILOVA (1958) on the phenology of *Chloridea obsoleta* in Central Asia. She came to the conclusion that in cases where the wintering stock is formed mainly from pupae of the late dates of pupation, the larvae of which developed at low temperatures, one should expect low numbers of these pests in the

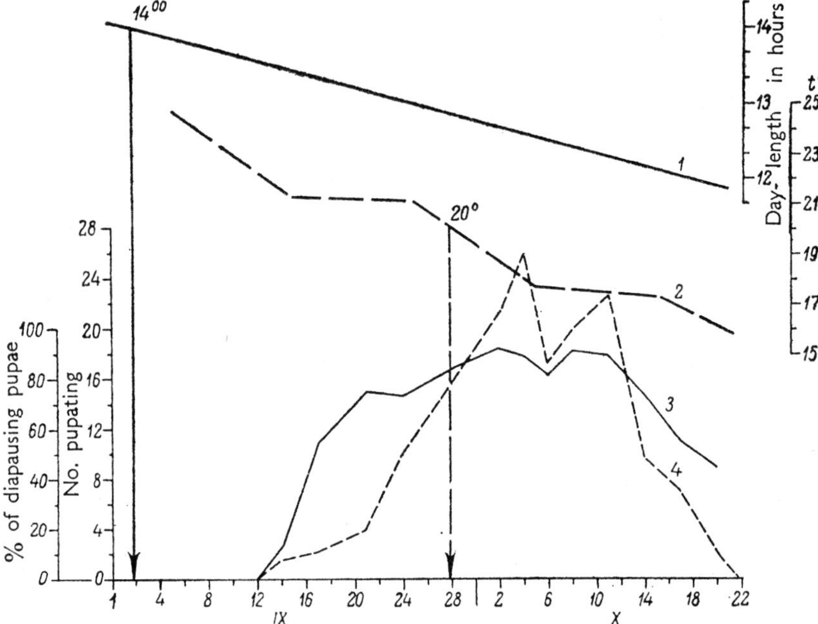

FIG. 58. The effect of autumn temperature conditions on the onset of diapause in pupae of *Chloridea obsoleta* in Azerbaijan (after Komarova, 1959).

1, the day-length; 2, the 10-day-average temperature in Sabirabad in 1954; 3, the percentage of diapausing pupae; 4, changes in pupation.
Arrows: the critical day-length and the onset of temperature inhibiting formation of diapause.

following season, since on account of the characteristics of the photoperiodic reaction in the larvae such pupae would not be cold-resistant.

Even from these selected examples it may be seen that variation in photoperiodic reaction under the influence of unusual temperature conditions has a detrimental effect on the future numbers of the population. An additional generation, which appears in warm years, does not as a rule contribute to the overwintering stock, and in consequence the numbers may be greatly diminished in the following year. Therefore a change in critical day-length caused by temperature must not be regarded as an adaptation to fluctuations in temperature conditions in a single locality. Apparently it is an adaptation to geographical variations in the temperature conditions, which provides greater possibilities for the spread of a population.

3. The causes of variation in insect phenology within the range of a species

The significance of intraspecific variation in physiological reactions becomes clear on analysis of the seasonal cycles in different climatic zones. We shall restrict our discussion to three species that show different forms of adaptation to geographical conditions.

(1) *Acronycta rumicis*. The geographical variation in phenology observed in *Acronycta rumicis* is typical of polycyclic species (DANILEVSKII, 1957a, 1957b).

Fig. 59 shows seasonal fluctuations in day-length, including twilight, in accordance with geographical latitude, and the phenology of this species in different zones. The first spring adults appear everywhere with the arrival of a stable temperature of 12°-14°. In Leningrad this is in the first 10 days of June; in the forest-steppe zone (Poltava) at the beginning of May; and in Sukhumi at the beginning of April. The main emergence usually begins 10 or 15 days later, and sometimes is greatly protracted.

The rest of the cycle proceeds differently in different zones. The number of generations is determined primarily by the sum-total of effective heat during the vegetative period. It agrees well with calculations made on the basis of the experimentally-established sum-total of effective temperatures, which is taken as 525-550 day-degrees above 10° for the full cycle (see Table 27).

In Leningrad province, temperature conditions during the summer (570 day-degrees) provide for development of only one generation, the pupae of which always enter diapause. The larvae develop during very long days (from 22 to 18 hours), but at temperatures always below 20°. In such conditions only obligatory diapause (as is seen from the data in Fig. 36) is possible in the

Leningrad race, in which the tendency to continuous development is completely suppressed at temperatures of 20° and under, even with 24-hour illumination. This feature of the Leningrad race, absent in the more southerly races, has a clearly adaptational character, which provides a monocyclic type of development in

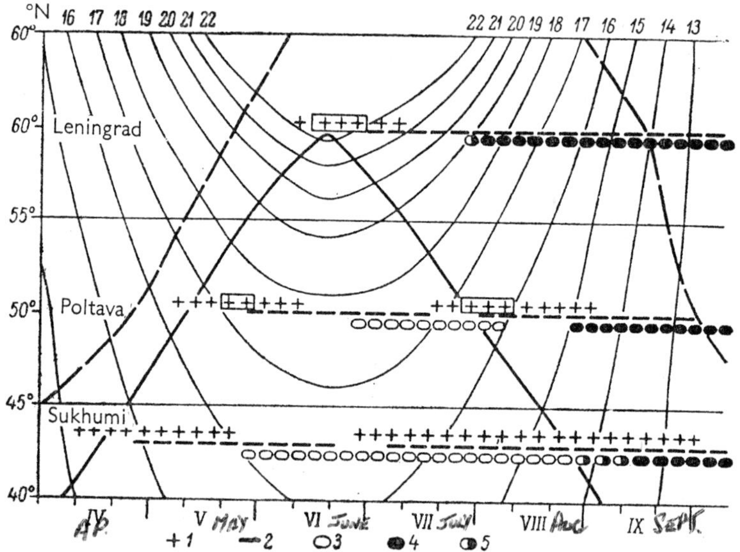

FIG. 59. The connection between the phenology of *Acronycta rumicis* in different natural zones and latitudinal fluctuations in day-length.

– – –: the limits of the period with temperature above 10°; ——: the limits of the period with day-length inducing non-diapause development; system of curves, changes in day-length.

1, adults (mass flight in rectangles); 2, larvae; 3, developing pupae; 4, diapausing pupae; 5, developing and diapausing pupae.

the long-day conditions of northern latitudes, where the active period is too short for two generations.

The phenology of *Acronycta rumicis* in the forest-steppe zone (Poltava), where this species develops in two generations, has been discussed above. From a comparison of the phenological patterns and experimental data on the reaction to the temperature and light conditions (see Fig. 36) it is easy to see that the absence of diapause in the first generation and its onset in the second may be due solely to the photoperiodic reaction observed in the local

(Belgorod-type) race. The reaction of other local races is clearly out of harmony with conditions in the forest-steppe zone. For instance, the Leningrad race, which is distinguished by a very high critical threshold (over 18°), would have to enter diapause even during the period of maximum day-length, i.e. in the first generation. For the Sukhumi race, on the other hand, the day-length at latitude 50°N. is too great even during the development of the second generation, and consequently there would be an emergence of third-generation adults, for whose further development the temperature would be too low.

In Sukhumi the temperature conditions (2,100 day-degrees) would theoretically enable four generations to develop, although MILYANOVSKII (1956a) observed only three, partly overlapping one another. The last adults are observed up to October, and larvae are still found in November. Individuals developing during the summer up to the beginning of September, i.e. in days longer than 14 hours 30 minutes, produce developing pupae, but later ones produce only diapausing pupae. Such phenology agrees only with the critical threshold of the Sukhumi form (see Figs. 30 and 36).

In this way the physiological characteristics of local races observed in laboratory experiments fully explain not only the variation in the number of generations with latitude but also the close agreement of the seasonal cycles with local climatic conditions.

(2) The Cabbage Moth *Barathra brassicae.* This species is distributed almost throughout the Palaearctic, except in the far north, from Western Europe to the shore of the Pacific Ocean and Japan. In the south it reaches the shore and islands of the Mediterranean, the subtropical zone of Asia Minor, and the mountain districts of north-western India and southern China; it is also known in North America. In spite of the extreme diversity of climatic conditions in this vast territory, the Cabbage Moth is a serious pest almost everywhere. Such exceptional ecological adaptability must be due to variability in seasonal-cyclic adaptations. Material received by our laboratory and investigated by Masaki (UCHIDA and MASAKI, 1954; MASAKI, 1956a, 1956b, 1957b, 1957c) relating to the Japanese form of the species enables us to discuss in general terms the features of zonal-geographical adaptations of the Cabbage Moth in different parts of its range.

Like *Acronycta rumicis*, *Barathra brassicae* is a polycyclic species with facultative diapause in the pupal stage. Its biology has been relatively well investigated within its European range and in Japan, but there are very few experimental data in the literature on the dependence of its development on external conditions. According to L. A. Arapova, for its Sumy and Batum populations the upper limit for development of all stages is slightly above 30°, and at 32° complete dying-off takes place. The optimum zone for development is between 16° and 25°. The lower threshold of effective temperatures, calculated from rates of development, is near 10°, but fluctuates somewhat in different stages. The sum-total of effective temperatures for full development in optimal conditions is 560-580 day-degrees, and with allowance for the period of maturation of the adults it may be taken as 600 day-degrees in round figures.

Among other biological characteristics we must mention the polyphagous habits of the larvae (KOZHANCHIKOV, 1950b) and their very hygrophilic nature, which are probably connected with their cryptic mode of life and their nocturnal activity, which reduce their effective day-length in comparison with species living in the open.

Diapausing pupae have considerable frost-resistance and survive freezing down to −18° and −19° (see Table 28). Since the pupae hibernate comparatively deep in the soil (as far as 9-12 cm down), this level of frost-resistance assures their survival even in northern regions with severe winters.

An outstanding feature of the diapausing pupae of the Cabbage Moth is their high resistance to desiccation, especially notable at high temperatures, in which pupae of *Acronycta rumicis* and most other species perish comparatively rapidly from dehydration (Table 39). This feature of the Cabbage Moth plays a leading role in the formation of its seasonal cycle in the southern districts of its range.

The geographical variation in photoperiodic reaction in the European and Caucasian forms of the Cabbage Moth leads to a gradual reduction in critical day-length in the southern forms as compared with the more northerly ones (see Fig. 31). Table 40 presents additional data relating the changes in critical day-length in various local races to the temperatures at which the larvae develop.

TABLE 39

Losses in weight (in mg per g of live weight in 10 days) of diapausing pupae depending on temperature and atmospheric humidity

Species	Relative atmospheric humidity (%)	Temperature					
		5	10	15	20	25	30
Barathra brassicae	40	2·2	2·7	3·5	4·0	5·0	5·2
	75	2·0	2·2	2·0	3·0	2·8	4·0
Acronycta rumicis	40	7·5	17·5	18·7	30·0	50·5	70·0
	75	9·5	10·0	14·5	15·0	16·5	32·5

TABLE 40

The effect of day-length and temperature on the onset of diapause in *Barathra brassicae* pupae (percentage diapausing)

Population	Temperature during larval development (°)	Day-length in hours							
		12	14	15	16	17	18	20	24
Leningrad	18	100	100	100	100	—	100	94	97
(60° N.)	25	100	100	100	91	70	57	35	25
Sumy	18	100	100	100	100	83	0	5	0
(51° N.)	25	100	97	87	3	0	0	0	0
Adzharian	18	100	100	100	0	2	0	2	0
(41° N.)	25	100	68	12	4	25	0	0	0

As with other polycyclic species, in the western part of the range of the Cabbage Moth the number of generations increases towards the south. In this respect we may divide the territory of the European part of the USSR and the Caucasus into three zones. North of the 53rd and 54th parallels of latitude only one generation develops, the pupae of which undergo diapause. Although occasionally one observes emergence of second-generation adults, their offspring do not succeed in developing and have no agricultural significance. The second zone, in which two generations regularly develop and become pests, embraces the forest-steppe and the steppe as far south as the northern Caucasus. In the warmest districts of the Black Sea coast and Transcaucasia three generations are observed. In the mountains, however, there is a decrease in the number of generations with altitude, down to one generation at an altitude of 1500 m. The phenology and conditions of development in the various zones are shown in Fig. 60.

The number of generations that develop depends directly on the temperature and the duration of the active period. It coincides with that calculated from the sum-total of effective temperatures, i.e. 600 day-degrees above 10°. The special features of the photoperiodic reaction in local races revealed by experiments, and their dependence on temperature, enable us to find the causes of some features of the preparation for diapause that have not been understood previously.

Monocyclism in the Cabbage Moth in the conditions of Leningrad province (Fig. 60, *a*) is due to the same causes as in *Acronycta rumicis*. The low summer temperature, which even in July is below 18°, not only gives an effective total too low for a second generation but also induces diapause, suppressing the photoperiodic reaction. In experiments with the Leningrad population (Table 40) at this temperature, even with continuous light, all pupae entered diapause. In the few years, however, when the temperature during the developmental period reaches 18°, one may expect to find a small number of active pupae. Apparently this explains the occasional appearance of adults at the end of August.

Phenological data available for other localities in the northern zone—Moscow (KAL'BERGENOV, 1951) and Sverdlovsk (NEDOVODIEV, 1953)—are similar to those for Leningrad. The temperature during the period of larval development does not exceed 18°, and the pupae there also always undergo diapause. In Moscow, however, in particularly warm years (e.g. in 1931) a partial emergence of second-generation adults has been observed (CHESNOKOV, 1936).

The similarity in the seasonal cycles of the Cabbage Moth in different parts of the northern zone shows that local populations react to the temperature and light conditions in the same way as the Leningrad population, and consequently they may be referred to as a single geographical race. In southern parts of the northern zone, because of the higher temperature, second-generation adults occur more frequently, which sometimes leads to a noticeable reduction in the number of hibernating pupae (CHESNOKOV,

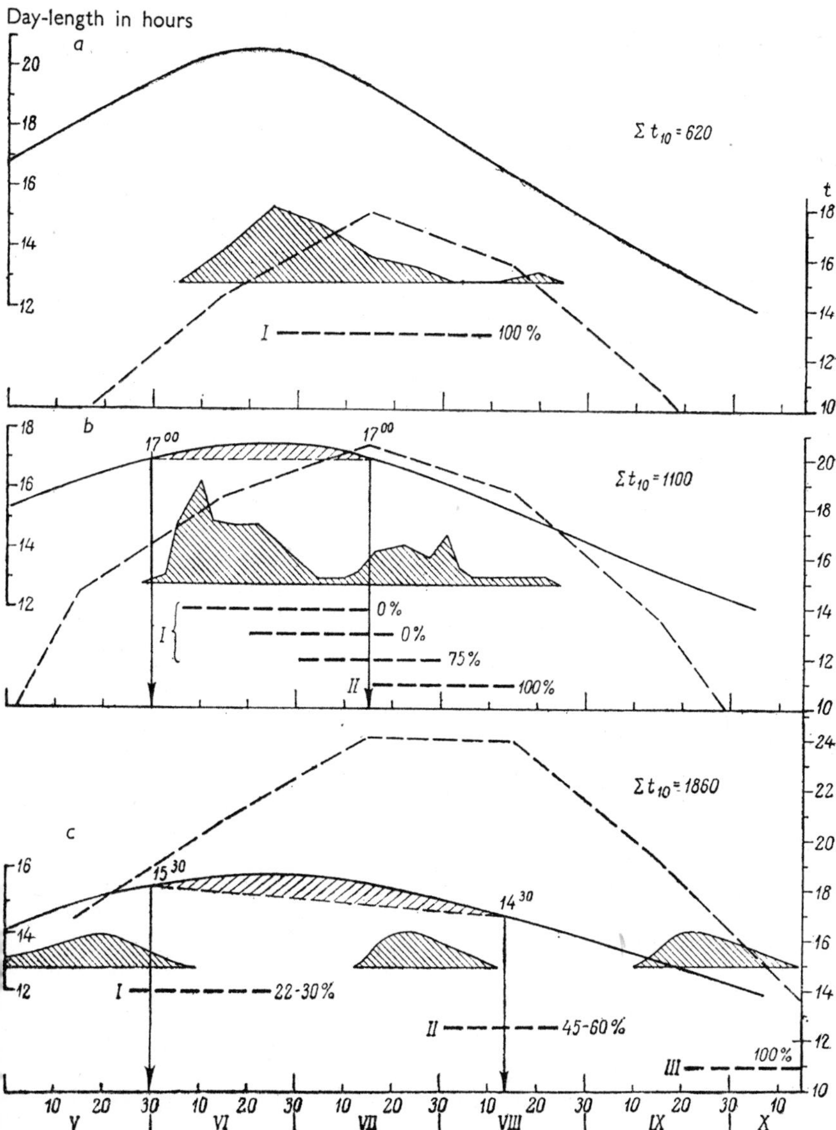

FIG. 60. The pattern of development of *Barathra brassicae* in different natural zones.

a, Leningrad province (60°N.); *b*, Voronezh province (62°N.); *c*, eastern Georgia (42°N.).
Arrows: critical day-length; *Light shading*: day-length inducing non-diapause development; *Curves*: flight of adults. *Roman numerals*: generations. *Heavy broken lines*: larvae. Figures denote percentage of diapausing pupae.

1936). Judging by the fragmentary phenological data, a race similar in its seasonal-cyclic reaction is distributed in the east throughout Siberia as far as Irkutsk.

In southern regions of the range of the Cabbage Moth its phenology is more complex than that of *Acronycta rumicis*.

At about the 50th parallel of latitude in the forest-steppe zone, in accordance with the sum-total of effective temperatures during the active period (1100 to 1300 day-degrees), a second generation, which succeeds in completing its development, is observed every year. A considerable proportion of first-generation pupae, however, enter diapause and hibernate: in Zhitomir and Kiev provinces from 10% to 50% of the first generation undergo diapause (KRISHTAL' and PETRUKHA, 1949); in Kharkov province about 40%, and in Voronezh province about 45% (KONAKOV, 1927); and in the neighbourhood of Saratov 70%-80% (KLEMENTS, 1958). This affects the numbers in the second generation. According to the records made by KONAKOV (1926) in Voronezh province, second-generation adults formed only 30% of the total number trapped. A similar proportion is found in specimens taken in light-traps at the Poltava experimental station. It is characteristic that the numbers of *Acronycta rumicis*, *Polia dissimilis*, and other species that do not undergo diapause in the first generation are always much higher in the second generation.

The reason for the onset of diapause in the first generation has not yet been discovered; there has only been noted a distinct connection with the dates of larval development. According to the observations of KONAKOV (1926) and KLEMENTS (1958), diapause is absent only in early pupae; later the number of active pupae falls off rapidly. It is not possible to explain this phenomenon as an effect of temperature, but it serves as a direct indication of the dependence on seasonal variation in day-length. Let us examine the extent to which the photoperiodic reaction of the forest-steppe race of the Cabbage Moth explains its phenology in this zone.

Fig. 60, *b* shows the patterns of emergence of adults, periods of development, and percentage in diapause, according to the observations of KONAKOV (1926) in Voronezh province. The day-length, as in all other species with cryptic modes of life, is taken as including half of the twilight period. According to data from experiments with the Sumy populations of Cabbage Moths (see Table 40), the critical day-length at the temperature of 19° to 20° observed in nature should lie between 16 hours 30 minutes and 17 hours.

As can be seen from the diagram, the period when the day-length exceeds this figure is very limited, lasting from about the end of May until mid-July. Since the adults appear comparatively late—at the beginning of June—and their period of activity is much prolonged, first-generation larvae are found from June 10 to mid-August, and the development of a large proportion of them takes place when the day-length is below the critical level. Therefore it is easy to understand why about half of them enter diapause. Konakov stressed the fact that active pupae develop only from larvae hatched before June 20; of those appearing at the beginning of July about 70% undergo diapause, and later ones produce only hibernating pupae. This fully agrees with the photoperiodic conditions. From Fig. 60, *b* it is seen that the development of the first set of larvae takes place during the long-day period, and that of later ones when the day-length is at the critical level or below it. The rapid increase in the number of diapausing individuals results in an abrupt fall in the number of second-generation adults, starting in early August.

Second-generation larvae, even those produced by the earliest adults, develop in late July and August in short-day conditions, and all of them enter diapause. The temperature at that time fluctuates within the same range as at the beginning of the development of the first generation. Therefore the deciding role played by photoperiodic conditions is particularly evident.

The method of analysis used also well explains the difference in the numbers of generations of the Cabbage Moth at stations on the flood-plain and on high ground in the Saratov district. According to KLEMENTS (1958), on the higher ground the Cabbage Moth produces two generations, but even in the first many remain in the pupal stage to hibernate. The phenological periods of development and the external conditions there are similar to those described for Voronezh province. First-generation larvae begin to appear on June 10, but maximum hatching takes place in the first 10 days of July. The critical day-length occurs in mid-July, which explains the high percentage of diapausing pupae (up to 70-85%).

In the Volga flood-plain only one generation ever develops.

Because of prolonged spring flooding, the development of pupae and the emergence of adults are much delayed there. The first larvae appear only in the second ten days of July, and most of the larvae, according to Klements, hatch in early August. This coincides in time with the development of second-generation larvae in the unflooded areas. As day-length by then is already well below the critical level, in both cases diapause must inevitably be induced.

The phenology of the Cabbage Moth is most complex in the Caucasus. According to Dolidze (1957a, 1957b, 1957c), in low-lying districts of Georgia up to an altitude of 500 m the moth develops in three generations; up to 1100-1200 m it has two, and at 1300-1700 m only one. Calculations of the effective temperatures for points at these altitudes show very good agreement with these data. In the low-lying zone (Tiflis, 409 m) the sum-total of temperatures above 10° is 1860 day-degrees, which enables three generations to develop. In the intermediate zone (Dusheti, 890 m) it falls to 1230 day-degrees, closely corresponding to two generations. At an altitude of 1715 m (Akhalkalaki) the sum-total of temperatures is 590 day-degrees, i.e. it reaches the limit for a single generation.

The phenology of the Cabbage Moth in the low-lying zone, according to Dolidze, is shown in Fig. 60, *c*. The adults appear in late April, and mass flights of them begin in mid-May at a temperature of 17·6°; the second generation appears in the second ten days of July, and the third in mid-September. The intervals between separate generations also agree closely with those calculated from the sum-totals of effective temperatures.

In spite of the long duration of the active period of growth and the high temperature, diapausing pupae appear even in the first generation; their number increases in the second and reaches 100% in the third. The reason for this lies in the relatively high critical threshold for the southern race of the Cabbage Moth (see Table 40) and in the short day-length in these latitudes. Since the effective day-length in mid-summer in the latitude of Tiflis does not exceed 15 hours 30 minutes, one must always expect a certain percentage of diapause. The actual amount of it will depend on temperature conditions during the larval developmental period. A predominance of active development is possible only from June 10 to August 10. In the third generation development takes place entirely in day-lengths of less than 13 hours, and diapause will occur irrespective of the temperature.

Dolidze's observations on the life-history of diapausing pupae of the first generation are interesting. A considerable proportion of them (25%-30%) do not hibernate and resume development in autumn, producing adults at the same time as the third generation.

Consequently the Cabbage Moth undergoes a short diapause of the summer type in Georgian conditions. Instances of the resumption of development by diapausing pupae that were kept for two or three months at a temperature of 25° were also observed in our experiments. These characteristics of diapause in the southern race recall the biology of the Cabbage Moth in the subtropical zone of Japan.

In Japan the variation in the phenology of the Cabbage Moth with geographical latitude is of a very unusual kind. According to MASAKI (1956a), in Hokkaido (Sapporo, 43°N.) the moth develops from July through September in two successive generations, of which the second undergoes diapause. Farther south, in spite of the rapid increase in the sum-total of effective heat, the number of generations does not increase, and even on the Ryukyu Islands (Amami, 28° 23′ N.), where the year-round temperature is considerably above the threshold for development and six or seven generations might be expected, only two are actually observed. Only on Hokkaido is there no interruption between the summer generations. In all more southerly districts development takes place during the spring and autumn periods of moderate temperature; there is a summer break between the generations, which increases progressively towards the south and in Amami even exceeds the winter resting period in duration.

The role of physiological adaptations of local races in these phenomena was demonstrated by MASAKI (1956a) by means of parallel investigations of 14 populations from different points in Japan, from northern Hokkaido to the Ryukyus. Comparing his data with those given above, we may observe differences in the geographical variation of seasonal-cyclic reactions of the Japanese and European forms of the Cabbage Moth.

Only the northern populations from the island of Hokkaido react to photoperiodic conditions in the way usual for the European form, developing continuously in long-day and diapausing in short-day conditions.

The critical threshold for the Sapporo population at a temperature of 24° is 15 hours (Uchida and Masaki, 1954), i.e. it corresponds approximately to that of our forest-steppe form. All the more southerly forms, even at a high temperature (24°-28°), produce diapausing pupae both in short-day (12 hours) and in long-day (16 hours) conditions, and in effect are monocyclic.

The type of diapause, however, varies greatly according to the light conditions in which preparation for it takes place. A short day (12 hours) induces prolonged diapause of the winter type, which is uniform in all populations. Low temperature is necessary for its reactivation. At a temperature of 26°, without cooling, it lasts from 190 days to a year or more.

A long day induces short-term diapause of the summer type, which normally ends without cooling. Its duration is specific for each population and increases regularly in the more southerly races (Fig. 61). Thus in populations from Hirosaki (northern Honshu) with a constant temperature of 26° summer diapause lasts less than two months, but in populations from Amami it lasts more than four months and is scarcely distinguishable from winter diapause. The differences in photoperiodic reaction and duration of diapause have an adaptational character. In Masaki's experiments they remained unchanged throughout two or three laboratory generations.

The duration of summer diapause induced by long days depends to a great extent on the temperature at which the pupae are kept. Thus in populations from southern Japan diapause lasted 70 days at a temperature of 26°, 33 days at 19°, and only 19 days at 15°. Summer diapause may not appear at all if the pupae encounter a temperature that is low but still effective for development. Consequently its appearance depends not only on conditions affecting the larvae but also on the influence of temperature on the pupae.

The results of Masaki's experimental investigations fully explain the unusual phenology of the Cabbage Moth in the subtropical climatic conditions in Japan. They show that even in southern latitudes the photoperiodic conditions are still the main regulator of seasonal development. There is no doubt that the capacity for prolonged summer rest is connected with the exceptionally high resistance of the Cabbage Moth pupae to the desiccating effect of high temperature.

The adaptational significance of summer diapause is less clear. It is mostly observed where the average monthly temperature exceeds 24°. In laboratory conditions such temperatures have not yet proved detrimental to the development of the pre-imaginal stages of the Cabbage Moth, but in nature they must be accompanied by sublethal overheating. It is possible that the moderate temperature-optimum of the adults, characteristic of the majority of nocturnal Lepidoptera, is of great importance in this connection.

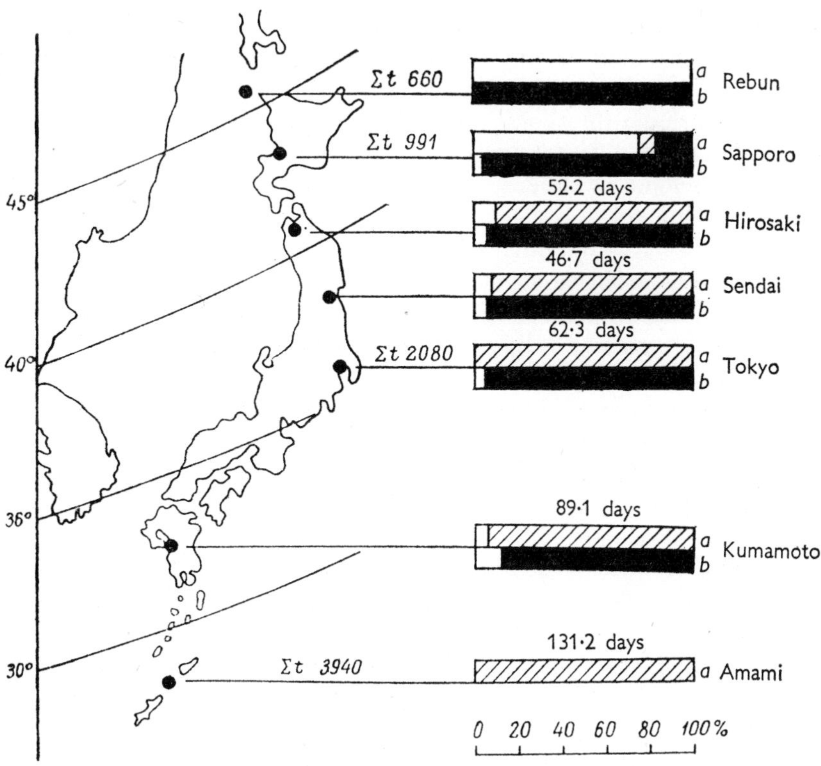

FIG. 61. The characteristics of the seasonal development and diapause of *Barathra brassicae* in Japan (from Masaki, 1956).

The diagram shows the percentage of different types of pupae as a result of the influence on larvae of (*a*) long and (*b*) short days. *White*: active pupae; *shaded*: short diapause of summer type (figures show duration); *black*: winter diapause.

The fact that the ranges of the two main physiological races in Japan are separated by the Tsugaru Strait is evidence of the important role played in their formation and distribution by historical factors acting together with ecological factors. This applies also to the existence of the northern type of seasonal-cyclic reactions in the race from the island of Hokkaido, in whose fauna northern elements are abundantly represented.

As a result of the analysis of geographical variation in the seasonal cycles of the Cabbage Moth in the western part of the Palaearctic and in Japan, one gets an impression of essential differences in their physiological mechanisms. Whereas in the European form this variation consists mainly in changes in the photoperiodic threshold, in the Japanese form it consists in the evolution of different types of diapause in accordance with the photoperiodic conditions. The forms investigated by us, however, are distributed only between 60° and 40°N, while the Japanese race with its summer diapause occupies a range from 40° to 28°N. It is very probable that in the most southerly regions of the western Palaearctic the tendency towards the evolution of summer diapause, already noted in our Transcaucasian form, will intensify to such an extent that the seasonal cycle will pass into the Japanese type. We may surmise that this is one of the common methods of adaptation of northern forms to subtropical climates.

(3) The Satin Moth *Leucoma salicis*. The Satin Moth is interesting as an example of a species which retains a monocyclic type of development throughout almost the whole extent of its vast range. Only in a few districts in the extreme south do two generations develop. The main outlines of its biology are well known. Larvae of the second and third instars hibernate in cracks in bark. Statements about overwintering eggs (RIMSKII-KORSAKOV and GUSEV, 1949) have not been confirmed. Spring development is comparatively rapid, and adults appear in midsummer. The larvae, which hatch early, enter diapause after two or three weeks of feeding, and go into hibernation long before the onset of cold weather.

A similar type of seasonal cycle is characteristic of many dendrophilic Lepidoptera, e.g. *Euproctis chrysorrhoea*, *E. similis*, and *Dasychira fascelina*. Their universal monocyclism has up to now been explained by the theory that diapause is an inevitable stage in larval development and is induced by internal causes, irrespective of external conditons (KOZHANCHIKOV, 1948, 1950a). But since the facultative character of diapause in these species has been demonstrated experimentally (GEISPITS, 1953), it is evident that in nature also their seasonal cycles are under the direct control of external conditions. On the basis of eco-physiological data, we shall try to discover the causes of monocyclic development in localities differing in climate and in the conditions which cause polycyclism in the southern regions.

The features of the photoperiodic reaction in the Satin Moth have been described above. In places where only one generation is observed, from Leningrad to the Ukraine and southern Kazakhstan, a race with a single type of reaction to the light conditions occurs (see Fig. 49). At a temperature of 23°-25° non-diapause development of this race is possible only with a day-length of over 20 hours. To this we must add that only larvae of the youngest instars are sensitive to light. Individual variation in the reaction is very great, and even at the optimal day-length not all the larvae develop. Among the offspring of different females the number that develop fluctuates from 20% to 60%. The temperature is of very great importance. At 20° photoperiodic reaction is completely suppressed and all larvae enter obligatory diapause.

When these data are considered in conjunction with geographical variations in temperature and in day-length they lead to an unusual conclusion. A combination of conditions necessary for non-diapause development—temperatures over 20° and day-lengths over 18 hours—is not found anywhere. Consequently the above race cannot produce more than one generation anywhere in natural conditions, but in different climatic conditions different factors are of primary importance in this respect.

Table 41 presents data on the conditions during the development of young Satin Moth larvae in the places from which the populations investigated in our experiments were obtained. In Leningrad province, where the larvae hatch during days still long enough for active development, photoperiodic reaction is not displayed, because the temperature is too low. In southern regions (the Ukraine and southern Kazakhstan) partial active development is possible in the temperature conditions, but inadequate day-length induces the onset of complete diapause. It is obvious that farther south, because of the still shorter day, monocyclic development will be retained in this race, regardless of high temperature.

TABLE 41

The principal elements of phenology and external conditions during the development of the three youngest instars of *Leucoma salicis* larvae in different geographical regions

Place	Geo-graphical latitude	Time of flight of adults	Development of young larvae	Conditions for development of young larvae		% of diapausing larvae	
				Tempera-ture (°)	Day-length (in hours and minutes)	In nature	Expected from experimental data
Leningrad province	60° N.	20 VI-15 VIII	15 VII-25 VIII	17-15	20.40-16.25	100	100
Ukraine	50° N.	1 VII-30 VII	15 VII-15 VIII	21-19	17.20-15.30	100	100
Southern Kazakhstan (altitude 800-1100 m)	43° N.	1 VII-20 VII	15 VII-15 VIII	22-20	16.00-14.50	100	100
Southern Armenia (altitude 860 m)	40° N.						
1st generation		1 VI-15 VI	10 VI-30 VI	21-24	16.00-15.05	partial diapause	10-20
2nd generation		5 VIII-25 VIII	20 VIII-10 IX	24-22	14.30-13.35	usually 100	100
Southern Armenia, highlands (altitude 1950 m)	40° N.	1 VIII-15 VIII	25 VIII-25 IX	16-12	14.30-13.00	100	100

It is by the same mechanism, apparently, that monocyclism is retained everywhere by *Euproctis chrysorrhoea* and *E. similis*.

There is another unexplained element in the phenology of the Satin Moth, to which Geispits has drawn attention in the above-quoted work. Everywhere from Leningrad to the southern limits of the range of the monocyclic race the adults appear at very close calendar dates. This is seen from the dates listed in Table 41. Even in Sukhumi, according to MILYANOVSKII (1956a), the adults appear in June and July, which almost coincides with the dates for the northern provinces. Since in the south effective temperatures in spring begin much earlier and their sum-total is considerably greater, we must conclude that there are some undiscovered conditions reducing the rate of development. Judging by phenological data, the above phenomenon is characteristic of many monocyclic species of insects.

GEISPITS (1953) has expressed the opinion, based on the results of experiments with *Euproctis chrysorrhoea*, that the delaying factor is the short day of southern latitudes, which retards spring reactivation of hibernating pupae and the rate of their further development. We do not have at our disposal, however, sufficient experimental and field data on the Satin Moth to verify this very plausible theory.

The southern limit of distribution of the monocyclic form of the Satin Moth is apparently determined by summer and autumn conditions. As diapause begins there at midsummer, diapausing larvae are exposed for a long time to high temperatures. Such conditions are obviously unfavourable for them. In laboratory experiments at a temperature above 20° and relative humidity of 60%-70%, death from desiccation commenced among diapausing larvae in 1½ to 2 months. In these circumstances probably lies the reason for the formation of a special polycyclic race of the Satin Moth in the Mediterranean climatic conditions of southern Europe, in Transcaucasia, and in certain areas of Central Asia (Kirghizia).

In its photoperiodic reaction the southern Armenian race differs greatly from the monocyclic ones (see Fig. 49). At a temperature of 25°, even with a short day (9 to 12 hours), diapause does not commence in all larvae, and with a day of more than 13 hours only active development is observed in the first generation. In larvae that feed on older willow leaves (second generation) the critical threshold is raised considerably. As is seen from the data presented in Table 42, temperature has a very strong effect on the photoperiodic reaction in the larvae: at 15° diapause is induced in any light conditions.

TABLE 42

The effect of day-length and temperature on the onset of diapause in *Leucoma salicis* larvae (percentage diapausing)

Population	Temperature of experiment (°)	Day-length in hours							
		12	14	15	16	17	18	20	24
Leningrad	25	100	100	100	100	100	99·2	81·0	100
	20	100	100	100	100	100	100	100	100
Belgorod	25	100	100	100	100	100	91·5	77·5	100
	20	100	100	100	100	100	100	100	100
Alma-Ata	23·5	100	100	100	100	—	88·6	87·4	45·1
Southern Armenian	25	66·3	0	0	0	0	0	0	0
	20	100	100	—	51·0	—	45·3	14·9	5·6
	15	100	100	—	100	—	100	—	100

These experimental data are in full agreement with the results of phenological observations by AVAKYAN (1953) on the seasonal course of development of the Satin Moth in the valleys of southern Armenia, where it produces two generations. The development of overwintering larvae begins there at the end of April, and adults appear by the beginning of June. Larvae of the next generation hatch in mid-June. Development of the first three instars, as is seen from Table 41, takes place during 16-hour days and at temperatures somewhat higher than 20°. In such conditions, according to experimental data, one may expect to find a moderate number—approximately 25%—of diapausing larvae. According to Avakyan's observations, some of the first-generation larvae (percentage unknown) actually go into hibernation, but they usually do not survive till autumn, and the wintering stock is made up from the next generation. Pre-diapause development of the second generation takes place from the last ten days of August to early September, when day-length decreases to 14 hours. At temperatures below 25° in such conditions practically complete diapause must result, but with high temperatures development of the early larvae may continue. Therefore it is understandable that during the warm autumn of 1953 partial development of a third generation was observed. The same type of phenology has been described for the Satin Moth in Yugoslavia (SERAFIMOVSKI, 1954). Apparently a race, physiologically very close to the southern Armenian one, occurs there.

In the mountain districts of Armenia the Satin Moth produces only one generation, which fact AVAKYAN (1953) correctly attributes to the influence of a much colder climate. Field observations have shown that at altitudes above 2,000 m the development of hibernating larvae begins at the end of May, i.e. a month later than in the Ararat valley. Because of the low temperature they develop slowly, and the adults appear only in early August, when second-generation adults are already flying in the valley. The young larvae go into hibernation at the end of September.

The phenological data are not sufficient for us to decide to which race the mountain populations belong. Comparison of the data presented in Tables 41 and 42 leads to the conclusion that in the temperature conditions obtaining in the highlands a single generation with full diapause may occur both in the northern (monocyclic) and in the southern (polycyclic) race. Experimental investigation of the mountain populations may provide valuable information on the origin and the interrelations of the two principal forms of the Satin Moth.

The potential capacity of the northern race of the Satin Moth for continuous development, as we have seen, is not realized anywhere in natural conditions. This poses the question of the biological significance of its photoperiodic reaction. Apparently in this case it is not a special ecological adaptation, but only a vestige of an earlier regulatory system. Therefore, as with the majority of other species that have photoperiodic regulation of seasonal development, the original form must be considered to be the polycyclic southern race, in spite of the fact that at present it has a restricted and even an interrupted range. The northern race, which probably evolved in a mountain climate, has occupied the greater part of the present range of the species.

4. The possibility of spread and acclimatization of local races

From analysis of geographical variations in phenology we may make an important deduction.

Perfect adaptation of the photoperiodic reaction of separate geographical populations to local conditions of climate and light lessens their ecological adaptability and ability to spread, actively or passively, even within the range of the species. Calculation shows that the transportation of forms adapted to the photoperiodic and temperature conditions of a particular zone into districts with different conditions must lead to such profound disharmony between their seasonal cycles and the climatic rhythm that acclimatization will prove to be impossible. This must be especially manifest in the case of the transfer of southern, relatively short-day, forms to more northern districts with a long summer day. In such cases the impossibility of timely initiation of diapause results in mortality during hibernation. On the other hand, when northern forms move to southern regions diapause will begin too early, and the wintering phases will be exposed for a long time to the action of high temperatures, which also can lead to unfavourable consequences. Changes in the norms of photoperiodic reaction under the influence of the temperature conditions can only partially correct the lack of co-ordination of the cycle, but cannot eliminate it entirely.

At the same time, experimental investigations have not disclosed any considerable intraspecific geographical variation in temperature requirements during the period of active growth and development, or of frost-resistance in the diapausing stages. This enables us to deduce that temperature adaptations cannot play a substantial role in the phenomena of distribution and acclimatization within the range of a species.

In the light of existing views on the factors which restrict the distribution and the possibility of acclimatization of insects, these conclusions may seem surprising. Up to the present intraspecific seasonal-cyclic adaptations, as a restricting factor, have not been taken into account at all, and primary importance has been ascribed to temperature and food adaptations and to biotic relations.

In order to check our conclusions experimentally, we set up

experiments in the rearing of southern populations of several species of Lepidoptera in the field conditions of the northern zone. The most complete data were obtained for *Acronycta rumicis* (DANILEVSKII, 1957a). Various geographical populations of this species—Leningrad, Belgorod, and Sukhumi—were reared simultaneously in the vicinity of Leningrad for the three periods that

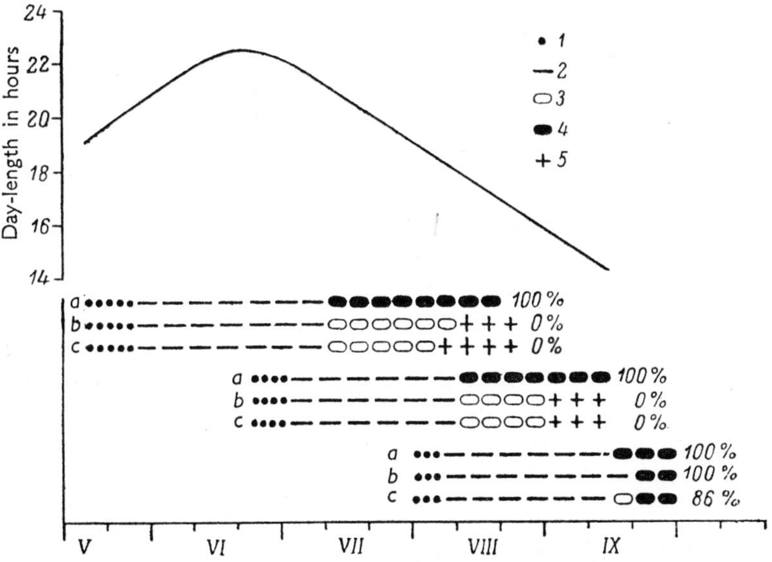

FIG. 62. The development of different populations of *Acronycta rumicis* in natural conditions in Leningrad province.

Populations: *a*, Leningrad; *b*, Belgorod; *c*, Sukhumi. The figures denote the percentage of diapausing pupae.
1, eggs; 2, larvae; 3, developing pupae; 4, diapausing pupae; 5, adults.

correspond to the average natural phenology of the local population. The pattern of the experiments and the principal results are given in Fig. 62. These data show, above all, the synchronous development of all three populations and consequently the uniform dependence of their rate of growth on temperature. According to microclimatic measurements, the sum-total of effective temperatures for the larvae amounted to from 248 to 260 day-degrees in the different series, which closely coincides with the values calculated from laboratory data. It is important also that in field conditions no differences were observed in the viability of the various populations. Even in autumn no signs of depression of the southern forms, as compared with the local one, were observed. The weight of pupae and the fecundity of adults obtained from them remained normal.

Therefore the temperature conditions during the active period do not limit the spread of local populations within the range of a species. Nevertheless, very wide differences in the formation of wintering stages are observed among them. The Leningrad population, as was to be expected, produced only diapausing pupae. Both of the southern populations differed markedly from it. In the first two series the larvae completed their development and pupated long before the arrival of their critical day-length. As a result all the pupae developed and produced adults, none remaining to form the wintering stock. Only in the last series did the day-length in September, together with the temperature, prove to be below the critical level for the Belgorod and near the threshold for the Sukhumi population; therefore diapause occurred in all pupae of the former and in 80% of the latter.

The results of observations on what happened afterwards to the diapausing pupae are of importance in finally settling the question of the possibility of adapting southern forms to the conditions in Leningrad province. In the following year adults of all three populations emerged simultaneously, at the usual dates (June 13 to 21) for the local form, from pupae that had overwintered in natural conditions. Larvae obtained from them developed before the beginning of August in long-day conditions, and therefore the southern forms did not produce diapausing pupae capable of hibernation.

The experiments made therefore confirmed that it was impossible to acclimatize the southern forms of *Acronycta rumicis* in the north. The deciding factor is the lack of harmony between their photoperiodic reaction and the conditions that obtain there during the period of development of the local form.

GEISPITS (1958) traced the development in Leningrad of two geographical populations of the Pine Moth *Dendrolimus pini*, which is especially interesting as this species develops everywhere in a single generation. When specimens of the Voronezh population and the local population were reared simultaneously during periods normal for Leningrad province (egg-laying on July 11, emergence of larvae on July 26), all larvae of the Leningrad form entered diapause at the end of September. Larvae of the southern form remained active until late autumn and perished, not having prepared for hibernation. That was due to the fact that they require a shorter day than does the Leningrad form to prepare for diapause (see Table 26). As such a condition comes late, at the beginning of September, and as the southern form requires not fewer than 50 days at low temperature to complete its preparation for diapause, the larvae encountered the frost period while still in an active and not a frost-resistant state.

The lack of adaptability of a southern form to the photoperiodic conditions of northern latitudes is also clearly exhibited in *Dasychira pudibunda.* A unique feature of the seasonal cycle in this species is that, in addition to pupal diapause in winter, its larval development is checked in summer by the long days. According to the observations of K. F. Geispits in Leningrad, larvae of the local form renew active development after the summer check in mid-August, and pupate in mid-September. For the Sukhumi form, which is adapted to the shorter day of southern latitudes, day-length is still too great at that time and the larvae remain in a state of arrested development. The stimulating day-length for them (less than 14 hours) comes only in the second half of September, i.e. when further development and pupation are inhibited by the temperature being too low. In an experiment, larvae of this form continued feeding until mid-October and perished with the onset of frost.

Therefore the photoperiodic adaptations of local races limit the possibilities of movements within the species' range, in species which differ widely in their biology and seasonal cycles. The same results were obtained with several other Lepidoptera. The Sukhumi forms of *Pieris brassicae*, *Spilosoma menthastri*, and *Barathra brassicae* did not enter diapause at the phenological dates normal for the Leningrad forms, although in their natural environment the pupae of these Sukhumi forms entered diapause at later periods of development in cold autumns and underwent normal hibernation.

Restricted adaptability to a new climatic environment, however, does not always appear to such an extent. For instance, the Satin Moth *Leucoma salicis*, when transported from Belgorod province to Leningrad, develops there normally and enters hibernation at the same time as the local form. This has a natural explanation in the fact that, unlike the majority of other species, the Satin Moth is represented by the same physiological race in both the forest-steppe zone and the north. One might expect that interchange of populations of *Pieris brassicae* between these zones would also present no difficulties, since they are found in laboratory experiments to be identical in their photoperiodic reaction. Therefore a method based on climatic similarities is inadequate for estimating the possibilities of acclimatization, as the deciding factor is not the region of origin of a species but the extent of the physiological differences between populations, which is not identical in different species.

The adaptational possibilities of local populations depend also on the relative roles played by temperature and light in regulating diapause. Forms in which diapause has little relation to temperature have more difficulty in adapting themselves to conditions in zones foreign to them. This may be seen from the following examples.

The Sukhumi form of the Corn Borer *Pyrausta nubilalis*, according to Du Chzhen'-ven', is distinguished by a very stable photoperiodic threshold, which at temperatures from 18° to 25° remains unchanged at 15 hours 30 minutes. When this form was reared at different periods of the year in Leningrad conditions diapause did not occur, and even larvae of the latest series, developing from July 15 to early September, all pupated, in spite of the fact that in the last instar they had already experienced a period of very low temperature. It is of interest to note that larvae of another form of this species, coming from northern Ukraine (Glukhov), whose critical threshold at a temperature of 25° is 17 hours but at lower temperatures is much higher, did not pupate, and all entered diapause.

Observations on the Armenian form of *Leucoma salicis* are particularly illuminating. At high temperature (25°) it differs sharply from the Leningrad form, and even in short days it develops partially without diapause; but at lower temperatures the differences between them are smoothed out. At 18°, even with a long day (20 hours), more than half of the larvae of the Armenian form enter diapause, and at 15° all of them enter diapause with any light conditions. The critical threshold rises only when the larvae feed on more mature willow leaves.

In field conditions in Leningrad province larvae of the Armenian form, obtained in the first half of summer (egg-laying June 3, hatching June 23), developed without interruption and produced second-generation adults in late August. But when they developed during periods corresponding to the normal phenology of the Leningrad form (egg-laying July 24, hatching August 7) larvae of the southern form, on reaching the second instar, all went into hibernation simultaneously with the local form. The day-length during their development period was still considerable—from 18 hours to 16 hours 30 minutes—and the temperature for most of the period was fairly high (19°-20°), but towards the end of their second instar it suddenly fell to 11°, which apparently determined the rapid onset of diapause. Such sharp differences in preparation for the wintering stages in accordance with the periods of development were probably due to the weather conditions during the summer of 1959. In ordinary years one may expect only some individuals to go into hibernation. A certain number of diapausing individuals were observed during investigation of the southern forms of *Trachea atriplicis*, *Loxostege sticticalis*, and several other species, whose photoperiodic reactions have not yet been adequately studied. In general all of these data confirm the limited possibility of extending southern forms towards the north, as they require a short day-length for the formation of a wintering stock.

With regard to the opposite process, i.e. the southward movement of northern forms adapted to long days and a short growing period, we have no direct field observations at our disposal. There are no grounds for doubting that in this case also acclimatization will be difficult and will be determined to a considerable extent by the resistance of the diapausing stages to high temperature and drought. Therefore different species would have different possibilities of extending their range southward.

The significance of the observed facts is obvious, not only with regard to a number of general problems in insect ecology, but also in problems of a purely practical nature.

We have to take account of the adaptation of races to local conditions and their physiological differences when we are dividing the ranges of pest species into ecological regions and forecasting the extent of plagues of them due to mass reproduction.

The data obtained show the necessity of reviewing the present scope and methods of acclimatizing parasitic and predatory insects used for the biological control of pests. The casual selection of forms for acclimatization, without consideration of the specific adaptation of local races to a definite rhythm of climate and to zonal characteristics of the light conditions, is apparently one of the chief reasons for the lack of success in acclimatizing entomophagous insects that has been observed not only in the introduction of foreign species but also in transportation within the range of a species.

Finally, a knowledge of intraspecific differentiation enables us to discover, from an ecological point of view, the paths of invasion of pests barred by quarantine regulations, and to determine the degree to which they are a danger in other geographical areas.

Further investigations, combining eco-physiological and field methods, will enable us to solve these important problems.

APPENDIX

LIST OF SPECIES OF INSECTS AND MITES WHOSE REACTION TO DAY-LENGTH HAS BEEN INVESTIGATED

In the column 'Type of reaction' the following abbreviations are used: L = long-day type of reaction; S = short-day type; M = intermediate type; N = photoperiodically-neutral species.

In the column 'Author', LSU stands for Leningrad State University.

Name of species	Phenomena regulated by day-length	Type of reaction	Author
LEPIDOPTERA			
Tortricidae			
Laspeyresia molesta Busck.	Prepupal diapause	L	Dickson and Sanders, 1945; Dickson, 1949
Enarmonia (Carpocapsa) pomonella L.	,, ,,	L	Dickson, 1949
Polychrosis botrana Schiff.	Pupal diapause	L	Komarova, 1949, 1954
Acalla fimbriana Thnbg. = *lubricana* Mn.	Imaginal diapause	L	Kuznetsov, 1955
Tortrix viridana L.	—	N	LSU lab. data
Pandemis corylana F.	Larval diapause	L	Danilevskii, 1957a
Pandemis ribeana Hb.	,, ,,	L	Danilevskii, 1956
Capua reticulana Hb.	,, ,,	L	Danilevskii, 1957a
Cacoecia podana Sc.	,, ,,	L	Danilevskii, 1956
Cacoecia rosana L.	—	N	LSU lab. data
Zygaenidae			
Harrisina brillians	Pupal diapause	L	Smith and Langston, 1953
Plutellidae			
Plutella maculipennis Curt.	—	N	Atwal, 1955
Gelechiidae			
Gelechia malvella Hb.	Prepupal diapause	L	LSU lab. data

Name of species	Phenomena regulated by day-length	Type of reaction	Author
Pyralididae			
Chilo suppresalis Wlk.	Larval diapause	L	Inouye and Kamano, 1957
Plodia interpunctella Hb.	Prepupal diapause	L	Danilevskii, 1956
Loxostege sticticalis L.	,, ,,	L	
Loxostege verticalis L.	,, ,,	L	
Pyraustidae			
Pyrausta nubilalis Hb.	,, ,,	L	Mutchmor and Beckel, 1958, 1959; Mutchmor, 1959; Beck and Hanec, 1960
Pieridae			
Aporia crataegi L.	—	N	Maslennikova, 1958
Pieris brassicae L.	Pupal diapause	L	Danilevskii and Geispits, 1948; Geispits, 1953; Doskočil, 1956a; Maslennikova, 1958, 1959; Bünning and Joerrens, 1959; Danilevskii and Goryshin, 1960
Pieris rapae L.	,, ,,	L	Danilevskii, 1956
Pieris napi L.	,, ,,	L	LSU lab. data
Papilionidae			
Papilio podalirius L.	,, ,,	L	Wohlfahrt, 1957
Nymphalidae			
Araschnia levana-prorsa L.	Pupal diapause, seasonal dimorphism	L	Danilevskii, 1948; Müller, 1955a, 1955c, 1956, 1957b, 1959
Vanessa io L.	Imaginal diapause	L	LSU lab. data
Sphingidae			
Sphinx ligustri L.	—	N	LSU lab. data
Smerinthus ocellatus L.	Pupal diapause	L	Danilevskii, 1956, 1957a
Smerinthus populi L.	,, ,,	L	
Notodontidae			
Lophopteryx camelina L.	Pupal diapause	L	LSU lab. data
Pygaera pigra Hufn.	,, ,,	L	Danilevskii, 1948

Name of species	Phenomena regulated by day-length	Type of reaction	Author
Geometridae			
Abraxas miranda Butl.	Pupal diapause	S	Masaki, 1957a, 1958
Bombycidae			
Bombyx mori L.	Embr. diapause	S	Kogure, 1933
Attacidae			
Antheraea pernyi Guer., polycyclic form	Pupal diapause	L	Tanaka, 1944-53; Andrianova, 1948; Belov, 1951
A. pernyi, monocyclic form	,, ,,	S	Danilevskii and Geispits, 1948
Lasiocampidae			
Dendrolimus pini L.	Larval diapause	L	Geispits, 1949, 1953, 1957
Dendrolimus sibiricus Ischtv.	,, ,,	L	LSU lab. data
Cosmotriche potatoria L.	Rate of larval growth	L	Kuznetsova, 1955
Lymantriidae			
Orgyia antiqua L.	Embr. diapause	L	Doskočil, 1956, 1957a, 1957b
Euproctis similis Fuessl.	Larval diapause	M	Geispits, 1953; Kuznetsova, 1955
Euproctis chrysorrhoea L.	,, ,,	M	
Leucoma salicis L., northern forms	,, ,,	M	
L. salicis, southern forms	,, ,,	L	LSU lab. data
Dasychira pudibunda L.	Growth rate, number of larval moults	S	Geispits, 1953
Lymantria dispar L.	—	N	LSU lab. data
Arctiidae			
Arctia caia L.	Larval diapause	L	LSU lab. data
Arctia aulica L.	,, ,,	L	
Arctia villica L.	—	N	
Parasemia plantaginis L.	Larval diapause		Danilevskii and Goryshin, 1960

Name of species	Phenomena regulated by day-length	Type of reaction	Author
Arctiidae (*cont.*)			
Spilosoma menthastri Esp.	Pupal diapause	L	Danilevskii, 1957a, 1957b
Spilosoma lubricipeda L.	,, ,,	L	LSU lab. data
Hyphantria cunea Dr.	,, ,,	L	Jermi and Saringer, 1955
Lithosia griseola Hb.	Larval diapause	L	LSU lab. data
Cymbidae			
Hylophila prasinana L.	Pupal diapause, seasonal dimorphism	L	LSU lab. data
Noctuidae			
Acronycta rumicis L.	Pupal diapause	L	Danilevskii, 1948, 1956, 1957a, 1957b; Danilevskii and Glinyanaya, 1949, 1950; Goryshin, 1955; Geispits, 1957; Danilevskii and Goryshin, 1960
Acronycta megacephala F.	,, ,,	L	Danilevskii, 1957a
Acronycta leporina L.	,, ,,	L	Danilevskii, 1957a
Acronycta psi L.	,, ,,	L	Danilevskii, 1957a
Demas coryli L.	,, ,,	L	Danilevskii, 1957a
Barathra brassicae L.	,, ,,	L	Way, Hopkins and Smith, 1949; Matsumoto, Santa and Otuka, 1953; Otuka and Santa, 1955; Uchida and Masaki, 1954; Masaki, 1956a, 1957b
Polia oleracea L.	,, ,,	L	Way, Hopkins and Smith, 1949; Way and Hopkins, 1950
Polia contigua Vill.	,, ,,	L	LSU lab. data
Polia dissimilis Kn.	,, ,,	L	Danilevskii, 1956
Trachea atriplicis L.	,, ,,	L	LSU lab. data
Athetis ambigua F.	Larval diapause	L	LSU lab. data
Agrotis C-nigrum L.	,, ,,	L	Danilevskii, 1956

Name of species	Phenomena regulated by day-length	Type of reaction	Author
Noctuidae (*cont.*)			
Agrotis triangulum Hufn.	Rate of larval growth	S	LSU lab. data
Agrotis puta Hb.	—	N	LSU lab. data
Agrotis segetum Schiff.	Rate of larval growth	L	LSU lab. data
Agrotis occulta L.	,, ,, ,,	L	LSU lab. data
Agrotis saucia Hb.	,, ,, ,,	L	LSU lab. data
Chloridea obsoleta F.	Pupal diapause	L	Goryshin, 1953, 1958b; Manuilova, 1958; Komarova, 1959
Chloridea dipsacea L.	,, ,,	L	Goryshin, 1953, 1958b
Chloridea peltigera Schiff.	—	N	Goryshin, 1953, 1958b
Melicleptria scutosa Schiff.	Pupal diapause	L	Goryshin, 1953, 1958b
DIPTERA			
Culicidae			
Anopheles maculipennis messeae Fall.	Diapause in females	L	Danilevskii, 1956; Danilevskii and Glinyanaya, 1958; Vinogradova, 1958, 1960
A. m. sacharovi Favre	Accumulation of fat in females		Khodukin and Lisova, 1954
A. m. atroparvus Thiel	Diapause in females	L	Vinogradova, 1960
Anopheles hyrcanus Pall.	,, ,,	L	Vinogradova, 1960
Anopheles superpictus Gr.	,, ,,	L	Vinogradova, 1960
Anopheles pulcherrimus Th.	Rate of larval growth	L	Vinogradova, 1960
Anopheles bifurcatus L.	Larval diapause	L	Khodukin and Lisova, 1953
Anopheles barberi Coq.	,, ,,	L	Baker, 1935
Culex pipiens pipiens, L.	Diapause in females	L	Tate and Vincent, 1936; Danilevskii and Glinyanaya, 1958; Vinogradova, 1958, 1960
C. p. molestus Forsk.	—	N	Vinogradova, 1960
Aedes triseriatus Say	Larval diapause	L	Love and Whelchel, 1955; Baker, 1935

Name of species	Phenomena regulated by day-length	Type of reaction	Author
Tendipedidae			
Metriocnemus knabi Coq.	Larval diapause	L	Paris and Jenner, 1959
Heleidae			
Culicoides guttipennis Coq.	,, ,,	L	Baker, 1935
Muscidae			
Musca domestica L.	—	N	LSU lab. data
Hylemyia brassicae Bouche	Pupal diapause	L	Hughes, 1960
Pegomyia hyosciami Pz.	,, ,,	L	LSU lab. data
Larvivoridae			
Protophormia terrae-novae R. D.	Imaginal diapause	L	LSU lab. data
HYMENOPTERA			
Tenthredinidae			
Athalia colibri Chr.	Prepupal diapause	L	Stepanova, 1959
Lygaeonematus compressicornis F.	,, ,,	L	Danilevskii, 1956
Braconidae			
Apanteles glomeratus L.	,, ,,	L	Geispits and Kyao, 1953; Maslennikova, 1958, 1959a
Apanteles spurius Wesm.	,, ,,	L	Geispits and Kyao, 1953
Chalcididae			
Pteromalus puparum L.	,, ,,	L	Maslennikova, 1958
Trichogramma evanescens Wstw.	Larval diapause	L	Maslennikova, 1959b

Name of species	Phenomena regulated by day-length	Type of reaction	Author
NEUROPTERA			
Chrysopidae			
Chrysopa sp.	Prepupal diapause	L	Danilevskii, 1956
COLEOPTERA			
Chrysomelidae			
Leptinotarsa decemlineata Say	Imaginal diapause	L	De Wilde, 1954-59; Jermi and Saringer, 1955; Goryshin, 1956, 1958a; Węgorek, 1959
Chrysomela fastuosa Sc.	,, ,,	L	Danilevskii, 1956
Phaedon cochleariae F.	,, ,,	L	Way, Hopkins and Smith, 1949
Haltica saliceti Ws.	,, ,,	L	Kuznetsova, 1955
Coccinellidae			
Coccinella septempunctata L.	—	N	Hodek, 1958
HOMOPTERA			
AUCHENORRHYNCHA			
Jassidae (Cicadellidae)			
Euscelis plebejus Fall.	Seasonal forms; size, colour	—	Müller, 1954, 1955a, 1955b, 1959
Euscelis lineolatus Br.	Structure of genitalia	—	Müller, 1957b, 1958b
Euscelis ohausi Wg.	Size, colour	—	Müller, 1957b, 1958b
Nephotettix cincticeps Uhler	Larval diapause; seasonal forms	L	Kisimoto, 1959a, 1959b

Name of species	Phenomena regulated by day-length	Type of reaction	Author
Delphacidae (Araepidae)			
Stenocranus minutus F.	Imaginal diapause; size, colour	L	Müller, 1957a, 1958a, 1959
Delphacodes striatella Fall.	Larval diapause; size of wings	S	Kisimoto, 1956
Sternorrhyncha Psyllidae			
Psylla pyri L.	Imaginal diapause; seasonal forms	L	Bonnemaison and Missonier, 1956a, 1956b
Aphididae			
Aphis forbesi Weed	Parthenogenesis and sexual forms, seasonal cyclomorphoses	—	Marcovitch, 1924
Aphis sorbi Kalt. (?)	,,	—	Marcovitch, 1924
Aphis chloris Koch	,,	—	Wilson, 1938
Aphis fabae Sc. (=*rumicis* L.)	,,	—	Davidson, 1929; De Fluiter, 1950
Capitophorus hippophaes Walk.	,,	—	Marcovitch, 1924
Brevicoryne brassicae L.	,,	—	Bonnemaison, 1951
Myzus persicae Sulz.	,,	—	Bonnemaison, 1951
Sappaphis plantaginea Pass.	,,	—	Bonnemaison, 1951
Acyrthosiphon pisum Harr.	,,	—	Kenten, 1955
Macrosiphum solanifolii Ptch. (=*euphorbiae* Thom.)	,,	—	Shull, 1928, 1929, 1930; Bonnemaison, 1951
Megoura viciae Buck.	,,	—	Lees, 1959a, 1959b
ORTHOPTERA Tetrigidae			
Acrydium arenosum	Imaginal diapause	L	Sabrosky, Larsen and Nabours, 1933
Acrididae			
Nomadacris septemfasciata Serv.	,, ,,	L	Norris and Richards, 1958; Norris, 1959
Schistocerca gregaria Forsk.	Duration of sexual maturity	—	Norris, 1957

Name of species	Phenomena regulated by day-length	Type of reaction	Author
ODONATA			
Aeschnidae			
Anax imperator Leach.	Larval diapause	M?	Corbet, 1954, 1955, 1956
ACARINA			
Tetranychidae			
Tetranychus urticae Koch	Diapause in females	L	Bondarenko, 1950, 1958; Lees, 1953a; Bondarenko and Kuan Khai-yuan', 1958; Geispits, 1960
Metatetranychus ulmi Koch	Embr. diapause	L	Lees, 1950, 1953a, 1953b; Miller, 1950; Geispits, 1960
Metatetranychus bioculatus W.-M.	—	N	Lees, 1953a
Ixodidae			
Dermacentor variabilis Say	Activity, hibernation	—	Smith and Cole, 1941

BIBLIOGRAPHY

Russian List

This includes all publications in the Russian language, with a couple in Ukrainian. The few publications by Russian authors in other languages are included in the 'Non-Russian List'.

(Abbreviations: M., Moscow; L., Leningrad; MSU, Moscow State University; LSU, Leningrad State University.)

ANDRIANOVA, N. S., 1948. The effect of light on growth and development of the Chinese Oak Silkworm. In the book *Culture of the Chinese Oak Silkworm in the USSR*. Sel'khozgiz, M., 38-47.

ARISTOV, M. T., 1932. Insect pests of the orchard. Sel'khozgiz, M.-L., 90-95.

AVAKYAN, G. D., 1953. New data on the biology of the Satin Moth. *Bull. Acad. Sci. Armen. SSR*, **6**, 10: 83-87.

BABAYAN, A. S., 1958. The biological characteristics of the Mallow Moth (*Pectinophora malvella* Hb.) on cotton plants. *Trans. Agric. Inst. Armen. SSR.* The Mallow Moth and methods of controlling it, 1: 21-48.

BEKLEMISHCHEV, V. N., 1944. *Ecology of the Malaria Mosquito*. Medgiz, M.

BELOV, P. F., 1951. Studies on the stages of development of the Chinese Oak Silkworm in connection with control of voltinism in it. In the book *The Chinese Oak Silkworm* (Trans. of the sericulture section's conferences on silkworm-breeding in 1949 and 1950). Sel'khozgiz, M., 5-61.

BONDARENKO, N. V., 1950. The effect of a shortened day on the annual cycle of development of the Common Spider Mite. *Rep. Acad. Sci. USSR*, **70**, 6: 1077-1080.

1958. The characteristics of diapause in the Spider Mite (*Tetranychus urticae* Koch.). *Zool. Zh.*, **37**, 7: 1012-1023.

BONDARENKO, N. V., and KUAN KHAI-YUAN', 1958. The characteristics of the onset of diapause in different geographical populations of the Spider Mite. *Rep. Acad. Sci. USSR*, **119**, 6: 1247-1250.

CHESNOKOV, P. G., 1936. The distribution and economic importance of crucifer-leaf-eating pests in vegetable culture. VASKhNIL, L., 3-90.

CHETVERIKOV, S. S., 1940. The selection of the Chinese Oak Silkworm (*Antheraea pernyi* Guer.) for univoltinism. In the book *Selection and Acclimatization of Oak Silkworms*. Sel'khozgiz, M., 16-22.

CHUGUNIN, YA. V., 1939. The results of studies of the Codling Moth in the Crimea. In the book *Trans. of the Crimea Fruit Station, 1916-1938*. M., **2**: 255-282.

DANILEVSKII, A. S., 1940. Experiments in the ecological analysis of the distribution and possibilities of acclimatization of the Tree-of-heaven Silkworm. *Zool. Zh.*, **19**, 1: 26-44.

1946. The significance of the resting stages in the life cycles and distribution of insects. *Sci. Bull. LSU*, **10**: 27-30.

1947. Feeding the Chinese Oak Silkworm on birch. In the book *Yellow Disease in the Bombyx and the Chinese Oak Silkworm*. Sel'khozgiz, M., 126-138.

1948. The photoperiodic reaction of insects in conditions of artificial light. *Rep. Acad. Sci. USSR*, **60**, 3: 481-484.

1949. The dependence of the geographical distribution of insects on ecological characteristics of their life cycles. *Entomol. Obozr.*, **30**, 3-4: 194-207.

1950. The temperature conditions of reactivation of diapausing stages of insects. *Trans. Leningrad Nat. Hist. Soc.*, **70**, 4: 90-107.

1951. The conditions of multi-annual diapause in Lepidoptera. *Entomol. Obozr.*, **31**, 3-4: 386-392.

1956. Photoperiodism as the regulator of seasonal cycles in insects. *N. A. Kholodkovskii Memorial Lectures*, 1954-1955. Acad. Sci. USSR, M.-L., 32-55.

1957a. Photoperiodism as a factor in the formation of geographical races of insects. *Entomol. Obozr.*, **36**, 1: 6-27.

1957b. Seasonal rhythms and intraspecific geographical differentiation in insects. *Bull. LSU*, **21**: 93-105.

DANILEVSKII, A. S., and K. F. GEISPITS, 1948. The effect of the daily periodicity of light on seasonal cycles of insects. *Rep. Acad. Sci. USSR*, **59**, 2: 237-240.

DANILEVSKII, A. S., and E. I. GLINYANAYA, 1949. The effect of the relation between the dark and light periods of the day on insect development. *Rep. Acad. Sci. USSR*, **68**, 4: 785-788.

1950. The effect of the rhythm of light and temperature on the onset of diapause in insects. *Rep. Acad. Sci. USSR*, **71**, 5: 963-966.

1958. The dependence of the gonotrophic cycle and imaginal diapause in bloodsucking mosquitoes on changes in day-length. *Sci. Mem. of LSU*, **240**: 34-51.

DANILEVSKII, A. S., and N. I. GORYSHIN, 1960. The relation between temperature and light conditions in regulating diapause in insects. *Trans. Peterhof Biol. Inst.*, LSU, **18**: 147-168.

DETINOVA, T. S., 1945. The effect of internal secretions on the maturation of sex organs and imaginal diapause in the common malaria mosquito. *Zool. Zh.*, **24**, 5: 291-298.

DOLIDZE, G. V., 1957a. Studies of the most important cabbage-head pests and the improvement of methods of controlling them in

Eastern Georgian conditions. Candidate's thesis. Acad. Sci. Georg. SSR, Tiflis.

1957b. A study of the ecology of the Cabbage Moth (*Barathra brassicae* L.) in Georgia. *Trans. Inst. Plant Protection, Acad. Sci. Georg. SSR*, **12**: 79-100.

1957c. Study of cabbage-head insect pests in Eastern Georgia. *Trans. Acad. Sci. Georg. SSR*, **18**, 1: 83-90.

EMME, A. M., 1953. Some theoretical questions on diapause in insects. *Usp. sovr. Biol.* (*Progress in modern Biology*), **35**, 3: 395-424.

GEISPITS, K. F., 1949. Light as a factor regulating the developmental cycle of the Pine Moth. *Rep. Acad. Sci. USSR, new ser.*, **68**, 4: 781-784.

1953. The reaction of univoltine Lepidoptera to day-length. *Entomol. Obozr.*, **33**: 17-31.

1957. The mechanism of acceptance of light stimuli in the photoperiodic reaction of Lepidoptera larvae. *Zool. Zh.*, **36**, 4: 548-560.

1958. The adaptational significance of the photoperiodic reaction and its role in the ecology of the Pine Moth (*Dendrolimus pini* L.). *Sci. Mem. of LSU*, **240**: 21-33.

1960. The effect of the conditions in which preceding generations were reared on the photoperiodic reaction of geographical forms of the Cotton Spider Mite (*Tetranychus urticae* Koch.). *Trans. Peterhof Biol. Inst.*, LSU, **18**: 169-177.

GEISPITS, K. F., and N. N. KYAO, 1953. The effect of the duration of light on the development of some ichneumon flies (Hymenoptera, Braconidae). *Entomol. Obozr.*, **33**: 32-35.

GORYSHIN, N. I., 1953. The ecological analysis of the seasonal cycle of development of the Cotton-boll Worm in northern cotton-growing districts. Candidate's thesis, LSU.

1955. The relation between light and temperature factors in the photoperiodic reaction in insects. *Entomol. Obozr.*, **34**: 9-14.

1956. The photoperiodic reaction in the Colorado Beetle (*Leptinotarsa decemlineata* Say). *Rep. Acad. Sci. USSR*, **109**: 205-208.

1958a. The effect of day-length on the onset of diapause in the Colorado Beetle (*Leptinotarsa decemlineata* Say). In the book *The Colorado Beetle*. Acad. Sci. USSR, M., **2**: 136-149.

1958b. The ecological analysis of the seasonal cycle of development of the Cotton-boll Worm (*Chloridea obsoleta* F.) in the northern areas of its range. *Sci. Mem. of LSU*, **240**: 3-20.

IVANOVA, S. A., 1936. Seasonal changes in the sex glands of animals, and factors inducing them. *Usp. sovr. Biol.* (*Progress in modern Biology*), **5**, 6: 1087-1095.

KAL'BERGENOV, G. K., 1951. The biological and ecological bases for measures of Cabbage Moth control in the conditions of Moscow province. Candidate's thesis, MSU, 1-12.

KARLASH, K. V., 1954. Rozvitok i zhittezdatnist' lyalechok dubovogo shovkopryada zalezhno vid umov zberigannya ikh v osinn'ozimovii period. (In Ukrainian.) In the book *Ekologiya Dubovogo Sholkopryada*. Acad. Sci. Ukrain. SSR, 62-89.

KARPOVA, A. I., 1959. The development and diet of the Corn Borer *Pyrausta nubilalis* Hb. (Lepidoptera, Pyralidae) in new maize-growing districts. *Entomol. Obozr.*, **38**, 4: 724-733.

KHODUKIN, N. I., and A. I. LISOVA, 1953. The effect of the light rhythm on the development of diapausing larvae of *Anopheles bifurcatus* L. *Med. Parasitol. and parasitic Diseases*, **4**: 357-360.

1954. The effect of the light rhythm on fat development in *Anopheles maculipennis sacharovi* Fav. *Trans. Inst. Zool. Parasitol., Acad. Sci. Uzbek SSR*, **3**: 31-35.

KLEMENTS, A. K., 1958. The Cabbage Moth and measures for its control. *Trans. Sci-prod. Conf. on protection of plants from pests and diseases in the south-east.* Saratov Book Publ., 119-128.

KOMAROVA, O. S., 1949. Factors inducing diapause in the Grape Berry Moth. *Rep. Acad. Sci. USSR*, **68**, 4: 789-792.

1954. The life cycle and conditions of development of the Grape Berry Moth (*Polychrosis botrana* Schiff.). *Zool. Zh.*, **33**, 1: 102-113.

1959. The formation of wintering stock and pupal diapause in the Cotton-boll Worm. *Entomol. Obozr.*, **38**, 2: 352-361.

KONAKOV, N. N., 1927. The biology of flight of moths, from syrup-trap data at the Ramonskaya selection station in 1926. *Sb. SSU, Izd. Sort. sem. upr. sakharotresta.* Kiev, **2**, (10): 77-79.

KOVAL'SKAYA, T., 1958. The effect of the physiological state of the Colorado Beetle (*Leptinotarsa decemlineata* Say), at the time of entering hibernation, on the duration of diapause and mortality during hibernation. In the book *The Colorado Beetle*. Acad. Sci. USSR, M., **2**: 66-73.

KOZHANCHIKOV, I. V., 1935a. The role of anaerobic processes in larval diapause of some members of the Pyralidae. *Rep. Acad. Sci. USSR*, **2**, 3-4: 322-327.

1935b. Experimental investigations on the effect of temperature on the development of the Beet Webworm. *Zasch. Rast.* (*Plant Protection*), **7**: 44-63.

1936. The significance of ecological factors in the distribution of the Cabbage White Butterfly *Pieris brassicae* L. *Zashch. Rast.* (*Plant Protection*), **11**: 40-57.

1937a. The growth and physiological state of insects in relation to the influence of ecological factors. *Zool. Zh.*, **16**, 1: 88-106.

1937b. Moths, subfamily Agrotinae. Fauna of the USSR. *Lepidoptera*, **13**, No. 3: 28-63.

1938a. Experiments and observations on the effect of temperature on the development of pupae of the Cotton-boll Worm *Heliothis obsoleta* F. *Zashch. Rast.* (*Plant Protection*), **16**: 27-34.

1938b. The geographical distribution and physiological characteristics of *Pyrausta nubilalis* Hb. *Zool. Zh.*, **17**, 2: 246-259.

1939a. Thermostable respiration as a condition of cold-resistance in insects. *Zool. Zh.*, **18**, 1: 86-98.

1939b. Characteristics of the development of pupae of the Cabbage Maggot (*Hylemyia brassicae* Bouche) in different environmental conditions. *Bull. Adv. course of appl. Zool. and Phytopathol.*, **7**: 5-14.

1939c. The role of the thermal factor in the development and distribution of leaf-eaters (*Phaedon cochleariae* F. and *Gastroidea viridula* Deg.). *Bull. Adv. course of appl. Zool. and Phytopathol.*, **9**: 5-30.

1941. The distribution and annual fluctuation in numbers of Cutworms and Beet Webworms in accordance with temperature and humidity. *Zool. Zh.*, **20**, 1: 30-45.

1948. Hibernation and diapause in Lepidoptera, fam. Orgyidae (Lepidoptera, Insecta). *Bull. Acad. Sci. USSR, Biol. ser.*, **6**: 653-673.

1949. The amplitude of the daily temperature fluctuation as a factor in larval development of the Chinese Oak Silkworm (*Antheraea pernyi* Guer.). *Rep. Acad. Sci. USSR*, **62**, 2: 381-384.

1950a. Tussock Moths (Orgyidae). Fauna of the USSR. *Lepidoptera*, **12**: 1-583.

1950b. The conditions for a change to a new plant diet by the Cabbage Moth (*Barathra brassicae* L.). *Rep. Acad. Sci. USSR*, **73**, 2: 385-387.

1950c. The developmental cycle and geographical distribution of the Winter Moth (*Operophtera brumata* L.). *Entomol. Obozr.*, **31**, 1-2: 178-197.

KRISHTAL', O. P., and O. I. PETRUKHA, 1949. *Shkidniki bobovikh ta zlakovikh roslin.* (In Ukrainian.) Univ. of Kiev, **1**: 236-238.

KUZNETSOV, V. I., 1955. The leafrollers *Peronea lubricana* Mn. and *Peronea fimbriana* Thnbg. as forms of a single species. *Entomol. Obozr.*, **34**: 124-128.

1958. The zonal distribution of Lepidoptera and the formation of a fauna of forest and orchard pests in the mountains of western Kopet-Dagh. *Sci. Mem. of LSU*, **240**: 122-147.

KUZNETSOVA, I. A., 1955. Changes in fatty tissue as a result of the photoperiodic reaction and diapause in insects. *Zool. Zh.*, **34**, 3: 532-541.

LADYZHENSKAYA, L. A., 1935. The effects of temperature and humidity on the changes in pupation and the emergence of adults of the Corn Borer. *Zashch. Rast.* (*Plant Protection*), **4**: 79-86.

LARCHENKO, K. I., 1937. The developmental cycle of the fat body in the Beet Webworm and the Cutworm, and its connection with maturation and fertility. *Entomol. Obozr.*, **27**, 1-2: 29-75.

1949. The principles of development and reproduction in the Cutworm (*Agrotis segetum* Schiff.). *Bull. Acad. Sci. USSR, Biol. ser.*, **4**: 470-494.

1955. Diet and diapause in the Colorado Beetle (*Leptinotarsa decem-*

lineata Say). In the book *The Colorado Beetle*. Acad. Sci. USSR, M., 1: 42-59.

1956. The laws of ontogenesis in insects. *Trans. Zool. Inst. Acad. Sci. USSR*, **23**: 5-214.

1958a. The conditions of diet and diapause in the Colorado Beetle (*Leptinotarsa decemlineata* Say). In the book *The Colorado Beetle*. Acad. Sci. USSR, M., 2: 36-52.

1958b. The duration of development in the Colorado Beetle (*Leptinotarsa decemlineata* Say) depending on temperature. In the book *The Colorado Beetle*. Acad. Sci. USSR, M., 2: 81-92.

1958c. Forecasting the dates of development of the Colorado Beetle (*Leptinotarsa decemlineata* Say) in the Polish People's Republic. In the book *The Colorado Beetle*. Acad. Sci. USSR, M., 2: 93-105.

1958d. The phenological dates of development of the Colorado Beetle (*Leptinotarsa decemlineata* Say) and their connection with its distribution and fluctuations in numbers. In the book *The Colorado Beetle*. Acad. Sci. USSR, M., 2: 106-115.

LOBASHEV, M. E., and V. B. SAVVATEEV, 1959. *The physiology of the Daily Rhythm of Animals*. Acad. Sci. USSR, M.-L., 1-259.

LOZINA-LOZINSKII, L. K., 1937. Cold-resistance and anabiosis in Corn Borer larvae. *Zool. Zh.*, **16**, 4: 614-642.

1942. The resistance of insects to freezing. *Priroda* (*Nature*), **3-4**: 65-76.

1952. Viability and anabiosis in animals at low temperature. *Bull. of the P. F. Lesgaft Nat. Hist. Inst.*, **25**: 3-32.

LOZINA-LOZINSKII, L. K., and S. S. SOKOLOV, 1938. Cold-resistance of eggs of *Locusta migratoria*. *Zool. Zh.*, **17**, 1: 91-101.

LYUI KHUN-SHEN, 1960. The hormonal mechanism of voltinism in the silkworm (*Bombyx mori* L.) Candidate's thesis. Tashkent, Agric. Inst.

MAYR, E., 1947. Systematics and the origin of species. Foreign lit. publ. agency, M., 1-502.

MANUILOVA, T. D., 1958. Some remarks on devising methods of forecasting the numbers of the Cotton-boll Worm. *Coll. sc. Works, Entom. Sect., Cent. Asian Br. of VIZR*, Tashkent, 11-15.

MASLENNIKOVA, V. A., 1958. The conditions determining diapause in the parasitic Hymenoptera *Apanteles glomeratus* L. (Braconidae) and *Pteromalus puparum* (Chalcididae). *Entomol. Obozr.*, **37**, 3: 538-545.

1959a. The relation between the seasonal cycles of geographical populations of *Apanteles glomeratus* L. and its host *Pieris brassicae* L. *Entomol. Obozr.*, **38**, 3: 517-522.

1959b. Hibernation and diapause in *Trichogramma evanescens* Westw. *Bull. LSU*, **3**: 91-96.

MILYANOVSKII, E. S., 1956a. The lepidopterous fauna (Macrolepidoptera) of Abkhazia. *Trans. Zool. Inst. Acad. Sci. Georg. SSR*, **15**: 51-110.

1956b. Reasons for the absence of certain species of Lepidoptera from the Black Sea coast of Abkhazia. *Zool. Zh.*, **35**, 8: 1170-1176.

MKRTUMYAN, K. L., 1958. The role of different food plants in the development of the Mallow Moth in the Armenian SSR. *Trans. Agric. Inst. Armen. SSR.* The Mallow Moth and methods of controlling it. **1**: 69-79.

MONCHADSKII, A. S., 1935. The role of contact moisture after winter diapause in Corn Borer larvae. *Zashch. Rast.* (*Plant Protection*), **3**: 39-50.

NEDOVODIEV, P. F., 1953. Insect pests of cruciferous-vegetable culture in southern districts of Sverdlovsk province. Candidate's thesis, M.

PANTYUKHOV, G. A., 1956. Geographical variations in cold-resistance in several insects. *Zool. Zh.*, **35**, 9: 1312-1324.

1959. Temperature adaptations of geographical forms of several insects. *Thesis report at session IV of All-Union Entom. Soc.* Acad. Sci. USSR, M.-L., **1**: 121-122.

POSPELOV, V. P., 1910. *Post-embryonic Development and Imaginal Diapause in Lepidoptera.* Kiev, 1-248.

RIMSKII-KORSAKOV, M. N., V. I. GUSEV, *et al.*, 1949. *Forest Entomology.* Goslesbumizdat, M.-L., 1-507.

RUBTSOV, I. A., 1941. The influence of temperature and humidity on the development of eggs and larvae of the Cotton-boll Worm. *Bull. Zashch. Rast.* (*Plant Protection*), **1**: 9-19.

SAKHAROV, N. L., 1928. A study of cold-resistance in insects. *Zh. opytn. agronom. Yugo-vost.* (*J. expt. Agronomy in the Southeast*), **6**, 2: 85-104.

SAKHAROV, N. L., 1930 see SACHAROV, N. in the non-Russian list.

SAMYGIN, G. A., 1946. Photoperiodism in plants (review of literature and tables). *Trans. of K. A. Timiryazev Inst. of Plant Physiology*, **3**, 2: 129-162.

SHAPOSHNIKOV, G. KH., 1959. Changes of host and diapause in aphids (Aphididae) in the process of adaptation to the annual cycles of their food plants. *Entomol. Obozr.*, **38**, 3: 483-504.

SHARONOV, V. V., 1945. *Tables for the Calculation of Natural Light and Visibility.* Acad. Sci. USSR, M.-L., 1-198.

SHEL'DESHOVA, G. G., 1956. The biology and ecological characteristics of the Pear Moth (*Carpocapsa pyrivora* Danil.). Candidate's thesis. Zool. Inst. Acad. Sci. USSR, 1-14.

SHIPITSYNA, N. K., 1957a. Characteristic features of the autumn phenological development of *Anopheles maculipennis* in the Soviet Union. In the book *Seasonal Phenomena in the Life of Malaria Mosquitoes in the Soviet Union.* Inst. of Malaria and med. Parasitol., M., 306-333.

1957b. Seasonal periodicity in the life of the malaria mosquito *Anopheles maculipennis* and the importance of studying it for anti-malaria measures in the Soviet Union. In the book *Seasonal*

Phenomena in the Life of Malaria Mosquitoes in the Soviet Union. Inst. of Malaria and med. Parasitol., M., 485-517.

1959. Effect of decrease in daylight on onset of diapause in *Anopheles maculipennis* Mg. *Med. Parasitol. and parasit. Diseases*, **1**: 4-17.

SHUMAKOV, E. M., and L. A. YAKHIMOVICH, 1950. Peculiarities of the embryonic development of the Asiatic locust (*Locusta migratoria* L.) as a result of certain external environmental conditions. *Zool. Zh.*, **29**, 4: 327-340.

STEPANOVA, L. A., 1959. Experimental investigations of the ecology of the Turnip Fly *Athalia colibri* Christ. (Hymenoptera, Tenthredinidae). *Trans. Karel. Br. of Acad. Sci. USSR*, **14**: 138-150.

USHAKOV, B. P., 1956. The heat-resistance of cellular proteins in cold-blooded animals in connection with specific adaptation to the temperature conditions in which they live. *Zh. Obshch. Biol.* (*J. gen. Biol.*), **17**, 2: 154-160.

1958. The conservation of protoplasm of a species in poikilothermal animals. *Zool. Zh.*, **37**, 5: 693-706.

1959a. The heat-resistance of tissues as one of the diagnostic characteristics of species in poikilothermal animals. *Zool. Zh.*, **38**, 9: 1292-1302.

1959b. The mechanism of adaptation in cells of the animal organism. *Tsitologiya* (*Cytology*), **1**, 1: 35-47.

1959c. The physiology of cells and the problem of speciation in zoology. *Tsitologiya* (*Cytology*), **1**, 5: 541-565.

USHATINSKAYA, R. S., 1949. The control of several processes in the bodies of insects at low temperatures. *Rep. Acad. Sci. USSR*, **68**, 6: 1101-1104.

1957. *The Basis of Cold-resistance in Insects.* Acad. Sci. USSR, M., 1-314.

VASIL'EV, V. P., 1951. The ecological conditions of development and the zonal division of the range of the Codling Moth in the Ukrainian SSR. *Coll. works on plant protection, Ukrainian Fruit-growing Inst.* Kiev and Khar'kov, **32**: 4-50.

VENGOREK, V., see WĘGOREK, W.

VINOGRADOVA, E. B., 1958. The photoperiodic reaction in the malaria mosquito (*Anopheles maculipennis messeae* Fall.). *Sci. Mem. of LSU*, **240**: 52-60.

1960. The experimental investigation of ecological factors inducing imaginal diapause in bloodsucking mosquitoes (Diptera, Culicidae). *Entomol. Obozr.*, **39**, 2: 327-340.

WĘGOREK, W., 1958a. The investigation of hibernation in the Colorado Beetle (*Leptinotarsa decemlineata* Say) on the basis of its physiology. In the book *The Colorado Beetle.* Acad. Sci. USSR, M., **2**: 53-65.

1958b. The biology and ecology of the Colorado Beetle (*Leptinotarsa decemlineata* Say) in the Polish People's Republic. In the book *The Colorado Beetle.* Acad. Sci. USSR, M., **2**: 74-80.

1958c. The effect of day-length and quality of food on the biology of the Colorado Beetle (*Leptinotarsa decemlineata* Say). In the book *The Colorado Beetle*. Acad. Sci. USSR, M., **2**: 129-135.

WĘGOREK, W., see also in the non-Russian list for his publications in Polish.

ZOLOTAREV, E. KH., 1938. Summer and autumn diets of larvae of the Chinese Oak Silkworm and their effect on pupal diapause. *Zool. Zh.*, **17**, 4: 662-663.

1940a. Data on the ecology of voltinism in the Chinese Oak Silkworm. *Zool. Zh.*, **30**, 4: 631-645.

1940b. The causes of the onset of pupal diapause in the Chinese Oak Silkworm and methods of controlling it. In the book *Selection and Acclimatization of Chinese Oak Silkworms*. Sel'khozgiz, M., 39-62.

1947. Diapause and development of pupae of the Chinese Oak Silkworm. *Zool. Zh.*, **26**, 1: 539-544.

1948. The biology of pupal diapause in the Chinese Oak Silkworm. In the book *Rearing Chinese Oak Silkworms in the USSR*. Sel'khozgiz, M., 48-63.

1950a. Some characteristics of the development of the Chinese Oak Silkworm in connection with the occurrence of diapause in its ontogenesis. *Bull. MSU*, **6**: 93-100.

1950b. The development of larvae of the Whitethorn Butterfly (*Aporia crataegi* L.) during hibernation. *Zool. Zh.*, **29**, 2: 152-158.

NON-RUSSIAN LIST

This includes a few publications by Russians in non-Russian languages

ANDREWARTHA, H. G., 1943. Diapause in the eggs of *Austroicetes cruciata* Sauss., with particular reference to the influence of temperature on the elimination of diapause. *Bull. entom. Res.*, **34**: 1-17.

1944. The influence of temperature on the elimination of diapause from eggs of the race of *Austroicetes cruciata* Sauss. (Acrididae) occurring in Western Australia. *Aust. J. exp. Biol. med. Sci.*, **22**: 17-20.

1952. Diapause in relation to the ecology of insects. *Biol. Rev.*, **27**: 50-107.

ANDREWARTHA, H. G., and L. C. BIRCH, 1954. *The Distribution and Abundance of Animals*. Chicago.

ARBUTHNOT, K. D., 1944. Strains of the European Corn Borer in the United States. *Techn. Bull. U.S. Dept. Agr.*, **869**: 1-20.

ATWAL, A. S., 1955. Influence of temperature, photoperiod and food on the speed of development, longevity, fecundity, and other qualities of the Diamondback Moth (*Plutella maculipennis* Curtis). *Aust. J. Zool.*, **3** (**2**): 185-221.

BABCOCK, K. W., 1927a. The European Corn Borer, *Pyrausta nubilalis* Hübn. I. A discussion of its dormant period. *Ecology*, **8**: 45-59.

1927b. The European Corn Borer, *Pyrausta nubilalis* Hübn. II. A discussion of its seasonal history in relation to various climates. *Ecology*, **8**: 177-193.

BAKER, F. C., 1935. The effect of photoperiodism on resting tree-hole mosquito larvae. *Canad. Entom.*, **67**: 149-153.

BECK, S. D., and W. HANEC, 1960. Diapause in the European Corn Borer *Pyrausta nubilalis* Hübn. *J. Ins. Physiol.*, **4**: 304-318.

BENOIT, J., 1950. Reproduction, caractères sexuels et hormones. Déterminisme du cycle sexuel saisonnier. *Traité de Zoologie*, **15**: 384-478.

BIRCH, L. C., and H. G. ANDREWARTHA, 1942. The influence of moisture on the eggs of *Austroicetes cruciata* Sauss., with reference to their ability to survive desiccation. *Aust. J. exp. Biol. med. Sci.*, **20**: 1-8.

BODENHEIMER, F. S., 1926. Ueber die Voraussage der Generationenzahl von Insecten. III. *Angew. Entom.*, **12**: 91.

BONNEMAISON, L., 1951. Contribution à l'étude des facteurs provoquant l'apparition des formes ailées et sexuées chez les Aphidinae. *Ann. Epiphyt.*, **2**: 1-380.

BONNEMAISON, L., et J. MISSONNIER, 1955a. Influence du photopériodisme sur le déterminisme des formes estivales ou hivernales et de la diapause chez *Psylla pyri* L. *C. r. Acad. Sci.*, Paris, **240**: 1277-1279.

1955. Recherches sur le déterminisme des formes estivales ou hivernales et de la diapause chez le psylle du poirier (*Psylla pyri* L.). *Ann. Epiphyt.*: 417-528.

BONNEMAISON, L., 1956. Déterminisme de l'apparition des larves estivales de *Periphyllus* (Aphidine). *C. r. Acad. Sci.*, Paris, **243**: 1166-1168.

BRADLEY, W. G., and K. D. ARBUTHNOT, 1938. The relation of the host physiology to the development of the Braconid parasite *Chelonus annulipes*. *Ann. entom. Soc. Amer.*, **31**: 359-365.

BROWNING, T. O., 1952a. The influence of temperature on the completion of diapause in the eggs of *Gryllulus commodus* Walker. *Aust. J. sci. Res.*, *B*, **5**: 112-127.

1952b. On the rate of completion of diapause development at constant temperatures in the eggs of *Gryllulus commodus* Walker. *Aust. J. sci. Res.*, *B*, **5**: 344-353.

BUCKLIN, D. H., 1953. Termination of diapause in grasshopper embryos cultured in vitro. *Anat. Rev.*, **117**: 539.

BÜNNING, E., and G. JOERRENS, 1959. Versuche zur photoperiodischen Diapauseinduktion bei *Pieris brassicae* L. *Naturwiss.*, **46**, 17: 518-519.

BUTENANDT, A., and P. KARLSON, 1954. Über die Isolierung eines metamorphose-Hormons der Insekten in kristallisierter Form. *Z. Naturf.*, **96**: 389-391.

CHURCH, N. S., 1953. Initiation of post-diapause development and reinstatement of diapause in *Cephus cinctus* Nort. (quoted by LEES, 1955).

1955a. Hormones and the termination and reinduction of diapause in *Cephus cinctus* Nort. *Canad. J. Zool.*, **33**, 5: 339-369.

1955b. Moisture and diapause in the Wheat Stem Saw-fly *Cephus cinctus* Nort. *Canad. Entom.*, **87**, 2: 85-97.

CORBET, P. S., 1954. Seasonal regulation in British dragon-flies. *Nature*, **174**: 655.

1955. A critical response to changing length of day in an insect. *Nature*, **175**: 338-339.

1956. Environmental factors influencing the induction and termination of diapause in the Emperor Dragon-fly *Anax imperator* Leach. *J. exp. Biol.*, **33**, 1: 1-14.

COUSIN, G., 1932. Étude expérimentale de la diapause des insectes. *Bull. Biol., suppl.*, **15**: 1-341.

DAVIDSON, J., 1929. On the occurrence of parthenogenetic and sexual forms in *Aphis rumicis* L. with special reference to the influence of environmental factors. *Ann. appl. Biol.*, **16**, 1: 104-134.

DAWSON, R. W., 1931. The problem of voltinism and dormancy in the Polyphemus Moth (*Telea polyphemus* Cramer). *J. exp. Zool.*, **59**: 87-132.

DICKSON, R. C., 1949. Factors governing the induction of diapause in the Oriental Fruit Moth. *Ann. entom. Soc. Amer.*, **42**: 511-537.

DICKSON, R. C., and E. J. SANDERS, 1945. Factors inducing diapause in the Oriental Fruit Moth. *J. econ. Entom.*, **38**, 5: 605-606.

DOSKOCIL, J., 1954. Příspěvek k poznání diapausy hmyzu. 1. Vliv délky osvětlení na vznik diapausy. *Věstník Československ. zool. Společn.*, **18**, 2: 139-145.

1956. Diapausa u *Orgyia antiqua* L. *Věstník Českoslov. zool. Společn.*, **20**, 2: 186-187.

1957a. Příspěvek k poznání diapausy hmyzu. 2. Vliv délky osvětlení na vznik diapausy vajíček. *Věstník Českoslov. zool. Společn.*, **21**, 3: 273-283.

1957b. Příspěvek k poznání diapausy hmyzu. 3. Diapausa vajíček *Orgyia antiqua* L. Časopis. *Českoslov. Společn. entom.*, **54**, 3: 213-216.

DUCLAUX, M. E., 1869. De l'influence du froid de l'hiver sur le développement de l'embryon du ver à soie, et sur l'éclosion de la graine. *C. r. Acad. Sci.*, Paris, **69**: 1021-1022.

1871. Études physiologiques sur la graine de ver à soie. *Ann. Chim. Phys. ser. IV*, **24**: 290-306.

1876. De l'action physiologique qu'exercent sur les graines de ver à soie des temperatures inférieures à zéro. *C. r. Acad. Sci.*, Paris, **83**: 1049-1051.

FUKAYA, M., 1950. On the factor inducing the dormancy of the Rice Borer, *Chilo simplex* Butler. *Trans. VIII Internat. Congr. Entom., Stockholm*: 223-225.

FUKUDA, S., 1951a. Alteration of voltinism in the silkworm by decapitating the pupa. *Zool. Mag. Japan*, **60**: 119-121.

1951b. Factors determining the production of non-diapause eggs in the silkworm. *Proc. Imp. Acad. Japan*, **27**, 9: 582-586.

1951c. The production of the diapause eggs by transplanting the suboesophageal ganglion in the silkworm. *Proc. Imp. Acad. Japan*, **27**: 672-677.

1952. Function of the pupal brain and suboesophageal ganglion in the production of non-diapause and diapause eggs in the silkworm. *Annot. Zool. Japan*, **25**: 149-155.

1953a. Determination of voltinism in the univoltine silkworm. *Proc. Imp. Acad. Japan*, **29**, 7: 381-384.

1953b. Determination of voltinism in the multi-voltine silkworm. *Proc. Imp. Acad. Japan*, **29**, 7: 385-389.

1953c. Alteration of voltinism in the silkworm following transection of pupal oesophageal connectives. *Proc. Imp. Acad. Japan*, **29**: 389-391.

GARLICK, W. C., 1948. A five-year field study of Codling Moth larval habits and adult emergence. *Scient. Agric.*, **28**: 273-292.

GOLDSCHMIDT, R., 1934. Limantria. *Bibl. genet.*, **11**: 1-186.

GREVILLIUS, A. Y., 1905. Zur Kenntnis der Biologie des Goldafters (*Euproctis chrysorrhoea*) und der durch denselben verursachten Beschädigungen. *Bot. Zbl., Abt.* 2, Beihefte, **18**: 222-322.

GRISON, P., 1947. Développement sans diapause des chenilles de *Euproctis phaeorrhoea* L. *C. r. Acad. Sci.*, Paris, **225**: 1089-1090.

1949. Effects d'implantation de cerveaux chez le Doriphore (*Leptinotarsa decemlineata* Say) en diapause. *C. r. Acad. Sci.*, Paris, **228**: 428-430.

HAMILTON, A. G., 1936. The relation of humidity and temperature to the development of three species of African locusts—*Locusta migratoria migratorioides, Schistocerca gregaria, Nomadacris septemfasciata. Trans. Entom. Soc., Lond.*, **85**: 1-60.

HASEGAWA, K., 1952. Studies on the voltinism in the silkworm, *Bombyx mori* L. with special reference to the organs concerning determination of voltinism. *J. Fac. Agr. Tottori Univ.*, **1**: 83-124.

1957. The diapause hormone of the silkworm, *Bombyx mori. Nature*, **179**: 1300-1301.

HELLER, J., 1926. Chemische Untersuchungen über die Metamorphose der Insekten. III. Über die ,,subitane" und ,,latent" Entwicklung. *Biochem. Z.*, **169**: 208-234.

HINTON, H. E., 1953. The initiation, maintenance and rupture of diapause: a new theory. *Entomologist*, **86**, 12: 278-291.

1957. Some aspects of diapause. *Science Progress*, **178**: 307-320.

HODEK, J., 1958. The influence of temperature, relative humidity and photoperiodicity on the speed of development in *Coccinella septempunctata* L. *Acta Soc. entom. Cechoslov.*, Praga, **55**: 124-141.

HODSON, A. C., and C. J. WEINMAN, 1945. Factors affecting recovery from diapause and hatching of eggs of the Forest Tent caterpillar, *Malacosoma disstria* Hbn. *Techn. Bull. Minn. Agric. Exp. Sta.*, **170**: 1-31.

HUGHES, R. D., 1960. Induction of diapause in *Erioischia brassicae* Bouche (Diptera, Anthomyidae). *J. exp. Biol.*, **37**, 2: 218-223.

INOUYE, H., and S. KAMANO, 1957. The effects of photoperiod and temperature on the induction of diapause in the Rice Stem Borer, *Chilo suppressalis* Walk. *Jap. J. appl. Entom. Zool.*, I: 100-105.

JANISCH, E., and H. MAERCKS, 1933. Licht und Insektenentwicklung. *Z. Morph. Ökol. Tiere*, **26**, 3: 372-384.

JERMI, T., and G. SARINGER, 1955. Die Rolle der Photoperiode in der Auslösung der Diapause des Kartoffelkäfers (*Leptinotarsa decemlineata* Say) und des amerikanischen weissen Bärenspinners (*Hyphantria cunea* Drury). *Acta agron. Acad. sci., Hung.*, **5**, 3-4: 419-440.

JOLY, P., 1945. La function ovarienne et son contrôle humoral chez les Dytiscides. *Arch. Zool. exp. gen.*, **84**: 49-164.

JONES, B. M., 1956a. Endocrine activity during insect embryogenesis. Function of the ventral head glands in locust embryos (*Locustana pardalina* and *Locusta migratoria*). *J. exp. Biol.*, **33**, 1: 174-185.

1956b. Endocrine activity during insect embryogenesis. Control of events in development following the embryonic moult (*Locusta migratoria* and *Locustana pardalina*). *J. exp. Biol.*, **33**, 4: 685-696.

KAISILA, J., 1954. Über das Vorkommen zweier Generationen bei den finnischen Grosschmetterlinge im allgemeinen und besonders im Sommer 1953. *Suom. Hyönteistiettellinen Aikakauskiya*, **20**, 1: 20-40.

KENTEN, J., 1955. The effect of photoperiod and temperature on reproduction in *Acyrthosiphon pisum* (Harris) and on the forms produced. *Bull. entom. Res.*, **46**: 599-624.

KEVAN, D. K., 1944. The bionomics of the Neotropical Cornstalk Borer, *Diatraea lineolata* Wlk. in Trinidad. *Bull. entom. Res.*, **35**: 23-30.

KISIMOTO, R., 1956. Effect of diapause in the fourth larval instar on the determination of wing-form in the adult of Small Brown Planthopper, *Delphacodes striatella* Fallen. *Ōyō-K̄ontyū*, **12**: 202-210.

1959a. Studies on the diapause in the Planthoppers and Leafhoppers. III. Sensitivity of various larval stages to photoperiod and the forms of ensuing adults in the Green Rice Leafhopper, *Nephotettix cincticeps* Uhler. *Japan. J. appl. Entom. Zool.*, **3**, 3: 200-207.

1959b. Studies on the diapause in the Planthoppers and Leafhoppers. Arrest of development in the fourth and fifth larval stage induced by short photoperiod in the Green Rice Leafhopper, *Nephotettix bipunctatus cincticeps* Uhler. *Japan. J. appl. Entom. Zool.*, **3**, 1: 49-54.

KLEIN, H. Z., 1932. Studien zur Ökologie und Epidemiologie der Kohlweißlinge. I. Der Einfluss der Temperatur und Luftfeuchtigkeit auf Entwicklung und Mortalität von *Pieris brassicae*. *Z. wiss. Insektenbiol.*, **26**: 395-448.

KOGURE, M., 1933. The influence of light and temperature on certain characters of the silkworm—*Bombyx mori*. *J. Dept. Agr. Kyushu Univ.*, **4**: 1-93.

KOT, J., 1958. Możliwości adaptacji gasienic owocówki jabłokówki (*Carpocapsa pomonella* L.) do pólnocnych warunków zimøwania. *Ekologia Polska, ser. B*, **4**, 2: 173-176.

KOZANTSCHIKOW, I. W. (=KOZHANCHIKOV, I. V.), 1938c. Physiological conditions of cold-hardiness in insects. *Bull. entom. Res.*, **29**, 3: 253-262.

KOZHANCHIKOV, I. V., see also in the Russian List.

KÜTHE, K., 1937. Zur Biologie und Bekämpfung des Apfelwicklers (*Carpocapsa pomonella*). *Z. angew. Entom.*, **24**, 1-4: 129-144.

LE BERRE, J. R., 1953. Contribution à l'étude biologique du criquet migrateur des Landes (*Locusta migratoria gallica* Rem.). *Bull. Biol. France Belg.*, **87**: 227-273.

LEES, A. D., 1950. Diapause and photoperiodism in the Fruit Tree Spider Mite (*Metatetranychus ulmi* Koch.). *Nature*, **166**: 874-875.

1953a. Environmental factors controlling the evocation and termination of diapause in the Fruit Tree Red Spider Mite *Metatetranychus ulmi* Koch. *Ann. appl. Biol.*, **40**: 449-486.

1953b. The significance of the light and dark phases in the photoperiodic control of diapause in *Metatetranychus ulmi* Koch. *Ann. appl. Biol.*, **40**, 3: 487-497.

1954. Photoperiodism in Arthropods. *Proc. I Internat. Photobiol. Congr.*, Amsterdam: 36-45.

1955. The physiology of diapause in arthropods. *Cambridge Monogr. exper. Biol.*, **4**: 1-151.

1956. The physiology and biochemistry of diapause. *Ann. Rev. Entom.*, **1**: 1-16.

1959a. Photoperiodism in insects and mites. In the book *Photoperiodism and Related Phenomena in Plants and Animals*. Ed. R. B. Withrow, Washington: 585-600.

1959b. The role of photoperiod and temperature in the determination of parthenogenetic and sexual forms in the aphid *Megoura viciae* Buckton. I. The influence of these factors on apterous virginoparae and their progeny. *J. Inst. Physiol.*, **3**: 92-117.

LOVE, G. J., and J. G. WHELCHEL, 1955. Photoperiodism and the development of *Aedes triseriatus*. *Ecology*, **36**, 2: 340-342.

MAERCKS, H., 1934. Untersuchungen zur Ökologie des Kohlweisslings (*Pieris brassicae* L.). Die Temperaturreaktionen und das Feuchtigkeitoptimum. *Z. Morph. Ökol. Tiere*, **28**: 692.

MARCHAL, P., 1936. Recherches sur la biologie et le développement des Hyménoptères parasites: Les Trichogrammes. *Ann. Epiphyt.*, **2**: 447-550.

MARCOVITCH, S., 1923. Plant lice and light exposure. *Science*, **58**: 537-538.

1924. The migration of the Aphididae and the appearance of the sexual forms as affected by the relative length of daily light exposure. *J. agric. Res.*, **27**: 513-522.

MASAKI, S., 1956a. The local variation in the diapause pattern of the Cabbage Moth, *Barathra brassicae* L., with particular reference to the aestival diapause. *Bull. Fac. Agric. Mie Univ.*, **13**: 29-46.

1956b. The effect of temperature on the termination of pupal diapause in *Barathra brassicae* L. *Japan. J. appl. Zool.*, **21**, 3: 97-107.

1957a. Ecological significance of diapause in the seasonal cycle of *Abraxis miranda* Btl. *Bull. Fac. Agric. Mie Univ.* **15**: 15-24.

1957b. Larval sensitive stage for the action of external factors controlling the occurrence of diapause in the Cabbage Moth pupa, *Barathra brassicae* L. *J. Fac. Agric. Hokkaido Univ.*, **50**, 3: 197-210.

1957c. Further experiments on the thermal relations of the Cabbage Moth pupa, *Barathra brassicae* L. *J. Fac. Agric. Hokkaido Univ.*, **50**, 3: 211-224.

1958. The response of a 'short-day' insect to certain external factors: the induction of diapause in *Abraxis miranda* Butl. *Japan. J. appl. Entom. Zool.*, **2**, 4: 285-294.

MATTHEE, J. J., 1951. The structure and physiology of the egg of *Locustana pardalina* Walk. *Sci. Bull. Dept. Agr. S. Afr.*, **316**: 1-83.

MILLER, L. W., 1950. Factors influencing diapause in the European Red Mite. *Nature*, **166**: 875.

MOROHOSHI, S., 1959. Hormonal studies on the diapause and non-diapause eggs of the silkworm *Bombyx mori* L. *J. insect Physiol.*, **3**, 1: 28-40.

MÜLLER, H. J., 1954. Der Saisondimorphismus bei Zikaden der Gattung *Euscelis* Brullé. *Beitr. Entom.*, **4**, 1: 1-56.

1955a. Die Bedeutung der Tageslänge für die Saisonformenbildung der Insekten, insbesondere bei den Zikaden. *Ber. 7. Wanderversamm. deut. Entom.* Berlin: 102-120.

1955b. Über den Einfluß der Tageslänge auf die Saisonformenprägung von *Euscelis plebejus* Fall. *Verh. deut. zool. Ges.* Tübingen, 1954: 307-316.

1955c. Die Saisonformenbildung von *Araschnia levana*, ein photoperiodisch gesteuerter Diapauseeffekt. *Naturwiss.*, **42**: 134-135.

1956. Die Wirkung verschiedener diurnaler Licht-Dunkel-Relationen auf die Saisonformenbildung von *Araschnia levana*. *Naturwiss.*, **43**: 503-504.

1957a. Über die Diapause von *Stenocranus minutus* Fabr. *Beitr. Entom.*, **7**, 3-4: 203-226.

1957b. Die Wirkung exogener Fartoren auf die zyklische Formenbildung der Insekten, insbesondere der Gattung *Euscelis* Brullé. *Zool. Jahrb. Abt. Syst. Ökol. Geograph. Tiere*, **85**, 4-5: 317-430.

1958a. Über den Einfluss der Photoperiode auf Diapause und Körpergrosse der Delphacide *Stenocranus minutus* Fabr. *Zool. Anz.*, **160**, 11-12: 294-312.

1958b. The taxonomic value of the male genitalia in Leafhoppers in the light of new studies on the seasonal forms of *Euscelis*. *Proc. X. Intern. Congr. Entom.*, **1**: 357-362.

1959. Tageslänge als Regulator des Gestaltwandels bei Insekten. *Umschau*, **2**: 36-39.

Müller, L., and H. Kautz, 1939. *Pieris bryoniae* O. und *Pieris napi* L. *Abh. Oesterr. entom. Ver.*, **1**: 1-191.

Muroga, H. 1951. On the consumption of inhibitory substance in silkworm eggs. *J. seric. Sci. Japan*, **20**: 92 (quoted by Lees, 1955).

Mutchmor, J. A., 1959. Some factors influencing the occurrence and size of the midsummer flight of the European Corn Borer, *Ostrinia nubilalis* (Hb.) in south-western Ontario. *Canad. Entom.*, **91**: 798-805.

Mutchmor, J. A., and W. E. Beckel, 1958. Importance of temperature and photoperiod in inducing diapause in the European Corn Borer *Pyrausta nubilalis* (Hb.). *Nature*, **181**: 204.

1959. Some factors affecting diapause in the European Corn Borer *Ostrinia nubilalis* (Lepidoptera, Pyralidae). *Canad. J. Zool.*, **37**: 161-168.

Neiswander, C. R., 1947. Variations in the seasonal history of the European Corn Borer in Ohio. *J. econ. Entom.*, **40**: 407-412.

Nitsch, I. P., and F. W. Went, 1959. The induction of flowering in *Xanthium pensylvanicum* under long days. In the book *Photoperiodism and Related Phenomena in Plants and Animals*. Ed. R. B. Withrow: 311-314.

Nordman, A. E., 1954. The geographical distribution in Europe of the migrations of the large white *Pieris brassicae*, and some remarks on their climatological causes. *Notul. entom.*, **34**: 99-106.

Norris, M. J., 1957. Factors affecting the rate of sexual maturation of the desert locust (*Schistocerca gregaria* Forsk.) in the laboratory. *Anti-locust Bull.*, **28**: 1-29.

1959. The influence of day-length on imaginal diapause in the Red Locust, *Nomadacris septemfasciata* Serv. *Entom. exp. et appl.*, **2**: 154-168.

Norris, M. J., and W. Richards, 1958. Influence of photoperiod on imaginal diapause in Acridids. *Nature*, **181**: 58.

Novak, V., 1959. *Insektenhormone*, Prag: 1-283.

OTUKA, M., and H. SANTA, 1955. Studies on the diapause in the Cabbage Army-Worm, *Barathra brassicae* L. III. The effect of the rhythm of light and darkness on the induction of diapause. *Bull. Nat. Inst. Agric. Sci., Tokyo (C)*, **5** : 49-56.

PARIS, O. H., and CH. E. JENNER, 1959. Photoperiodic control of diapause in the Pitcher-plant Midge *Metriocnemus knabi.* In the book *Photoperiodism and Related Phenomena in Plants and Animals.* Ed. R. B. Withrow, Washington: 601-624.

PARSONS, F. S., and G. ULLYET, 1934. Investigations on the control of the American and Red Bollworm of cotton in S. Africa. *Bull. entom. Res.*, **25** : 341-381.

PAYNE, N., 1926. The effect of environmental temperatures upon insect freezing points. *Ecology*, **7** : 99-106.

PAYNE, N. M., 1929. Absolute humidity as a factor in insect cold hardiness with a note on the effect of nutrition on cold hardiness. *Ann. entom. Soc. Amer.*, **22** (4): 601-620.

PEARSON, E. O., and B. L. MITCHELL, 1945. Report on the status and control of pests of cotton in the lower river districts of Nyasaland (quoted by LEES, 1955).

PEPPER, J. H., 1938. The effect of certain climatic factors on the distribution of the Beet Webworm (*Loxostege sticticalis*) in North America. *Ecology*, **19** : 565-571.

PETERSEN, B., 1947. Die geographische Variation einiger fennoskandischer Lepidopteren. *Zool. Bidr. Uppsala*, **26** : 329-531.

1949. On the evolution of *Pieris napi. Evolution*, **3**: 269-278.

PICTET, A., 1936. La zoogéographie experimentale dans ses rapports avec la génétique. *Mém. Mus. Hist. natur. Belgique, ser.* 2, **3** : 233-282.

1937. Sur des croissements de races géographiques de Lépidoptère de pays très éloignées *Mitt. Schweiz. ent. Ges.*, **16** : 706-715.

PREBBLE, M. L., 1941. The diapause and related phenomena in *Gilpinia polytoma* (Hartig.). I-V. *Canad. J. Res. (D)*, **19** : 295-454.

PROSSER, C. L., 1955. Physiological variation in animals. *Biol. Rev.*, **30** : 229-262.

1957. The species problem from the view-point of a physiologist. In the book *The Species Problem.* Washington: 339-369.

PUNT, A., 1950. The respiration of insects. *Physiol. comp.*, **2** : 59-74.

RAHM, U. H., 1952. Die innersekretorische Steuerung der postembryonalen Entwicklung von *Sialis lutaria* L. *Rev. suisse Zool.*, **59** : 173-237.

READIO, P. A., 1931. Dormancy in *Reduvius personatus. Ann. entom. Soc. Amer.*, **24** : 19-39.

ROBINSON, W., 1928. Relation of hydrophilic colloids to winter hardiness of insects. *Colloid Symposium Monograph*, **5** : 199-218.

ROSSI-ESPAGNET, A., 1957. Alcune osservazioni sul complesso *Culex pipiens* della provincia di Latina. *Rend. Ist. super. Sanità*, **20**, 11: 1045-1049.

ROUBAUD, E., 1928. L'anhydrobiose réactivante dans le cycle évolutif de la Pyrale du mais. *C. r. Acad. Sci.* Paris. **186**: 792-793.

SABROSKY, C. N., J. LARSEN, and R. K. NABOURS, 1933. Experiments with light upon reproduction, growth and diapause in Grouse Locusts (Acridinae, Tetriginae). *Trans. Kansas Acad. Sci.*, **36**: 298-300.

SACHAROV, N., 1930. Studies in cold resistance in insects. *Ecology*, 11: 505-517.

SACHAROV, N., see also SAKHAROV, N. L., in the Russian List.

SALT, G., 1941. The effects of hosts upon their insect parasites. *Biol. Rev.*, **16**: 239-264.

SALT, R. W., 1947. Some effects of temperature on the production and elimination of diapause in the Wheat Stem Saw-fly, *Cephus cinctus* Nort. *Canad. J. Res. (D)*, **25**, 2: 66-86.

1949. Water uptake in eggs of *Melanoplus bivittatus* (Say). *Canad. J. Res. (D)*, **27**: 236-242.

1952. Some aspects of moisture absorption and loss in eggs of *Melanoplus bivittatus* Say. *Canad. J. Zool.*, **30**: 55-82.

SANDERSON, E. D., 1908. The relation of temperature to the hibernation of insects. *J. econ. Entom.*, **1**: 56-65.

SCHNEIDER, F., 1950. Die Entwicklung des Syrphidenparasiten *Diplazon fissorius* Grav. in uni-, oligo- und polyvoltinen Wirten und sein Verhalten bei parasitärer Aktivierung der Diapauselarven durch *Diplazon pectoratorius* Grav. *Mitt. Schweiz. entom. Ges.*, **23**: 155-194.

1951. Einige physiologische Beziehungen zwischen Syrphidenlarven und ihren Parasiten. *Z. angew. Entom.*, **33**: 150-162.

SCHNEIDERMAN, H. A., and C. M. WILLIAMS, 1953. The physiology of insect diapause. VII. The respiratory metabolism of the *Cecropia* silkworm during diapause and metamorphosis. *Biol. Bull.*, **105**: 320-334.

SELLIER, R., 1949. Diapause larvaire et macroptérisme chez *Gryllus campestris*. *C. r. Acad. Sci.*, Paris, **228**: 2055-2056.

SERAFIMOVSKI, A., 1954. Ciclus razvića topolinog gubara u okolini Beograda. *Zashchita bila*, Belgrade, **25**: 18-41.

SHULL, A. E., 1928. Duration of light and the wings of the Aphid *Macrosiphum solanifolii*. *Roux' Arch. Entw. Mech.*, **113**: 210-239.

1929. The effect of intensity and duration of light and of duration of darkness, partly modified by temperature upon wing-production of aphids. *Roux' Arch. Entw. Mech.*, **115**: 825-851.

1930. Control of gamic and parthenogenetic reproduction in winged aphids by temperature and light. *Z. indukt. Abstamm. Vererbungslehre*, **55**: 108-126.

1943. Origin of diverse strains of an aphid species within a limited area. *Papers Michigan Acad. Sci., Arts and Letters, 28 (1942), P. II, Zool.*: 425-431.

SIEGLER, E. H., 1946. Susceptibility of hibernating Codling Moth larvae to low temperatures and the bound-water content. *J. agric. Res.*, **72**, 10: 329-340.

SIMMONDS, F. J., 1948. The influence of maternal physiology on the incidence of diapause. *Phil. Trans. Roy. Soc., B.*, **233**: 385-414.

SLIFER, E. H., 1938. The formation and structure of a special water-absorbing area in the membranes covering the grasshopper egg. *Quart. J. micr. Sci.*, **80**: 437-457.

1946. The effects of xylol and other solvents on diapause in the grasshopper egg, together with a possible explanation for the action of these agents. *J. exp. Zool.*, **102**: 333-356.

SMITH, J., and R. L. LANGSTON, 1953. Continuous laboratory propagation of Western Grape Leaf Skeletonizer and parasites by prevention of diapause. *J. econ. Entom.*, **46**, 3: 477-484.

SMITH, S. C., 1941. A new form of Spruce Saw-fly identified by means of cytology and parthenogenesis. *Sci. Agric.*, **21**: 254-303.

SQUIRE, F. A., 1939. Observations on the larval diapause of the Pink Bollworm, *Platyedra gossypiella* Saund. *Bull. entom. Res.*, **30**: 475-481.

1940. On the nature and origin of the diapause in *Platyedra gossypiella* Saund. *Bull. entom. Res.*, **31**: 1-6.

STEINBERG, D. M., and S. KAMENSKY, 1936. Les prémisses oecologiques de la diapause de *Loxostege sticticalis* L. *Bull. biol. Fr. Bdg.*, **70**, 2: 145-183.

SÜFFERT, F., 1924. Bestimmungsfactoren des Zeichnungsmuster beim Saison-Dimorphismus von *Araschnia levana-prorsa*. *Biol. Zbl.*, **44**: 173-188.

TANAKA, J., 1944. Effect of day-length on hibernation of the Chinese Oak Silkworm (quoted by LEES, 1955).

1950a. Studies on hibernation with special reference to photoperiodicity and breeding of the Chinese Tussar-Silkworm. I. *J. seric. Sci. Japan*, **19**: 358.

1950b. Studies on hibernation with special reference to photoperiodicity and breeding of the Chinese Tussar-Silkworm. II. *J. seric. Sci. Japan*, **19**: 429.

1950c. Studies on hibernation with special reference to photoperiodicity and breeding of the Chinese Tussar-Silkworm. III. *J. seric. Sci. Japan*, **19**: 580.

1951. Studies on hibernation with special reference to photoperiodicity and breeding of the Chinese Tussar-Silkworm. V. *J. seric. Sci. Japan*, **20**: 132.

1953. Genetics of the silkworm, *Bombyx mori*. *Advanc. Genet.*, **5**: 239-317.

TATE, P., and M. VINCENT, 1936. The biology of autogenous and anautogenous races of *Culex pipiens*. *Parasitology*, **28**: 115-145.

THERON, P., 1943. Experiments on terminating the diapause in larvae of Codling Moth. *J. entom. Soc. S. Africa*, **6**: 114-123.

THOMSEN, E. E., 1952. Functional significance of the neurosecretory brain cells and the corpus cardiacum in the female Blow-fly *Calliphora erythrocephala* Meig. *J. exp. Biol.*, **29**: 137-172.

TOWNSEND, M. T., 1926. The breaking-up of hibernation in the Codling Moth larva. *Ann. ent. Soc. Amer.*, **19**: 429-439.

TULESCHKOV, K., 1935. Über Ursachen der Überwinterung der *Lymantria dispar*, L. *monacha* und anderer Lymantriiden im Eistadium. *Z. angew. Entom.*, **22**: 97-117.

UCHIDA, T., and S. MASAKI, 1954. The effect of photoperiod on the induction of diapause in the Cabbage Moth, *Barathra brassicae* L. *Mem. Fac. Agric. Hokkaido Univ.*, **2**, 1: 85-95.

UMEYA, Y., 1926. Experiments of ovarian transplantation and blood transfusions in silkworms, with special reference to the alternation of voltinism (*Bombyx mori* L.). *Bull. seric. Exp. Stat. Chosen*, **1**: 1-27.

UMEYA, L., and C. HARADA, 1955. On the genetic determination of the voltinism of silkworms. *Japan. J. Gen.*, **30**: 158-162.

UVAROV, B. P., 1931. Insects and climate. *Trans. entom. Soc.*, **79**: 1-247.

VANCE, A. M., 1939. Occurrence and responses of a partial second generation of the European Corn Borer in the Lake States. *J. econ. Entom.*, **32**: 83-90.

VANDERZANT, E., and R. REISER, 1956a. Aseptic rearing of the Pink Boll-worm on synthetic media. *J. econ. Entom.*, **49**, 1: 7-10.

1956b. Studies of the nutrition of the Pink Boll-worm using purified casein media. *J. econ. Entom.*, **49**, 4: 454-458.

WAY, M. J., B. A. HOPKINS, and P. M. SMITH, 1949. Photoperiodism and diapause in insects. *Nature*, **164**: 615.

WAY, M. J., and B. A. HOPKINS, 1950. The influence of photoperiod and temperature on the induction of diapause in *Diataraxia oleracea* L. *J. exp. biol.*, **27**: 365-375.

WAY, M. J., P. M. SMITH, and B. A. HOPKINS, 1951. The selection and rearing of leaf-eating insects for use as test subjects in the study of insecticide. *Bull. entom. Res.*, **42**: 331-354.

WĘGOREK, W., see also in the Russian List, for his publications in Russian.

1957a. Badania nad biologią i ekologią stonki ziemniaczanej (*Leptinotarsa decemlineata* Say). *Roczniki nauk rolniczych*, **74-A-2**: 136-185.

1957b. Badania nad zimowaniem stonki ziemniaczanej (*Leptinotarsa decemlineata* Say). *Roczniki nauk rolniczych*, **74-A-2**: 315-338.

1959a. Stonka ziemniaczana (*Leptinotarsa decemlineata* Say). *Prace naukowe Inst. ochr. rośl.*, **1**, 2: 7-178.

1959b. Badania nad pośrednim i bezpośrednim wlywem fotoperiodu na rozwój i fiziologie stonki ziemniaczanej (*Leptinotarsa decemlineata* Say). *Prace naukowe Inst. ochr. rośl.*, **1**, 3: 5-35.

WENT, F. W., 1959. The periodic aspect of photoperiodism and thermoperiodicity. In the book *Photoperiodism and related phenomena in plants and animals*. Ed. R. B. Withrow: 551-564.

WIGGLESWORTH, V. B., 1934. The physiology of ecdysis in *Rhodnius prolixus*. II. Factors controlling moulting and metamorphosis. *Quart. J. micr. Sci.*, **77**: 191-222.

1936. The function of the corpus allatum in the growth and reproduction of *Rhodnius prolixus*. *Quart. J. micr. Sci.*, **79**: 91-121.

1939. Principles of insect physiology. London: 1-434.

1948. The function of the corpus allatum in *Rhodnius prolixus*. *J. exp. Biol.*, **25**: 1-14.

1952a. The thoracic gland in *Rhodnius prolixus* and its role in moulting. *J. exp. Biol.*, **29**: 561-570.

1952b. Hormone balance and the control of metamorphosis in *Rhodnius prolixus*. *J. exp. Biol.*, **29**: 620-631.

1954. The physiology of insect metamorphosis. *Cambridge Monogr. exp. Biol.*, **1**: 1-152.

WILDE, J. DE, 1954. Aspects of diapause in adult insects with special regard to the Colorado Beetle, *Leptinotarsa decemlineata* Say. *Arch. Neerl. Zool.*, **10**: 375-385.

1955. The significance of the photoperiod for the occurrence of diapause in the adult *Leptinotarsa decemlineata* Say. *Proc. I Internat. Photobiol. Congr.*, Amsterdam.

WILDE, J. DE, and H. BONGA, 1958. Observations on threshold intensity and sensitivity to different wave lengths of photoperiodic responses in the Colorado Beetle (*Leptinotarsa decemlineata* Say). *Entom. exp. et appl.*, **1**: 301-307.

WILDE, J. DE, 1958. Perception of the photoperiod by the Colorado potato Beetle (*Leptinotarsa decemlineata* Say). *Prox. X. Internat. Congr. Entom.*, 1956, **2**: 213-218.

1959a. Fotoperiodiciteit bij insecten. *Vakblad Biol.*, **39**, 9: 153-162.

1959b. Endocrine influence on behaviour and reproduction in insects. *Acta Physiol. pharmacol. Neerlandica*, **8**.

WILDE, J. DE, C. S. DUINTJER, and L. MOOK, 1959. Physiology of diapause in the adult Colorado Beetle (*Leptinotarsa decemlineata* Say)—I. The Photoperiod as a controlling factor. *J. ins. Physiol.*, **3**: 75-85.

WILLIAMS, C. B., 1930. *The Migration of Butterflies*. London: 1-475.

1939. The migrations of the Cabbage White Butterfly *Pieris brassicae* L. *Verh. VII Internat. Congr. Entom. Weimar*, **1**: 482-493.

WILLIAMS, C. M., 1946. Physiology of insect diapause: the role of the brain in the production and termination of pupal dormancy in the Giant Silkworm *Platysamia cecropia*. *Biol. Bull.*, **90**: 234-243.

1947. Physiology of insect diapause. II. Interaction between the pupal brain and prothoracic glands in the metamorphosis of the Giant Silkworm, *Platysamia cecropia*. *Biol. Bull.*, **93**: 89-98.

1952a. Physiology of insect diapause. IV. The brain and prothoracic glands as an endocrine system in the *cecropia* silkworm. *Biol. Bull.*, **103**: 120-138.

1952b. Morphogenesis and the metamorphosis of insects. *Harvey Lectures*, **47**: 126-155.

Wilson, F., 1938. Some experiments on the influence of environment upon the forms of *Aphis chloris* Koch. *Trans. Entom. Soc. Lond.*, **87**: 165-180.

Wishart, G., 1947. Further observation on the changes taking place in the Corn Borer population in Western Ontario. *Canad. Entomologist*, **79**: 81-83.

Withrow, R. B. (edit.), 1959. Photoperiodism and related phenomena in plants and animals. *Proc. Conf. Photoperiodism, 1957*. Washington: 1-203.

Wohlfahrt, T., 1957. Über den Einfluss von Licht, Futterqualität und Temperature auf Puppenruhe und Diapause des mitteleuropäischen Segelfalters *Iphiclides podalirius* L. *Tagunsber. 8. Wandervers. deut. Entom.*, Berlin, **II**: 6-14.

Wressell, H. B., 1952. Increase of the multivoltine strain of the European Corn Borer *Pyrausta nubilalis* Hb. in south-western Ontario. *Ann. Rep. entom. Soc. Ontario*, **83**: 43-47.

Zeeuw, D., 1957. Flowering of *Xanthium* under long-day conditions. *Nature*, **180**: 588.

INDEX OF INSECTS

INDEX OF PLANTS